Origins of Modernity

Published in the United States of America in 2005 by
Augustana College, 639-38th Street,
Rock Island, Illinois 61201-2296.

ISBN 0-9714345-2-2

Origins of Modernity

CATHERINE CARTER GOEBEL

Paul A. Anderson Chair in the Arts

Editor

ERRIN COPPLE

Research Assistant

AUGUSTANA COLLEGE

Rock Island, Illinois

"Modernity...to extract from fashion the poetry that resides in its historical envelope, to distill the eternal from the transitory...."

Charles Baudelaire, *The Painter of Modern Life (1863)*

Origins of Modernity

Catalogue Design
ELIZABETH PARKER DUCEY

Electronic Web Gallery
CYNTHIA WIEDEMANN EMPEN

"In such an age as this, painting should be understood, not looked on with blind wonder, nor considered only as a poetic aspiration, but as a pursuit, legitimate, scientific, and mechanical."

John Constable *(1776-1837)*

To my husband

Dr. Gary James Goebel

In celebration of our twenty-fifth anniversary

And many wonderful years

Of collaboration between art and science

And to our children Tom and Katie

A continued source of joy

And inspiration.

Catherine Carter Goebel

Professor of Art History

Paul A. Anderson Chair in the Arts

"*So there are such things as modern beauty and modern heroism!...The life of our city is rich in poetic and marvelous subjects.*"

Charles Baudelaire, *The Salon of 1846: On the Heroism of Modern Life*

Acknowledgments

The *Origins of Modernity* exhibition represents an important multidisciplinary collaboration at Augustana College. The works of art exhibited have been carefully selected, researched and documented by current and former students of the college as well as a number of members of the faculty and administration. The exhibition was designed to complement the winter liberal studies (LS 112) first-year curricular theme of the *Birth of Modern Times* as well as a number of other liberal arts courses at Augustana. This undertaking is largely supported through the Paul A. Anderson Endowment. The profound insight of alumnus Paul A. Anderson, whose successful life was cut tragically short in 1992, established this chair so that the beauty and intellectual stimulation of the visual arts would have a strong and lasting presence at Augustana. Paul wanted students to see original works of art in person and become knowledgeable about the aesthetics, meaning and history of that art within a supportive academic environment. These resources serve to enhance the teaching mission of the Art History Department as well as the College in general. Approximately one-half of the works exhibited here were purchased or gifted through the Anderson Endowment in order to develop a pedagogically-based art collection which represents a broad historic range from ancient Greek black and red-figure painting through contemporary printmaking. True to Paul's aims, this exhibition and catalogue serve to instruct those who have been involved in their production as well as those who read the text and study the collection. Even after the exhibition closes, these works of art and the related catalogue will continue to inform and educate those at Augustana as well as the community-at-large.

The Anderson Endowment has thus reinforced Paul's commitment toward the ideals of the College—service to church and community. Through building an art history teaching collection and supporting its related programming, his endowment has enriched many areas within Augustana College. This is the third major exhibition and catalogue supported through this endowment since my appointment as chair ten years ago and each has been a growing experience methodologically. *The Paul A. Anderson Art History Collection* (2001) catalogue consisted of research by faculty and administrators as well as art history majors and minors. The *Tracing Line Through Time: A Whistler Centenary Exhibition* (2002) publication included additional research by art history majors and minors as well as three senior art history capstone essays. This *Origins of Modernity* catalogue goes a step further in that it is even more inclusive, with contributors ranging from first-year LS through upper-class art history students, together with senior art history capstones. Yet, the vast majority of contributors are not art history majors or minors, thus students from a variety of viewpoints, informed through art historical research and analysis, have produced this catalogue. I hope that it will serve as a model for liberal arts/studies interaction. Augustana is cutting-edge in its approach toward using original works of art as teaching resources in the classroom (as important to our field as books in the library) and I am gratified that so many colleagues have been involved in this undertaking at a number of different levels. The catalogue and exhibition represent a most impressive collaboration of many committed people—scholars, administrators, professors, donors, lenders, art dealers and students—in my estimate, reflecting the ideals of the liberal arts education.

I have enjoyed overseeing the research, writing and editing for this publication. I know of no other college or university that is undertaking such projects with undergraduates. We are both building and celebrating a world-class art history teaching collection which enables Augustana students to engage in critical research and writing on original works of art. This project represents student engagement at every level before, during and after its publication, promising the same dynamic that I witnessed this year when this generation of students cited former students from previous catalogues as sources for information. I believe we are breaking new ground in the interdisciplinary use of the liberal arts museum as a classroom, and perhaps more importantly, with the classroom used as a relevant forum for original works of art. I am particularly grateful for further support for this catalogue which was provided by the granting of a Donald Anderson Faculty-Student Research Fellowship through the Lindstrom Foundation to Errin Copple (Class of 2005) to work as my research assistant last summer. Errin's fine scholarship, writing skills and work ethic greatly enhanced the quality of this publication. I am grateful for all of her dedication and support throughout the summer, only ending with her departure for graduate school at Vanderbilt University. In addition, I would like to acknowledge the support of the Augustana Humanities Fund Committee for granting this project an award through the Arts and Curriculum Fund, which helps enable the catalogue, as I had envisioned, to be free-of-charge and thus available to the entire community.

I would also like to thank my former art history professor and advisor, Thomas B. Brumbaugh, Professor Emeritus of Fine Arts, Vanderbilt University, whose gifts and loans of works of art collected through forty years of teaching have greatly impacted the teaching collection at Augustana College. Professor Brumbaugh ignited my own interest in art history and collecting original art and it was his superb example which inspired me toward the goal of building a teaching collection at Augustana. I am delighted that the Dr. Thomas B. Brumbaugh Art History Collection continues to stimulate present and future students as they study art history and other fields in the liberal arts that are enriched by this wonderful resource. And I am indebted to my sister, Patricia Deveau, for encouraging me to take my first art history class.

In addition to art contributions from Paul A. Anderson and Professor Thomas B. Brumbaugh, additional patrons who have lent and gifted artwork or made possible specific art acquisitions included in this exhibition are my mother Barbara L. Carter (in memory of my father Dr. Thomas William Carter), Jeff Abernathy (Dean of the College and Professor of English) and

Rebecca Wee (Associate Professor of English), Professor Irma Adelman, Drs. Richard and Paula Arnell, Paul A. Arnell, Audubon Elementary School, Art History Alumni in Honor of Dr. Mary Em Kirn (Professor Emerita of Art History), Mr. and Mrs. Victor H. and Isabel Bartolome, Mr. James Beebe ('88), Barbara Bradac (in Memory of Hubert A. and Ruth E. Boisvert), Betty L. Beer (and a memorial honoring William L. Beer), Dr. James K. Billman, Dan Churchill, Adam J. DeSimone, Al and Lynne DeSimone, David A. DeSimone, Elizabeth and John Ducey, Mr. Daryl Empen ('91) and Dr. Cynthia Empen ('92), the Reynold Emanuel and Johnnie Gause Leak Holmén Endowment for the Visual Arts, Sonja Knudsen (Professor Emerita of German), the Lohrey Family Limited Partnership, Mr. and Mrs. Frank Lufrano, Mr. and Mrs. Michael Moss, the Neville-Strass Collection, George and Pat Olson, The Olson-Brandelle North American Indian Art Collection, Thomas E. Rassieur, the Erick O. Schonstedt Inkstand Collection, Dr. Alex and Mrs. Martha Stone, Dr. Eugene C. and Mrs. Barbara B. Wittenstrom and Mr. Clarence F. and Mrs. Barbara B. Wittenstrom, Jr. (in Memory of their Parents, Rev. Clarence F. and Mrs. Edna A. Wittenstrom, Sr., Class of 1928, and in Memory of Their Grandparents, Rev. Carl Jr. and Mrs. Anna A. Johnson, Treasurer of Augustana College under President Andreen), and Dr. Karin Youngberg (Professor of English and Conrad Bergendoff Professor of Humanities). Additional funding support was provided by the Art and Art History Department, Augustana College Art Exhibits program, friends of Augustana College, Marcia A. Lutz Blust (Augustana '68) and Summer Chu Maurer Lawrence. We are particularly fortunate to exhibit for this occasion a large number of important works graciously and anonymously lent from private collections.

Our College administration has been tremendously supportive of this vast undertaking. I thank President Steven C. Bahls for his genuine and contagious enthusiasm for art and his fine essay on Pieter Bruegel for the catalogue; Jeff Abernathy, Vice President and Dean of the College, who has contributed substantial encouragement and support through many aspects of this project as well as his gift of Thomas Hart Benton's lithograph, *Sunday Morning*, and his insightful paper on this piece and its context for the catalogue; Al DeSimone, Vice President for Development, who in addition to gifting several pieces for this exhibition (*Declaration of Independence*, *Portrait of George Washington*, *Burial of Atala* and co-sponsorship of Paul Gauguin's woodcut, *Manao tupapau*), has been integral over the years toward defining programs and directions for the Paul A. Anderson Endowment, and Paul Pearson, Vice President of Business and Finance, for his general support for our many projects.

Many contributors to the catalogue must also be acknowledged. I especially thank my colleague, Mary Em Kirn, Professor Emerita of Art History, whose research on the oil sketch of Marie de' Medici by Sir Anthony Van Dyck provides important new information on this recent gift to the college. Mary has always been the ideal senior colleague, and continues as such during retirement, as she has additionally offered invaluable advice on the introductory essay, as did David Ellis, Assistant Professor of History, in order to make it more relevant to the general liberal arts curriculum. In addition, I am deeply grateful to Jeff Abernathy, Thomas Banks, Thomas Bengtson, David Ellis, Dell Jensen and Nancy Huse for not only offering insights for the introduction, but also reviewing it for editorial suggestions. Many members of the administration and faculty contributed essays on works of art related to their interests, including Jeff Abernathy, Steven Bahls, Thomas Banks, Daniel Connolly, Roger Crossley, Cynthia Empen, Nancy Huse, Taddy Kalas, Emil Kramer, Sherry Maurer, Michael Nolan, Margi Rogal and Karin Youngberg. There are many additional professors who have kindly acted as resources for this publication as noted in the entries for the exhibition checklist as well as many endnote citations. I would also like to acknowledge the considerable research and collection assistance of Alex Adelman, Bruce Duncan, Zeljko Lah, Carlton Neville and Stephanie Strass, Ron Povlich, Harris Schrank and John and Fay Ziemer.

The catalogue features the senior capstone essays of art history majors, Errin Copple (Art History, Classics), Dana Kau (Art History, Speech Communication) and Michael Skelton (Art History, Geography). Each of these students defined theses that not only related to works on exhibit, but also utilized methodological approaches that combined their double-majors. I appreciate the additional advice they received from a number of faculty resources, including Thomas Banks, Daniel Connolly and Sharon Varallo. In addition, many more students from a variety of majors and minors, ranging from first year through seniors, contributed essays on individual works in this exhibition. Senior writers from the class of 2005 include: Brian Allured, Wilder Anderson, Jennifer Banaszak, Matt Brownley, Errin Copple, Megan Crandall, Andrew Gustafson, Dana Kau, Nikki Kromphardt, Beth Luebke, Joe Marusarz, Jason Myers, Megan O'Brien and Michael Skelton. Contributors from the class of 2006 include: Paul Arnell, Alisha Boley, Kate Felde, David Freeman, Regina Gorham, Colleen Jaycox, Jennifer Johnson, Alisha Kumar, Carol Marquardsen, Scott Metzger, Stephanie Schneider, John Sexton, Kim Weidner and Ewa Wojewoda. Class of 2007 authors include: Beth Biercz, Mikeda Cannon, Beth Cloud, Mary Feeney, Katie Gedrimas, Chris Johnson, Katrina Kainz, Laura Kurczodyna, Jennifer Lams, Gayln Landem, Dan Pearson, Marissa Saunders, Preston Taylor, Kelly Volkert, Stephanie Walz, Jessica Whetzal, Jennifer Windmiller and Dana Zingato. And first-year contributors from the Class of 2008 include: Katie Arnold, John Bianchin, Jennifer Bock, Kaitlin Bradley, Tiffany Chezum, John Deery, Kady Fairfield, Jessica Feinman, Beth Gilmartin, Thomas J. Goebel, Julius Gylys, Randi Higel, Lisa Johnson, Aron Lees, Cristy Martinez, Mallory McClintock, Kristin McLinden, Anne Motto, Amanda Nordstrom, Courtney Olson, Katie Otter, Erin Reeverts, John Regan, Andrea Ritchie, J. D. Rotzoll, Joe Scurto, Johanna Voorhees and Jeffrey Weiland. Art history alumni have also provided essays for this publication, including: Paul Bacon ('90), James Beebe ('88), Cynthia Wiedemann Empen ('92) and Emily Vokt Ziemba ('98).

Sherry Case Maurer, Director of the Augustana College Art Museum and Collection, must be thanked for her many contributions to this project, particularly her preparation of the exhibition checklist and her help in proofreading and editing. Her impeccable eye for framing and displaying images for exhibition presents these diverse works to their optimal effect. Her preparations for this project were advanced by student work-study staff including Tiffany Chezum, Christina Montalto, Elizabeth Eyler, Michelle Neptune and Alison Tunnicliff. Preparators who have also assisted her were Al Bieg, Elizabeth Ducey and Cynthia Empen. Mimzi Haut of the Moline Art Gallery kindly lent her expertise toward framing a number of pieces on exhibit.

Director of the Staelens Family Art History Visual Resource Collection, Cynthia Wiedemann Empen, has also been essential to this venture. She must be noted for her many contributions toward editing and proofreading as well as checking citations. She also constructed an electronic web gallery of the works on exhibit which will facilitate their usage by faculty and students. She was assisted by work-study students including Sarah Altergott, Mikeda Cannon, Carly Griswold, Sarah Hauser and Carianne Meng. Dick Oberg photographed artwork for this publication. I would also like to acknowledge the assistance of the Thomas Tredway Library staff, particularly Margi Rogal, Reference Librarian. In addition, Information Technology

Services furthered this undertaking. Mary Doonan, College Controller, and Darlene Link, Director of Fiscal Operations, have continually reinforced our many endeavors.

Special thanks are extended to our graphic designer (and secretary) Elizabeth Ducey. Beth has spent the past nine months tirelessly working with me through the summer as well as many evenings and weekends. Her dedication to this project is laudable and her consummate eye for design is reflected in every beautiful page of this publication. She was assisted by work-study students Allison Gladfelter, Megan O'Connor and Kendra Shaddick. I am also indebted to Barbara Bradac, Creative Director, Office of Communication and Marketing, who offered initial advice and basic design templates based on her past work for *The Paul A. Anderson Art History Collection* and *Tracing Line Through Time: A Whistler Centenary Exhibition* catalogues. Fidlar Printing Company courteously provided professional resources toward the planning and production stages for this project. In addition, I wish to acknowledge James Konrad, Adjunct Assistant Professor of Art, for his skillful conservation of many of the paintings on exhibit. Barry Bauman, Conservator of Paintings and Fine Works of Art for Non-Profit Organizations, conserved pieces for this exhibition and expedited his sensitive restoration of the featured cover painting.

Finally, I want to generally thank all, too numerous to mention, who have in any way contributed to the successful completion of this exhibition and catalogue. I am most indebted to my husband, Dr. Gary James Goebel, who has always been patient, supportive and encouraging toward my many diverse professional projects. I am grateful to my mother, Barbara L. Carter, who introduced me to the beauty and importance of visual and written language and my late father, Dr. Thomas William Carter, whose example of excellence and service remain a beacon in my life. I especially want to thank my children, Tom and Katie, who tolerate with remarkably good humor, artwork and books scattered throughout our home and a mother who edits between tennis matches and various other activities. Without my family's enthusiasm and encouragement this project would never have been completed.

CATHERINE CARTER GOEBEL
Paul A. Anderson Chair in the Arts
Professor of Art History

"Observe carefully and extract from nature everything that can be extracted. Above all, light! Seek its radiance, its flash, render it down, hunt out its warmth."

Eugène Boudin *(1824-98)*

The Origins of Modernity

An Introduction

Catherine Carter Goebel

Works of art offer an ideal historical and multidisciplinary lens through which we might examine modernity as it relates to the various eras and themes under investigation. Diverse scholarly approaches are often used to explicate artwork, including stylistic analysis, iconographic (symbolic) language, sociological and psychological interpretation, as well as scientific and technical consideration. Art historians increasingly account for the context in which works of art were created and the manner in which such accomplishments mirror their time periods. By studying artwork from a given epoch, we can learn more about that time. Furthermore, as we trace the development of art along a timeline, we may note places where tradition and past styles (catalogue 2) have impacted the present (catalogue 79) as well as innovations that occur that are particular to a specific period.

catalogue 2

catalogue 79

Thus, the *Origins of Modernity* exhibition serves as a major pedagogical resource for teaching critical thinking, comparative analysis and chronological developments. Studying such original works of art, rather than merely consulting photographs or electronic images, is crucial for students because reproductions cannot adequately present perceptual subtleties of scale, surface, color and line quality or conceptual details found within the work's content. This art collection has been carefully developed in order to effectively complement the liberal arts curriculum of the college; it thus establishes an important visual education resource for students and faculty. As evidenced by this publication, undergraduates ranging from the first through senior year with a multitude of majors and minors have benefited from the opportunity of directly studying these outstanding works of art in person. And the benefit increases, as their writing further informs the next generation of students who might utilize this catalogue for their own research, creating an on-going dialogue with the work of art and with others who interpret it, designed to facilitate both contemplation and action.

The origins of modernity may be traced through a number of cultural and historical movements. In fact, the very nature of being *modern* may pertain to such a wide range of artistic periods that one must repeatedly attempt to frame modernity within its appropriate context. Many art historians, for example, feel nineteenth-century American expatriate artist James McNeill Whistler (catalogue 61) effectively defined the position of the modern artist. Whistler was a highly original individual who transformed Romantic alienation into a virtue and indeed made it a necessity for success. One cannot imagine a better role model for the modern pose than Whistler, an artist who flaunted patrons, sued a critic, enjoyed being incomprehensible and wrote a book to celebrate it all. In fact, his publication, *The Gentle Art of Making Enemies*, has long been hailed as a virtual sourcebook for modern artists.

catalogue 96

Jeff Abernathy, Dean of the College and Professor of English, proposes: "To be modern is to doubt the very certainties that have ever defined the human. It is both burden and promise, as demonstrated, for instance, in the tension we find in this collection between the rearward-glancing Thomas Hart Benton (catalogue 96) and the forward-looking Marc Chagall (catalogue 98). We see the twentieth century lurch forward despite the tension, passing—at times regretfully—into new awareness of a not-quite existential isolation. In reflecting on the *Origins of Modernity*, we consider the essential tensions of our community."

catalogue 98

In applying this term through the liberal arts model, itself a concept representing, according to Thomas Banks, Professor of Classics and Dorothy Parkander Professor of Literature, an "evolving human achievement, not a motionless given"[1] and across various disciplines within the liberal studies program, varied diverse definitions and interpretations result. Such complexity furnishes "introductions to the fundamental questions of the liberal arts...an ever-new resource for an unknown future."[2] And as with the classical basis for such examination, this exhibition begins with Greek civilization.

catalogue 61

Perhaps the very nature of being *modern*, implies constant flux as the *new* is evaluated, and often replaced, by the next generation. Nancy Huse, Professor of English, suggests the richness of such relativity: "*Modern* has seven listed meanings in the *Oxford English Dictionary*. Our students always know the first one, which focuses on the right-now...perhaps the most instructive thing about *modern* is that we see various shades and sparks in the word, so that it shelters and stimulates our favorite versions of history. I like to imagine faculty relativism overtaking, just for a moment, student certainty when we each say *modern*, and then in a curious dance changing partners. And back again. For me, the dance of words and meaning is the whole reason we partner up anyway."

In defining the historical *modern age*, productive interpretative disagreements ensue. As David Ellis, Assistant Professor of History, states: "Many historians in the west consider the modern era to have begun sometime around either 1500 or 1789. Those in the first camp point to a number of crucial developments that occurred within fifty years or so of 1500. These include the introduction of the movable printing press, European voyages of discovery and subsequent transcontinental exchanges, significant expansion and solidification of the Ottoman Empire…[and] the beginning of the Protestant Reformation(s) …Those who favor the time around 1789 (give or take fifty years) as the beginning of the modern era point to another cluster of comparably important events and processes that start around that time. These include important developments in imperialism…, the American Revolution…, the various phases of the French Revolution [and]…the beginnings of the Industrial Revolution…Historians of Europe often resort to a *modus vivendi* [an accommodation] that partly reconciles the two positions…[into a] distinction between the *early modern* and the *modern* eras."

The so-called *early modern* period might be traced in such Renaissance works as Giorgio Ghisi's engraving after Michelangelo's *The Erythraean Sibyl* (catalogue 5) at the Sistine Chapel in Rome. As he did in the famous scene of the *Creation of Adam*, from the same location, Michelangelo sought to reconcile classical idealism and anatomical investigation with Roman Catholicism. Such renderings reflect a careful balance of art and science with theology, reinforced by the artist's own deep faith and belief that if indeed man was made in God's image, then by studying cadavers the artist could both learn how to accurately portray the human figure and spiritually gain greater insight into the nature of God. In the same manner, Northern Renaissance master, Albrecht Dürer (catalogue 6), utilized architect Filippo Brunelleschi's mathematical invention of linear perspective, which improved upon ancient illusionism by effectively creating the look of a third dimension through a logical system of parallel and perpendicular lines on an otherwise two-dimensional surface.

catalogue 5

catalogue 6

Following on the heels of such innovations, the Reformation brought about profound changes in seventeenth-century Baroque subject matter. For example, Dutch etcher, Rembrandt Van Rijn, although illustrating a religious event in *Christ Preaching* (catalogue 12), adopted an approach which reflects less interest in the visionary side of religion and instead presents an approachable holy figure who, although emphasized through *chiaroscuro* (the contrast of light and shadow), seems to compete with the assemblage of interesting personalities surrounding him. Rembrandt was a master of atmosphere and characterization and his works responded to a growing interest in searching beyond classical idealism toward individuality. In similar manner, artist and diplomat, Peter Paul Rubens in *The Hunt of the Hippopotamus and the Crocodile* (catalogue 10) illustrated the quest for exoticism based in further voyages of discovery. The privileged humanistic position of man over nature is fragile, lending itself to a more emotional and precarious depiction, with a similar sort of modern appeal as today's action movies. Even the medium of printmaking reflects an increasing democratic approach to art by making it more accessible to a larger number of people, both by virtue of its multiple images as well as its resulting lower price.

catalogue 12

catalogue 10

3

catalogue 13

catalogue 25

In most recent art historical studies, however, the modern period seems to be most broadly defined by the eighteenth-century Enlightenment and the various important events that followed in its wake. In an era marked by a return to classicism and order, further fueled by the rediscovery of the lost Roman cities of Pompeii and Herculaneum and the consequent Neoclassical movement, Rococo images of decadent, pampered female Parisian aristocrats depicted as goddesses such as *Hebe* (catalogue 13) would soon be replaced by desperate women in revolt (catalogue 25), demanding a means by which to feed their children. Artists pursued the *Grand Tour*, considered an essential finishing element to gentlemen's formal education, and sculptors found a ready market for marble copies of ancient Greek and Roman works such as *Minerva* (catalogue 21). British entrepreneur Josiah

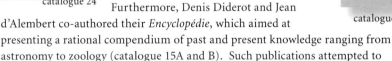

Wedgwood effectively marketed the classical for popular consumption through his invention of jasper ware (catalogue 24) which imitated ancient Roman glass. At the time, the so-called *father of art history*, Johann Winckelmann, encouraged young enthusiasts: "There is but one way for the moderns to become great, and perhaps unequaled; I mean by imitating the ancients."[3]

catalogue 24

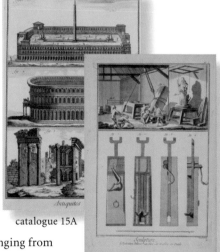

catalogue 15A

catalogue 21

Furthermore, Denis Diderot and Jean d'Alembert co-authored their *Encyclopédie*, which aimed at presenting a rational compendium of past and present knowledge ranging from astronomy to zoology (catalogue 15A and B). Such publications attempted to

catalogue 15B

catalogue 20

portray a rational new world devoid of superstition. At the same time, they made information more precise and available to a larger number of people. Artists such as Sebastiano visited Athens and Rome on the Grand Tour in order to examine and record such antiquities in person (catalogue 20), while academies in France and Britain, patronized by royalty, developed to reinforce appropriate artistic training and exhibition (catalogue 22) of didactic artwork. These art academies also determined the types and hierarchy for works of art. History was considered the highest level and consisted of stories from ancient or recent history, including religious or mythological subjects. It was the most prestigious since it was generally considered morally edifying. Also in descending order, the hierarchy included portraits, genre (scenes of everyday life), landscape and still life.

catalogue 22

catalogue 17

It seemed that the American Revolution would provide the perfect Enlightenment subject for artists of the day. Yet in a young country which prided itself on freedom from oppression, there were inherent challenges as to how to appropriately portray grand history painting related to the revolutionary cause. John Trumbull's image of the *Declaration of Independence* (catalogue 17), representing perhaps the triumph of Enlightenment philosophy, suffers from the very nature of the newly created country

catalogue 18

where straightforward Yankee realism and accuracy outweighed bombastic historicizing. Another problem arose in this new republic, without princes and popes, as to who would patronize such large, expensive works? The same quality might be seen in the consummate if unfinished portrait of *George Washington* (catalogue 18), which retains its credibility by portraying a simple, straightforward interpretation of the first president of the United States.

catalogue 27

Romanticism furnished many seeds for modernity. The image of the suffering artist found its source in such works as Francisco Goya's *The Sleep of Reason Produces Monsters* (catalogue 27), a self-portrait of the painter himself who, although a child of the Enlightenment, was disillusioned by intolerant rulers, peasant sorcery and ignorance as well as the Spanish Inquisition. An illness left him deaf, further isolating him from the aristocratic society of his patrons. This image breaks the barrier from the rational world to the imagination, which according to Goya, when accompanied by reason, was the "mother of the arts," yet when abandoned, produced "impossible monsters."[4] Goya's fascination with the subject of dreams opened a realm of mystery that would be the focus of twentieth-century Surrealists. At the same time, painters like Thomas Lawrence explored mortality through literary sources such as William Shakespeare. *Hamlet* (catalogue 28), for

catalogue 28

example, holds the skull of his former court jester, Yorick, a *memento mori* (reminder of death) in order to examine the frailty of the human condition. Both images and sources also touched upon the subject of depression and insanity, which would be further explored by twentieth-century psychology.

catalogue 29

Multiculturalism—or perhaps orientalism— was increasingly probed through images such as the *Burial of Atala* (catalogue 29), which illustrates the tug-of-war experienced in the New World by François-René de Chateaubriand's literary figure of Atala. She could only reconcile the pull between her religious conviction, illustrated by the priest on the right, and her love for the young Native American boy on the left, by tragically committing suicide. The piece, having elements of both Neoclassicism and Romanticism, might also be seen as illustrating the competing schools of the time. In the same manner,

catalogue 33

exotic subjects reflecting colonization were also explored through Sir David Wilkie's study (catalogue 33) for *Sir David Baird Discovering the Body of the Sultaun Tippoo Sahib* and Eugène Delacroix's sketches of lions (catalogue 34).

catalogue 34

Romanticism also accompanied the age of modern nineteenth-century science. Dell Jensen, Assistant Professor of Chemistry, has suggested: "Modernity cannot be defined without looking at the development of science, because it provided the basis for advancement and betterment of society through the understanding of the natural world. From this perspective, it can be said that modernity started with the great thinkers of the Renaissance (Leonardo da Vinci and Galileo Galilei). They were followed by many other individuals (Isaac Newton, Francis Bacon, Antoine Lavoisier and Benjamin Franklin) who made significant contributions to our understanding of the modern world…[Furthermore] John Dalton and Charles Darwin…laid the foundation for modern science. Dalton's Atomic Theory (1807) provided the basis for much of our understanding of chemistry and Darwin's book, *Origin of Species* (1859), solidified the concept of natural selection and evolution. During this four hundred year period, the world underwent profound changes and many of those changes involved the understanding of the natural world and its role in society." Yet, such a narrative of progress often sat uneasily with Romantics, whose appreciation for the power, beauty and uniqueness of nature was coupled with a bitter sense of the loss of mystery, which many expressed with poignant irony.

catalogue 31

Artistic parallels in science might be traced to John James Audubon's series, including *Whippoorwill* (1830—catalogue 31), which aimed at recording all the native birds of North America depicted in their natural habitats. The illustrator attempted to capture the immediacy of the specimens, either drawn from life or freshly shot and wired into position, exhibited against a blank background allowing them to be read in a careful analytical manner, with some aesthetic interpretation for effect. In similar manner, English Romantic painter John Constable beautifully combined the meteorological interests of his age with art through dozens of cloud studies, captured on sight through the invention of portable oil paints which allowed artists for the first time to paint outdoors directly from nature (catalogue 30A). Although Constable lovingly depicted the subtle nuances of cloud banks and individual trees; his scientific interest, like Michelangelo's before him, was reinforced by a profound belief that such natural phenomena were aspects of God's divine order. Yet never before had an artist so effectively captured the moods of nature, which would have immediate influence on the development of Realism and Impressionism in France.

catalogue 30A

American artist Thomas Cole would similarly straddle Romanticism and Realism. His *Voyage of Life* series raised

catalogue 35

landscape to the level of history through its predictable moral metaphor for the river of life, the meaning accessible to a large audience. In scene two of the four-part series, *Youth* (catalogue 35), the baby from scene one is now a young man in the summer of his youth (as well as that of landscape) who optimistically steers his boat with the hourglass masthead toward a castle in the sky. Although the elements are carefully and scientifically rendered after nature, Cole's greater purpose was to deliver the message of time's passing and the consequent *ages of man* inherent in history painting.

By the second half of the nineteenth century, artists had largely abandoned such themes and focused, with Impressionism's interests in capturing everyday life, on utilizing new theories such as the physics of light.

Michel-Eugène Chevreul published his law of simultaneous contrasts in 1839, which likely influenced Impressionist and Post-Impressionist approaches to color. Such Impressionist paintings as Henry Clifford's *Boating Scene* (catalogue 65) reflected these new ideas, as well as the utilization of atmospheric perspective based on the scientific observation that colors appear cooler and details less distinct in the distance. Such imagery also offered no apology for simply representing modern life, with no pretense of greater purpose.

catalogue 65

By the mid nineteenth century, following the Industrial Revolution, city populations were growing at rapid speed, as people moved from the countryside. This new middle class was accommodated by urban adjustments. Thomas Bengtson, Professor of Mathematics and Earl H. Beling Chair in Mathematics, has noted: "The fine arts were greatly affected by advances in technology and gains in wealth. Art came to be produced not only for the aristocracy, but rather for those with the means to pay for it. Subjects depicted in art changed to include themes of interest to a growing middle class. Entirely new subjects became available, too, such as railroads and buildings of inexpensive iron and steel. Technology provided new means, such as photography (catalogue 45) and steel engravings, with which to produce art…Consider *The Railway Station*

catalogue 45

(catalogue 50), 1866, an engraving after an original painting by William Powell Frith. The subject includes a train and a train station. Fifty years earlier, trains did not exist and neither did the architecture of an open iron lattice for the station. Steel engraving techniques had only recently become available, making the print affordable to a growing middle class."

catalogue 50

catalogue 52

In response to the growing bourgeoisie, newspapers and journals multiplied to educate and entertain the masses. Artists such as Charles Keene (catalogue 52), George du Maurier (catalogue 51) and Phil May (catalogue 53) delighted their audiences with narratives, astutely drawn and engraved, that illustrated the many facets of modern urban life. Yet their field, based on quick and brilliant sketches, would soon be eclipsed by photography.

catalogue 51

catalogue 53

Many artists and writers regretted the sweeping changes that accompanied urban modernity. As the new Paris was being designed by Baron Haussmann for Emperor Napoleon III, clearing away much of the historic medievalism of the city, artists such as Charles Meryon in *La Galerie Notre Dame* (catalogue 36) recorded national treasures that were now in jeopardy. In like manner, James McNeill Whistler depicted the colorful dockside views along the Thames River in London, such as *Black Lion Wharf* (catalogue 40), destined to be irrevocably erased through the building of an embankment. Although such changes brought large boulevards and better living conditions, there was a wistful sentimentality as to the price of *progress*. Decorative arts even reflected rejection of the mass production of post-Industrial Revolution society by designing functional art that retained careful craftsmanship, part of the *Arts and Crafts* movement, with results such as Emile Gallé's beautiful glass vase (catalogue 75) and the elegant bronze *Art Nouveau Style Inkstand* (catalogue 73).

catalogue 36

catalogue 40

catalogue 73

catalogue 75

With such renditions of modernity initially aided by technology, many artists further questioned the *advances* that they enabled. Whistler suggested: "The imitator is a poor kind of creature. If the man who paints only the tree, or flower, or other surface he sees before him were an artist, the king of artists would be the photographer."[5] Portraits (catalogue 45) and landscapes (catalogue 49) could now be captured on film, so what was left for an artist to do? Such modernist dilemmas might be illustrated by comparing Eugène Boudin's *Beach at Trouville* (1864—catalogue 42) with James McNeill Whistler's *Early Morning* (1878—catalogue 60). On the surface, though similar in composition and atmospheric effect, they both emerge from very distinct philosophies which ultimately defined the course of modern twentieth-century art.

catalogue 45

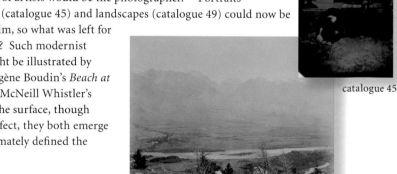
catalogue 49

catalogue 42

Both artists were initially influenced by writer and theorist Charles Baudelaire (catalogue 41), who postulated in his 1845 essay on the *heroism of modern life:* "We do not lack for subjects or colors with which to make epics. The painter, the true painter for whom we are searching, will be the one who can seize the epic quality of contemporary life and make us see and understand, with brush or with pencil, how great and poetic we are in our cravats and patent-leather boots....the true seekers may grant us the extraordinary joy of celebrating the advent of the *new!*"[6]

catalogue 60

catalogue 41

Boudin's works directly relate to such ideas as he was one of the first French artists to paint *en plein air*, before an outdoor subject, at fashionable bourgeois resorts. He aimed to capture the climatic effects of the landscape, as well as the fashionable participants who inhabited it. Like Constable, Boudin focused on the transient qualities of the atmosphere, yet in a more secularized Impressionist manner. His works would inspire his most direct follower, Claude Monet, the leader of the French Impressionist movement, who described the influence of Boudin: "Suddenly a veil was torn away. I had understood—I had realized what painting could be. By the single example of this painter devoted to his art with such independence, my destiny as a painter opened out to me."[7] By capturing instantaneous views, further informed through photography, portable tube oil paints and new scientific theories on light and color, such works epitomized the epic quality of modern life. Sketches and finished paintings now expressed the same sort of *unfinished* quality that invited the viewer's eye to complete the impression, ultimately leading to Paul Cézanne's description of Monet: "He is only an eye, but *my* God what an eye!"[8] Monet himself admitted the difficulty of achieving his goals: "It is enough to drive one raving mad, to render the weather, the atmosphere, the ambience...the sun sets so fast that I can't follow it."[9] Boudin and Monet thus shared the naturalist passion of Constable, devoid of his spiritual associations.

Whistler, on the other hand, by 1878 had evolved away from such Realist concerns and increasingly withdrew from competing with technology. Instead, he advocated the theory of *Art for Art's Sake*, a more elitist philosophy that placed aesthetics above replication. Analogies were made between the parallel connections of music, poetry and art, as he stated: "As music is the poetry of sound; so is painting the poetry of sight, and the subject-matter has nothing to do with harmony of sound or of colour."[10] In this manner, he reasserted his traditional position as an artistic genius who would *improve* the scenery: "Nature contains the elements, in colour and form, of all pictures, as the keyboard contains the notes of all music. But the artist is born to pick, and choose, and group with science, these elements, that the result may be beautiful—as the musician gathers his notes; and forms his chords, until he brings forth from chaos glorious harmony. To say to the painter, that Nature is to be taken as she is, is to say to the player, that he may sit on the piano."[11]

Given his *modern* sense of aesthetics, we can see Whistler's landscape, along the Thames River in London, softened and made more elegant through an atmospheric envelope. A critic at the time, in response to such effects, humorously suggested that perhaps there was no fog in London until Whistler created it. Whistler thus transformed the murky urban industrial landscape, as he described in his publication *The Gentle Art of Making Enemies*: "And when the evening mist clothes the riverside with poetry, as with a veil, and the poor buildings

catalogue 57

catalogue 54

catalogue 55

lose themselves in the dim sky, and the tall chimneys become campanile, and the warehouses are palaces in the night, and the whole city hangs in the heavens, and fairy-land is before us… Nature, who, for once, has sung in tune, sings her exquisite song to the artist alone, her son and her master—her son in that he loves her, her master in that he knows her….In all that is dainty and lovable he finds hints for his own combinations, and *thus* is Nature ever his resource and always at his service, and to him is naught refused."[12]

Whistler and Boudin were thus two leaders of the nineteenth century who developed works of art that were highly original, yet at the same time reflected the theories of artists and writers of their age. As in the case of these works, at times their images bore striking similarities to one another, yet in theory, they were at opposite ends of the spectrum. Boudin represented the scientific and technological advancements of the day that enabled artists to better portray perceptual realities of nature on their canvases. Whistler, on the other hand, offered a more conceptual response which encouraged the development of twentieth-century abstraction. Both clearly were beacons for the modern era.

Along with reactions to technology and science, new viewpoints were inspired from interactions with other cultures. In particular, the reopening of trade with Japan, virtually isolated from the West for one hundred fifty years, introduced Oriental porcelains, and perhaps more importantly, Japanese woodblock prints to an appreciative western market. The influence that such bold, cropped and flattened images had on nineteenth-century approaches might be demonstrated by comparing a Japanese pillar print (catalogue 57) with Impressionist Edgar Degas' etching of *Mary Cassatt at the Louvre* (catalogue 56), which acknowledged not only the subject of women in museums, but their training and acceptance as artists (catalogue 54). Such *Japonisme* (European adaptation of Japanese aesthetics) revolutionized modern art. Renaissance perspective was abandoned in favor of more abstracted artforms. Japanese *ukiyo-e* (images from the floating world) subjects also encouraged artists to pursue more common everyday scenes, exemplified by Cassatt's straightforward approach to maternal bonding in *The Manicure* (catalogue 55) and Degas' suggestion that the modern *Venus*, as a female nude, might be found in bourgeois households and houses of prostitution, as in *Le Bain* (catalogue 58).

catalogue 56

catalogue 58

Further multiculturalism—or orientalism—can be found in Post-Impressionist Paul Gauguin's intentionally primitive woodcut, *Watched by the Spirits of the Dead* (catalogue 78), inspired by his life in Tahiti and his response to native mythology. In like manner, African art (catalogue 80B) and its *magical* brutality would stimulate twentieth-century leaders such as Pablo Picasso and Henri Matisse to pursue more conceptualized and abstract directions. Matisse explored the emotive, expressionist qualities of such images, and Picasso, the more formal and geometric patterns. Lyric poet Guillaume Apollinaire (catalogue 87), one of the great critics of the early twentieth century, encouraged interpretation of such sources: "Consequently the artistic

catalogue 78

catalogue 87

catalogue 84

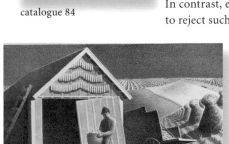

catalogue 84

'handwriting' of all kinds of styles—those of the hieratic Egyptians, the refined Greeks and the voluptuous Cambodians, the works of the ancient Peruvians, the African statuettes proportioned according to the passions which have inspired them—can interest an artist and help him to develop his personality."[13]

Artists Picasso and Georges Braque advanced the style of Cubism, as beautifully depicted in Perle Fine's *Sketch for a Cubist Still Life* (catalogue 90). Apollinaire recognized that these innovators built upon Whistler's aesthetic model and were "moving toward an entirely new art which will stand, with respect to painting as envisaged heretofore, as music stands to literature. It will be pure painting, just as music is pure literature."[14] Although still based in natural observation, the pieces of the still life are seemingly broken into parts and built along a mathematical grid. Color is secondary to form, the whole rejecting linear perspective, in favor of a sort of composite view consisting of the intersection of multiple viewpoints— presumably adding time, as a suggested fourth dimension, to the ensemble.

catalogue 80B

catalogue 90

Although nearing abstraction, it was the German Expressionists who accomplished the momentous break with reality. Apocalyptic imagery often appeared in the works of *Blue Rider* painters, German Franz Marc (catalogue 84) and Russian Vasily Kandinsky (catalogue 85) during the years preceding World War I. They responded to world events, not with the careful, mathematic precision of the Cubists, but instead with the expression of full emotive color and imagery, continuing the course of Whistler's philosophy. Kandinsky wrote in *Concerning the Spiritual in Art* (1911): "Color directly influences the soul. Color is the keyboard, the eyes are the hammers, the soul is the piano with many strings. The artist is the hand that plays, touching one key or another purposely, to cause vibrations in the soul."[15] Such interpretation led Kandinsky to ultimate abstraction based on pure color and line.

catalogue 96

In contrast, events leading to America's involvement in World War II encouraged artists to reject such European modernism in favor of familiar scenes of American genre, as illustrated in Grant Wood's *Seed Time and Harvest* (catalogue 95) and Thomas Hart Benton's *Sunday Morning* (catalogue 96). These works continued the comfortable realism of nineteenth-century depictions by artists such as Boudin. Wedged as they were between the Great Depression and the Second World War, they presented a sort of predictable pattern and perhaps even escapism during an age of profound

catalogue 85

catalogue 17

catalogue 18

uncertainty. These traditional images could just as well have been based on nineteenth-century imagery as twentieth and reflect a national preference for the observed fact, traceable back to such benchmarks as the *Declaration of Independence* (catalogue 17) and portrait of *George Washington* (catalogue 18).

catalogue 3B

catalogue 74

Such interactions between conceptual and perceptual viewpoints might be noted throughout this exhibition. One might discern renewed sources from the past, such as the beautiful patina of the ancient Roman glass bowl (catalogue 3B), an accident of nature's chemical process over time, scientifically replicated as an inkwell by the twentieth-century decorative artist, Louis Comfort Tiffany (catalogue 74). Also intriguing is the balance of the written word with visual imagery, as in the medieval illuminated manuscript (catalogue 4) contrasted against Henri de Toulouse-Lautrec's modernist advertising poster for the Moulin Rouge (catalogue 69). At the same time, the bold, clean elements of the Renaissance woodcut from Hans Holbein's *Dance of Death* (catalogue 7) might be traced in the disillusioned 1940s German workers of Erich Heckel (catalogue 97).

catalogue 4

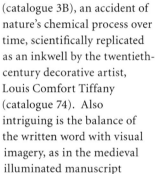

catalogue 7

catalogue 97

Within modernity, twentieth-century landscapes can vacillate between the ethereal visions of Marc Chagall (catalogue 98) and the classical metaphysical discomfort of Georgio de Chirico (catalogue 86B). We might even trace the same

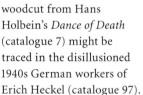

catalogue 69

catalogue 98

catalogue 99

abstracted curl of Alexander Calder (catalogue 99) in Fannie Nampeyo's Native American ceramic decoration (catalogue 91). Finally, one can only marvel at the visual concordance between Gavin Hamilton's elevated allegory of classical perfection in the *Allegorical Figure of Painting* (catalogue 19) as it translates into a mechanistic Art Deco-inspired woman, machine-like yet whimsical (catalogue 94) within a modern twentieth-century urban structure. What other comparisons, contrasts, distinctions and definitions might be observed? I invite you to examine the pieces in this exhibition, digest the information written in the catalogue, investigate even further and draw your own conclusions.

catalogue 86B

catalogue 91

[1] Thomas Banks, Professor of Classics, "An Introduction to the Liberal Arts for the AGES Reader," *Augustana General Education Studies: A Reader for First Year Students* (Rock Island: Augustana College, 2005), 1.

[2] Ibid.

[3] Johann Joachim Wickelmann, *Reflections on the Painting and Sculptures of the Greeks*, trans. Henry Fuseli (London, 1765), reprinted in Lorenz Eitner, ed., *Neoclassicism and Romanticism, 1750–1850: An Anthology of Sources and Documents* (New York: Harper & Row, 1989), 6.

[4] R. Stanley Johnson, trans., *Francisco Goya (1746–1828): Los Caprichos* (Chicago: R. S. Johnson Fine Art, 1992), 32.

[5] James McNeill Whistler, "The Red Rag," in *The Gentle Art of Making Enemies* (London: William Heinemann, 1892), 128.

[6] Charles Baudelaire, *The Salon of 1845*, reprinted in J. Mayne, trans., *The Mirror of Art* (London: Phaidon Press, 1955), 37.

[7] William C. Seitz, *Claude Monet* (New York: Harry N. Abrams, 1960), 13.

[8] Thomas Parsons and Iain Gale, *Post-Impressionism: The Rise of Modern Art: 1880-1920* (Toronto: NDE Publishing, 1999), 45.

[9] Claude Monet, letters to Gustave Geffroy, July and October, 1890, respectively, quoted in Seitz, 138.

[10] Whistler, "The Red Rag," 127.

[11] James McNeill Whistler, "Mr. Whistler's *Ten O'Clock*," *The Gentle Art of Making Enemies* (London: William Heinemann, 1892), 142-43.

[12] Ibid., 144-45.

[13] Guillaume Apollinaire, *La Phalange* (Paris, 15 December 1907), 483-4.

[14] Guillaume Apollinaire quoted in Marilyn Stokstad, *Art History*, revised second edition, volume two (Upper Saddle River: Pearson Prentice Hall, 2005), 1036.

[15] Vasily Kandinsky, *Concerning the Spiritual in Art* (1911), quoted in Stokstad, 1028.

catalogue 19

catalogue 94

Yan Face
Pablo Ruiz y Picasso (catalogue 100) 1963

Fire in the Kiln!

Picasso's Classical Modernism

Errin Copple

All avant-garde artists somehow find their roots in the past, whether by outright rebellion against it, a clever reinterpretation of it or merely by its reconstruction. Pablo y Ruiz Picasso, in creating his *Yan Face* vase (1963, catalogue 100), was no different. Through exploring the stylistic similarities as well as thematic ideas evident in comparison of two pieces from the Paul A. Anderson Art History

catalogue 1

Collection, the *Attic Black-figure Kylix* (ca. 500 B. C.E., catalogue 1) and *Red-figure dish with Running Female Figure with Wreath and Ivy-garnished Phiale* (ca. 330-320 B.C.E., catalogue 2), this essay will demonstrate how Picasso drew from the Classical Greek tradition. One key difference examined will be the fact that Picasso's vase was not meant to be functional but was designed as *fine* art, whereas the Greek pieces were intended primarily for use.

catalogue 2

Picasso's *Yan Face* vase is a red earthenware pitcher that was probably cast from a mold, then manipulated and painted. When observed, the top portion of the vase around the rim resembles a bird, the lower portion a face. The mouth of the vase has been pinched together to form the beak of the bird, which is distinguished by a few bold black strokes that delineate the beak and eyes. The face was painted on the belly of the pitcher, again in thick black lines, consisting of eyebrows, a mouth and a nose, the nose originating as two parallel lines above the mouth and moving upward to arch over the eyebrows. A handle was added and short black lines were painted horizontally across it. Similar lines were added sweeping back from the face behind the ears in order to represent hair.

With the combination of a red pot and black coloring, Picasso's pitcher recalls the ancient traditions of Greek vase painting, especially, in this case, of Archaic black-figure painting. With the combination of red ground and black paint, Picasso established strong ties to these ancient traditions. An example from this period is the *Attic Black-figure Kylix*. Kylixes were common Greek drinking cups. They often were used at *symposia*, all male drinking parties.[1] The adult male was the center of Greek society, entitled to vote, fight and, of course, attend the *symposia*. Educated from a young age, boys were trained mentally and physically, and brought up to value courage, honor and loyalty.

Despite an intensive educational program, the Greeks valued recreation. According to ancient sources, at their *symposia* the wine flowed as freely as the stories. And it was here that the myths were recounted. Contests of poetry and wit, as told in Plato's *Symposium*,[2] were some of the many diversions offered at these drinking parties. At the end of the evening any sobriety or aristocratic pretense would be lost within an atmosphere of congenial drunkenness. The most popular drinking cup for these events was the *kylix*. For this reason, many that exist today have been painted with humorous or erotic scenes, befitting the occasion of the *symposium*.

This particular *kylix* is a red clay cup decorated in the black-figure style, the technique of painting black figures over pale or reddish *terracotta*, baked clay. By etching into the black slip the paler clay beneath provides additional details. Finally, red and white paint were applied to the surface for extra touches.[3] The interior of this *kylix* is painted entirely black, except for the head of a *gorgon* in the bare reddish clay. The gorgon is detailed both by incising the black paint and by adding dabs of red to its mane.

catalogue 1

The gorgons were three sisters who were hideously ugly, female mythological creatures with hair made of snakes. According to tradition, they turned men who looked at them into stone. When the owner drained the contents of his cup, he was immediately confronted with this face staring at him. This is a comical image, although gorgons were initially illustrated for their protective functions.[4] The exterior of the cup is divided into black and red bands, the central red one holding the alternating images of lions, palmettes and eyes. When tipped upright, as it would be in drinking, the overall shape of the vessel forms a humorous face with two eyes in the band, handles for ears and a circular foot for a mouth.

Between the *Yan Face* vase and the *Black-figure kylix* many surface similarities exist. Perhaps the most obvious one is the earthy red clay that forms the backdrop for the black figures, which become the focus. The replication of this black and red pattern on pottery gives us our first clue that Picasso was looking to the past, perhaps for inspiration or perhaps to resolve something. The *Yan Face* vase is by no means the only pottery Picasso created that harkens back to Greek precedence. He made several pieces in the black-figure style and also explored an array of Classical subjects in his works, especially in those created during the time he spent in Antibes and Vallauris in the area of the Mediterranean Sea. Picasso remarked on his subject matter at this time, "It's strange—in Paris, I never draw fauns, centaurs or heroes from mythology, it's as if they live only here."[5]

catalogue 100

On this vase, Picasso did not, however, include a faun, but rather a bird and a human face seem to be the focal point. It was not unusual for human figures, especially women, to be portrayed as surface decoration or even as the body of the pot itself. The idea, held throughout history, associates women as empty vessels from which life springs. Picasso often portrayed women on his vases and clay pieces. He made several female depictions including many *tanagras*,[6] so-called because of their resemblance to Hellenistic statuettes by that name.[7]

In his younger days, Picasso was influenced by Post-Impressionist Paul Gauguin's ideas about creating from the earthy clay. Gauguin believed if God could form man out of the earth, why could the artist not do the same?[8] Similar to Picasso, Gauguin's work in clay was fairly obscure. History has generally focused on these artists' paintings and also, for Gauguin, on his wooden sculpture and woodcuts (catalogue 78). Gauguin preferred to create hand-shaped constructions rather than regularized objects from a wheel or mold.[9] In light of the large number of people portrayed on Picasso's clay, we might note an almost reverential quality to some of them.

Seemingly in contrast to Classicism, both Gauguin and Picasso were highly interested in primitivism. The rough exoticism of primal art drew their fascination and creative tools like many other modern artists. Gauguin

catalogue 78

believed, "Every barbarity is a return to youth. The great mistake is the Greek, however beautiful it may be."[10] Through his Tahitian woodcut, *Manao tupapau (Watched by the Spirits of the Dead*, 1894-1895, catalogue 78), Gauguin delved into both the mystery and the rougher style of primitive art. A girl is shown in the foreground lying on a bed while a haunting figure resides in the background. Whether exploring the dream world, the realm of spirits or both, he investigated topics contemplated in the primitive lands he visited. Even the very medium of woodcut relies on coarse imagery, as he emphasized, whose thick lines and scratches add to the primal effect. Gauguin was one of the first Europeans to *discover* primitive art and use it as a source, as Picasso would later reinforce with qualities inspired by African masks (catalogue 80A and 80B).

In the *Red-figure dish with Running Female Figure with Wreath and Ivy-garnished Phiale* (catalogue 2), the image of the entire female figure dominates. Similarities between Picasso's *Yan Face* vase and this *phiale* will help us gain a better understanding of the Classical influence on Picasso. A *phiale* is a shallow cup, probably used for drinking or pouring offerings.[11] It was done in the red-figure style, in which the figures are in red silhouette against the black slip background with additional black touches painted to indicate details on the red surface.

catalogue 80B

catalogue 80A

This style evolved from the black-figure in response to the changing demands of the market and became the dominant medium for several hundred years. Although potentially more difficult for the artist to paint in terms of negative space, leaving the central image positive in bare clay, details within the image were easier to add with a brush rather than through the previous necessity of etching. In this case, additional white paint creates the girl's necklace, bracelets, headband and other details. The central image is a running girl who is frozen on a decorated band beneath her feet. In her left hand she holds a wreath, and in her right a *phiale* similar to the one on which she is depicted. On the wall behind her hangs a fillet and decorative flowers. Large laurel leaves encircle her beneath the rim of the cup.

catalogue 2

An obvious similarity to Picasso's pitcher is the black on red coloring. However, perhaps even more interesting is the subject of the female. Instead of taking the shape of the vessel, she provides decoration for the cup. Frozen in an active pose, she looks behind her at the *phiale* that is in her hand, ironically the same object that the viewer would hold. We are led through her gaze to examine what she grasps. Perhaps it is a clue as to the bowl's purpose. In Picasso's piece the bird and the face portrayed on the vessel take the body of the vase as their own and force viewers to see the pitcher as a bird and as a face, transforming it in their minds. Both pieces require the viewer to take that extra step after first seeing it, to interpret the vessel and then to symbolically transform it.

Besides the face, Picasso's vase also has the image of a bird at its spout. Again, this tradition of zoomorphic images on pots was not new for Picasso, but had existed for thousands of years. *Vasilike* and *Kamares* wares of the Minoan culture were created some 1,500 years before the Greek gorgon *kylix* and the *Running Female Phiale*. The *Vasilike* style consisted of

catalogue 100

thick walled pots on which potters began experimenting by lengthening the spouts on pitchers. This was a forerunner to *Kamares* ware, which advanced to *eggshell* thin walls because of the availability of finer clay and the invention of the potter's wheel. Artists elongated pitcher spouts and added circles of clay to the area of eyes, which gave the jugs zoomorphic shapes resembling birds with their beak-spouted tops and clay eyes.[12] The human element was ignored and pots were painted with floral or patterned motifs. Picasso's pinched spout

catalogue 100

forming the beak of the bird is not nearly as elongated as *Vasilike* or *Kamares* spouts. However, the obvious parallels between these pitchers present a convincing connection with ancient sources.

Perhaps the main difference that distinguishes Picasso's *Yan Face* vase from the Greek *kylix*, besides the 2,500 year gap, centers on their function. While the form of each, one a pitcher the other a cup respectively, was designed to hold liquid, only one of them ever truly served that purpose. Picasso's was created as art—purely aesthetic and lacking in function. The Greek potter in making his piece was crafting a cup he knew would find its way toward much wine and presumably grateful lips. The worn paint on the handles demonstrates that the cup was indeed well used.[13]

Although the potter chose to decorate the *kylix* with bits of art, the cup was by no means considered a high art form, if it was even regarded as art at all. In the hierarchy of Greek art, pottery found its place at the bottom, preceded by gold and silver containers (their value was in the material more than craftsmanship, a Greek savings account of sorts), panel painting (at which the Greeks apparently excelled) and wall painting.[14] Of these art forms, however, it is only pottery that has survived for posterity. Greek panel paintings and wall paintings were not able to withstand time, so they unfortunately cannot be studied. Pottery, although artistic, was meant to be functional. It consisted primarily of utilitarian products decorated to entertain. People valued them, but they were not considered high art. Yet these pieces constitute the majority of the art that remains and provide most of our data for ancient Greek culture. Because of their high rate of survival most of our research is conducted on them.

An ancient market for these works definitely existed and Greek ceramicists adapted their style to the tastes of the buyers at home and abroad. But did these potters see themselves as artists? Did the utilitarian pots they painted constitute art? The loaded modern question of *what is art*? or even *who is the artist*? are not here meant to be debated. However, the majority of art historians would agree that these are indeed works of art. Perhaps the most relevant distinction lies in the fact that these pieces, unlike those by the twentieth-century artist Picasso, were meant to be used. The purpose of the gorgon *kylix*'s creation was to provide an attractive drinking cup for use

catalogue 1

at symposia that reflected both a mythological background as well as a sense of humor on the part of the artist.

Picasso's vase, on the other hand, was made, like traditional art in a museum, to be viewed and admired as art. Any art historian in his or her right mind would bodily remove the person that attempted to pour, say, wine into Picasso's vase. And in that manner, it defies the traditional purpose of a pitcher: to hold liquids, to pour. The value of the *Yan Face* vase is therefore visual and aesthetic, but truly not functional. Picasso, in designing it, aimed to create not a decorative piece designed for kitchen use but rather something for admiration and contemplation.

In crafting his clay pieces, however, Picasso did not completely work independently. A good majority of Picasso's clay works were created in the Madoura studio in Vallauris, a town on the French Riviera.[15] Picasso had first visited Vallauris with his friend Françoise Gilot in the summer of 1946 at the invitation of Georges and Suzanne Ramié to visit their pottery studio. The Ramiés were artists who had moved to Vallauris just a decade earlier. They had bought an old studio and hired a potter from the area to be their master craftsman. The next year Picasso returned to the town and to the Ramiés with a book full of sketches for ideas he wanted to create.[16] He continued to work there for another twenty years, eventually buying an abandoned factory in Vallauris to serve as his studio in 1952.[17]

Picasso himself did not throw the pots on which he painted. He had tried a few unsuccessful potting attempts and ultimately decided to let the *true* potters create the pots which he manipulated and painted. He would imagine and sketch out ideas for shapes he wanted and then have a potter achieve those forms on the wheel. Once the basic form was created, Picasso then worked toward his ultimate design, sometimes by adding clay pieces, bending the wet clay or etching into it while wet or dry. After manipulating the clay piece, he began experimenting with glazes and slips in order to form vibrant colors and patterns. He painted various characters and images on the pots, ranging broadly from birds to bikinis. Picasso, like the Greeks, definitely had a humorous side to his work, such as seen in the *Bikini*, where he took a normal bulbous shaped vase, tapered at the center, then expanding out again at the top and painted it with a bright yellow bikini. Similarly, he crafted the overly endowed male of *Priapus*, achieved by adding a tubular phallic extension to the black and white painted pot of a man.

In return for the use of their studio, Picasso gave the Ramiés permission to produce copies of some of his works and sell them for profit. These works were called *Edition Picasso* and were labeled with *Edition Picasso* and *Madoura* stamps. Picasso's *Yan Face* vase is one of these copies, number 99 out of the 300 made, which indicates another key difference between the Picasso and the *kylix* in the method of production.

The *kylix* was probably created by one artist and painted by another. Signed pieces were often labeled separately to include both who *made* and who *painted* the work. Potters were just as famous as painters. Picasso likewise only painted and altered the pots once they were already thrown. He may not have even touched the copies by the Ramiés. The replicas they made could have been copied from originals or possibly just from a design by Picasso. The great artist may have come by after the pitchers were formed and painted on the two faces, giving the vessel *life*, figuratively and aesthetically. However, it is more likely that with such a large number as 300 copies, workers in the studio painted the many pots according to his designs.

catalogue 61

One is now faced with the very real possibility that the hand of the artist never even touched the vase. What then? Can we call it a fake? Not really. These pieces, though not selling nearly as high as *original* Picassos, are still very desirable items. What accounts for this? Surely if the artist had no direct contact with the art, it must lose its value. However, this is not the case. I would attempt to explain it, as Walter Benjamin did, as the *aura of the artist*.[18] There is a certain aura attached to an artist that extends to whatever he creates, even if, as in Picasso's case, the artist never directly touched the piece. It is that invisible quality that surrounds an artist and often all that is associated with him.

catalogue 27

Throughout western history, artists have created with the help of workshops. In these workshops, *lesser* artists would assist the master in his creations: sometimes filling in landscape and background and sometimes creating the entire work of art based on a design by the chief artist. The master artist would then sign the finished work as his own, giving no credit to the workshop artists beneath him. This was not unusual. It happened quite often, and people of the respective time periods seemed to have no qualms. It was the *name* of the artist that mattered. In the last hundred years with the concept of the inspired genius artist (catalogue 27 and 61), the infiltration of *art for art's sake* ideas and, especially, the aura we now attach to them, the status of the modern artist has risen considerably. The name, the *image* of the artist, is indeed what matters most.

Looking at the American art scene at the time of the *Yan Face* vase's construction, this same idea was true. Separation of the artist from the art is nowhere more magnified during this time than with Andy Warhol and the Pop Art movement in the 1960s. Warhol created the designs for his silk-screens, but otherwise did not even touch them. He wished to be far removed from the art and its creation. Mass production was the very thing these artists replicated, taking popular culture out of the mainstream and placing it in a far from flattering light.

With the *Yan Face* vase, the possibility arises that the copies were not even hand thrown, but rather the pot may have been made from a mold and mechanically reproduced. While this form of reproduction allows for more copies of works, something seems lost in the process. With every copy, the authentic art in a sense depreciates.[19] One of the reasons Picasso did not allow the Ramiés to copy many of his pieces was that he feared that multiple

catalogue 44

copies would result in confusion over what was original (which it has).[20] This is similar to the dynamic associated with the influx of prints during the Renaissance. Prints became immensely popular (catalogue 6) because they allowed commoners to possess art which could now be affordable. In our time, lithographs (catalogue 44, 68, 69 and 79) and photography (catalogue 45 and 49) have become forms of artistic reproduction for dissemination to the masses.

The result of making art available to anyone[21] is the gradual decay of the aura surrounding the art. According to Benjamin this is brought on by "the desire of contemporary masses to bring things 'closer' spatially and humanly, which is just as ardent as their bent toward overcoming the uniqueness of every reality by accepting its reproduction."[22] Picasso himself believed in the genius of the artist and that art is not a problem to be solved or comprehended by the viewer but rather, is the outgrowth of the

artist. "Everyone wants to understand art," he stated once, "Why not try to understand the songs of a bird? Why does one love the night, flowers, everything around one, without trying to understand them? But in the case of a painting people have to *understand*."[23] The reproductions of *Yan Face* vase were created as a limited edition, with only 300 copies being made. This is a far cry from mass reproduction where anyone is able to obtain a copy. However, it is likewise far removed from a single original.

catalogue 6

The Greek pieces were also produced in a workshop. Unlike the *Yan Face* vase however, they were likely not mass-produced. Throughout the ages, art has been reproduced by students studying, masters spreading their art and outside people looking to make a profit. Mechanical reproduction differs from this; it is a technical reproduction to produce works in quantity. The only ways Greeks pursued this was through coinage and metal casting.[24] All other art was original. Perhaps because clay pots did not constitute a high art form, signatures on these pieces were rare until the sixth century B.C.E. when scholars believed Sophilos signed the first pot by an Athenian artist.[25] With signatures came the idea that artists were taking pride in their work or at least attempting to better market them. This could also reflect the changing position of the artist in Greek society. These pieces have the *aura* of authenticity because they are not replicas, but originals probably created for a specific event or person.

While Picasso drew heavily from his ancient ceramic predecessors, he had successfully created his own, entirely new style. He started with the basics—the ancient form of the medium, the terracotta red with black, the subject matter—and he transformed it. Throughout the evolution of his artistic career, Picasso continually sought new challenges and original ways to solve them. Ceramics were no exception. He used Classical influences to help him invent his own style, one that was never stagnant but in constant motion. By transforming the functional into *pure* art, Picasso took ceramics to an entirely new modern level.

[1] Barry B. Powell, *Classical Myth*, 3rd ed. (Upper Saddle River, New Jersey: Prentice-Hall Inc., 2001), 31.

[2] Plato, *Symposium*.

[3] Around 700 B.C.E. the black-figure style was invented in Corinth. However, from 530 B.C.E. on, red-figure replaced black as the main pottery style. It is interesting that Picasso chose to create his vases in the older Archaic style. John Boardman, *Athenian Black Figure Vases* (New York: Thames & Hudson, 2000), 9.

[4] David Caccioli, *The Paul A. Anderson Art History Collection*, ed. Catherine Carter Goebel (Rock Island: Augustana College, 2001), 16.

[5] Quoted in Marilyn McCully, ed., *Picasso: Painter and Sculptor in Clay* (New York: Harry N. Abrams, Inc., 1998), 28.

[6] They were named after the town of Tanagra in Boeotia in the present day area of Greece where a large number of them were found. Violaine Jeamme and John Fossey, "Tanagra, a Small World in Clay," *The Montreal Museum of Fine Arts, 2005*, http://www.mbam.qc.ca/en/expositions/exposition_45.html (1 May 2005).

[7] McCully, 36.

[8] *Picasso in Clay: Three Decades of Ceramics from the Marina Picasso Collection* (Santa Fe: Gerald Peters Gallery, Inc., 2000), 6.

[9] "Serious Play's Feat of Clay," *Times Literary Supplement*, no. 5286 (23 July 2004): 19.

[10] Quoted in Michel Ragon and Howard B. Garey, "In Praise of Sculpture," *Contemporary Art* no. 19/20 (1957): 16.

[11] Jane Borelli, *The Paul A. Anderson Art History Collection*, ed. Catherine Carter Goebel (Rock Island: Augustana College, 2001), 18.

[12] John Griffiths Pedley, *Greek Art and Archaeology*, 3rd ed. (Upper Saddle River, New Jersey: Prentice-Hall, Inc., 2002), 64.

[13] Borelli, 16.

[14] Carol Benson, "Women on Classical Greek Vases," *Magazine Antiques* 148, no. 6 (1995): 790.

[15] Vallauris is a small town in the south of France just a few miles from Antibes where Picasso had been working in the summer of 1946. It had been an important center for pottery in Roman times and possibly even as far back as in Greek times. Its name comes from *vallis auri* meaning *valley of gold*, the *gold* being its wealth of soft fine clay. In the years Picasso first came, the town was in an economic slump. Now, however, thanks to Picasso's notoriety, it thrives and is said to be the home of around one hundred potters. McCully, 12-13.

[16] McCully, 26.

[17] *Picasso in Clay*, 5.

[18] Walter Benjamin, "The Work of Art in the Age of Mechanical Reproduction," *Illuminations* (New York: Harcourt, Brace & World, 1968), 225.

[19] Benjamin, 223.

[20] McCully, 38.

[21] Especially in today's internet-driven age, images and reproductions of artwork are available with the click of a button.

[22] Benjamin, 225.

[23] Taken from a conversation recorded by Christian Zervos with the artist in 1935. Alfred H. Barr, Jr., *Picasso: Fifty Years of his Art* (New York: The Museum of Modern Art, 1980), 274.

[24] Benjamin, 220.

[25] Robin Osborne, *Archaic and Classical Greek Art, Oxford History of Art* (New York: Oxford University Press, 1998), 88.

Child on a Second Empire Balcony
John Dabour (catalogue 48) 1872

Dabour's New View:

Child on a Second Empire Balcony as a Visual Link from Impressionism to Modernism

Michael Skelton

The turn of the nineteenth century came ornately nestled into the coarse hands of modernism. The modernist period, reinforced through tough wrought iron tempered by the soft stroke of artisans, manufactured elevated views of the *new* Paris. During this time, elements from the Industrial Revolution, which occurred from the 1770s to 1830s in both France and the United States, appeared in works by many Impressionists.[1] John Dabour (1837–1905), an American Impressionist, captured such change by incorporating elevated viewpoints of figures within the city. He also emphasized the use of wrought iron in architectural design and hinted at the recreational activities of the bourgeoisie in open urban spaces. Evidence of Impressionist elements can be observed by analyzing his pastel entitled, *Child on a Second Empire Balcony* (1872—catalogue 48).

This beautiful piece was completed during the opening years of the French Impressionist era and depicts a young child posing behind a wrought iron railing along the edge of a balcony. She is standing directly in front of a room framed by curtains. This portrait creates points of interest based on the artist's method of elevating the viewpoint, hinting at the interior behind and inviting interpretation of what might be the object of her gaze, perhaps the functional landscape of industrialized Paris. The date suggests influences from early French Impressionism.

Although categorized as an American portrait painter, John Dabour was actually born in Smyrne, Turkey in 1837, and died in his New York apartment in 1905. For nine years he studied at the prestigious *Ecole Nationale des Beaux-Arts* (School of Fine Arts) in Paris under the direction of French painter, designer and engraver Philippe Auguste Jeanron,[2] who later accepted the position of superintendent of French art museums.[3] During this period, Dabour excelled at pastel drawings. While incorporating past tradition, he further advanced the pastel medium toward modernism.

By 1867, Dabour had relocated to the United States, settling in the Baltimore area where he had family ties. He continued the methods that he was taught in Paris, preferring pastel, which, although long established in France, was considered innovative in America. As a medium, pastel communicates a softer quality to most subjects. Several elements in the *Child on a Second Empire Balcony* link Dabour with the up and coming Parisian Impressionist movement. In fact, Dabour's decision to focus on this medium might have been influenced by fellow Impressionists, *Edgar Degas* (catalogue 56 and 58) and *Mary Cassatt* (catalogue 55), who also explored it. Unlike American expatriate Cassatt, however, Dabour maintained his mature career primarily in the United States.

catalogue 56

The preceding periods of eighteenth-century century Rococo and Neoclassicism also produced many fine pastel images in Europe. Gavin Hamilton's *Allegorical Figure of Painting* (1768-1785, catalogue 19), for example, presents a female figure in classical drapery contemplating her painting. Her strong profile and *contrapposto* position are typical characteristics of Neoclassicism. Similar to Dabour, Hamilton blended complementary colors to create subtle modeling, particularly evident in the lower portions of her clothing. In addition, Hamilton also included unblended colors, a technique later advanced by the *Impressionists* (catalogue 42, 43, 65, 66A and B) and *Post-Impressionists* (catalogue 67A and B, 68, 69 and 77). When viewed from an appropriate distance, *The Child on a Balcony* gains further definition through the details of her dress as well as the flowers entangling the railing.

catalogue 19

While in Paris, Dabour witnessed the city's post-Industrial Revolution transformation toward modernism under its ruler, Napoleon III. Louis Napoleon, the nephew of Emperor Napoleon Bonaparte, was elected president following the 1848 Revolution. He aimed to modernize the capital city, which had seen little improvement since the 1789 Revolution (catalogue 25). Through the use of modern building materials such as wrought iron, combined with innovative urban design, he and Baron Haussmann conceived of a *new* Paris.

catalogue 42

During the 1850s and 1860s, Paris was thus largely a construction zone, which resulted in large open boulevards lined with trees and tall apartment buildings. Many of these had balconies ornamented with cast iron railings that opened out toward the street, affording views of the many magnificent gardens and parks created within the city. As in London, train stations (catalogue 50) were constructed in glass and wrought iron. The areas around Notre Dame Cathedral and the Louvre were opened in order to accentuate these large monuments, while bridges were modernized for more efficient crossing along the Seine River (catalogue 43).

catalogue 68

catalogue 25

Upon completing his training in France, Dabour established himself as an American portrait painter. His clients included powerful

catalogue 50

politicians, statesmen and officers in the Civil War, now revered as heroes. His most famous works were portraits of Confederate General Robert E. Lee and Senator Simon Cameron. *Robert E. Lee*, a small half-length pastel, was completed in 1871, the year before *Child on a Second Empire Balcony*. After the Civil War, Lee was celebrated in the South as a national hero for having led the Confederate Army. Although he surrendered at Appomattox Court House, he was still hailed by many as the best general during the Civil War.

Dabour's works were included in two recorded exhibitions, a one-man show in 1879, which featured his red pastel series of portraits of Baltimore statesmen, and a posthumous display of his pastels at the 1922 French Salon. His works must have been highly regarded by the French Academy to have been included in this important exhibit.[5] His obituary, published in the *New York Times* in 1905, offers more information on the artist:

catalogue 43

> John Dabour, a portrait painter, better known in the south, died yesterday at his home 206 East 46th Street. He was 68 years old. Mr. Dabour was born in Smyrna and studied in Paris. At the age of 38 he came to this country and settled in Baltimore, where he painted portraits of many statesmen and society women. Among his best known works are portraits of Grant and Sherman. This painter is survived by three children, John, Emma, and Alice. Miss Emma Dabour is also a portrait painter.[6]

One of Dabour's children thus followed in his artistic footsteps. Like her father, Emma primarily pursued portraiture and was clearly an established painter during his lifetime, likely trained by him. It is interesting to speculate if the child in this depiction might indeed be one of Dabour's own children, perhaps even Emma.

Child on a Second Empire Balcony was presumably created in America since it was dated after Dabour's move to

catalogue 48

Baltimore, yet it still reflects Parisian influence. Perhaps he traveled between the two countries after his career was established in Baltimore and it might thus represent a Parisian location. When he arrived two years after the end of the Civil War, most American artists focused on Realism, based on photographic images of modern life. French avant-garde artists, on the other hand, were already experimenting with Impressionist techniques. This piece seems to reflect his serious training in France. The date is premature for American Impressionism but factors into the beginning of the French Impressionist movement through the elevated viewpoint of an urban bourgeois environment.

Child on a Second Empire Balcony presents a beautifully drawn child standing on the balcony of a Second Empire style apartment. During this period, young girls and boys were often dressed in the same sort of fashionable clothing of the time. This child is unidentified by gender, but for the purpose of this essay, one might assume it is a young girl. Her attire is a high-waisted, *à la classique* (in the classical manner) dress, typical of the time. The light and flowing quality emulated the ancient *wet drapery* style. Members of this class represented a new type of wealth, the *nouveau riche* (newly moneyed) through non-traditional mercantile and industrial methods, rather than aristocratic inheritance. The *nouveau riche* established a somewhat upper class form of the middle class. Expensive regal blue velvet and white lace sheer curtains behind the child evidence social status. These drapes effectively frame the child as if she is emerging

catalogue 48

onto a theatrical stage. Yet, her audience cannot help but wonder exactly where her gaze is directed. The young child looks upon some scene, probably an urban landscape garden, while holding a small portion of nature within her grasp. Landscaped public gardens were also an important aspect of the *new* Paris, bringing nature to the city.

In her left hand, she grasps a pink flower, a *trumpet petunia*, a native flower of France, which seems to have been symbolically plucked from the metal ivy entangling the wrought iron railing. In fact, a repeated pattern of this vegetation is seen throughout the image, from the lace sheers to the designs in both the center and bottom castings of the railing. This repeated three-petal floral pattern represents the royal insignia of France: the *fleur-de-lis*, the lily flower, symbol for the French monarchy. By the time this image was created, the royal aspect was read more as a generalized nationalistic symbol, and as such was incorporated into French architecture, as in the wrought iron.

Wrought iron was originally developed during the Middle Ages. The process can be traced back to the French iron guilds of Western Europe where young men began their apprenticeship at the age of fifteen, training to become master craftsmen.[7] Despite its long tradition, this material also established the modern appearance of Paris as it was incorporated into the architectural design for most of the new nineteenth-century structures. Wrought iron was clearly superior to steel for modern architecture. Wrought iron's *patina* strengthens the iron as it ages. Steel on the other hand, rusts and thus weakens as it ages.

In this image the young child leans against a wrought iron balcony railing, manufactured through molds and casting. Ore, coke and sand were the raw materials that, when heated, created a liquid that was then poured

detail, catalogue 48

into castings. When cooled, the liquid hardened into long iron rods of varying widths in diameter. These rods were custom shaped by heating the metal until red hot and manipulated by twisting or pressuring to the desired size and length. Castings allowed iron railings to be detailed with ornamentation, yet sold at cheaper rates than if they had been hand-worked. Casting molds permitted ornamentation to be placed anywhere on the section of iron or on the rails, the top and bottom lateral pieces of the railing. Pickets were the vertical segments of iron welded to the rails. Atop the pickets, finials ranged from family crests to spears or even tridents. Iron railings were unique and aesthetically pleasing to the natural surroundings that they enhanced.

In Dabour's image, the railing is highly decorative. The pickets are almost indistinguishable from the repeated pattern of foliage in the top castings, while the *fleur-de-lis* of the bottom castings are intertwined with vines. The polished architecture and decoration in this scene likely indicate that the location was either in France or in an urban American city emulating the chic appearances of Paris. The curvilinear patterns of the railing foreshadow the style of *Art Nouveau* (catalogue 70, 71, 72 and 73), which would develop in France during the next two decades. Dabour, like many artists of his time, used figures placed near wrought iron fences to depict modernity.

Stylistic characteristics common to modernist images are evident in this artwork. Overall, the composition appears orderly and balanced. The pale figure stands in the center, grounded among vibrant primary colors that create the palette for this image. The *chiaroscuro* (contrast of light and shadow) draws the viewer's attention toward her eyes. Her gaze suggests influences of works that Dabour might have seen while in Paris. In particular, the 1863 *Salon des Refusés*, exhibiting the rejected works from the official Salon exhibition, featured Edouard Manet's infamous *Le Déjeuner sur l'Herbe*, in which his model, Victorine Meurent, lunched

in the nude with two male students dressed in caps and gowns. She brazenly stared at her shocked bourgeois audience, an emblem of the modern *Venus*, the Parisian prostitute. Manet repeated this theme at the 1865 Salon exhibit with *Olympia*, once again featuring Meurent as a nude prostitute, this time staring out as she lounges in bed. This same disarming gaze is evident in Dabour's child, representing a possible similar longing for change.

Her look invokes an implied hidden meaning underlying the image. Her stoic expression and strong eye contact establish psychological contact which invites reaction from the audience. This emotional engagement is reminiscent of the early nineteenth-century Romantic period, which explored moods beneath the surface, similar to our questioning what the child is thinking and what is behind us that so captures her attention. The

catalogue 66A

child's eyes seem to proceed beyond the viewer, toward a presumed urban landscape as if something has completely caught her attention.

She seems captivated by what lies over the edge of the railing, possibly indirectly referring to Dabour's early fascination with new concepts of urban landscape. Before coming to America, his collection of art consisted of

detail, catalogue 66A

sketches and works completed in pastel and oil presumably sketched primarily in France. Along with his portraits, the rest of Dabour's portfolio consisted of landscape sketches of urban parks. These images were small in scale for efficient transporting. Urban gardens were becoming very popular on the East Coast in America as well during this time. Two works by Emma Ruff, an Impressionist/ Post-Impressionist working in Paris at the turn of the century, depict such urban open spaces representing new gathering places. One image entitled *Le Jardin du Luxembourg* (catalogue 66A) shows women gossiping along a manicured landscape with a fountain. Young children are seen running about the piece and enjoying games played during this period. A sweet young girl is depicted, nestling against her nursemaid's lap, while her mother looks on in the right foreground. She appears tired from pushing the hoop through the garden with her small stick.

The other image by Ruff, *Le Jardin des Tuileries* (catalogue 66B), again placed in a park, depicts a couple conversing on a bench in the left foreground while two young children find amusement by drawing in the dirt. The manicured garden in this image is quite similar to that of the other Ruff landscape and was typical of Parisian gardens of the time. Emma Ruff clearly painted her subjects from different vantage points. Dabour also represented the duality of the urban park as both a place of constant activity and a space inviting solitude toward contemplating intriguing subjects.

Other artists of the time who captured the recreation of the bourgeoisie include Max Klinger and Edouard Manet. Klinger's etching, *Action* (1881), depicts men and women involved in new modern activities. Roller skating became a popular diversion and city parks soon incorporated skate rinks that were designed within the urban landscape, just as skate parks are today. Not only was open space created within the city as a gathering point, but it was also specifically designed for recreation and the enjoyment of nature.

The Railway, 1873
Edouard Manet, (oil on canvas)
Gift of Horace Havemeyer in memory of his mother, Louisine W. Havemeyer,
Image © Board of Trustees, National Gallery of Art, Washington, D.C.

Edouard Manet's *The Railway* (1873) reflects a more relaxed view toward enjoying nature. A mother and child spend time at the edge of the common, reading and watching trains roll into the Saint-Lazare Train Station. His model for the woman was again Victorine Meurent, who had earlier posed for his shocking Realist works. She now represents an Impressionist bourgeois mother, rather than a dangerous prostitute. She holds a book in her hands, symbolizing that she is educated, and looks up from her reading as if interrupted by the audience. A small dog is curled in her lap suggesting fidelity and a softer Victorine. The child grips the pickets of the wrought iron fence as the trains presumably shake the ground she stands upon and catch her interest with the toot of their whistles. Contrasted with her mother, the child is gazing toward the trains, indicating that only the railing is keeping her separated from somewhere or something in the space beyond. *Child on a Second Empire Balcony* is similar in its psychological and complementary positioning of the child, but in Dabour's case, the child is turned toward the audience, making our confrontation with her more immediate.

While in Paris, Dabour experienced the rise of the bourgeoisie and the establishment of a *new* Paris as much of the old Romantic medieval city was destroyed in favor of *progress*. Sleek Second Empire buildings with mansard roofs were softened through balconies framed in wrought iron designs, delineating the framework as shoestrings lace shoes. Steel was present in both the interior and exterior of these modern structures. *New* Paris accommodated increasing populations with efficient maneuverability. As observed, the boulevards of Paris were congested due to this immense growth. Buildings were often designed at the edges of streets, forcing people to mix with buggies on transportation routes. Dabour gave viewers a vantage point from one such apartment complex.

By elevating one's perception of the landscape, through tall buildings decked with balconies, the views became grander. In 1870, landscape architect Frederick Olmstead indicated the importance of open space within communities. He promised that it would ensure a pleasing aesthetic value to the landscape and that the architect "was entitled to restrict the meaning to a large tract of land set apart by the public for the enjoyment of rural landscape, as distinguished from a public square, a public garden, or a promenade, fit only for more urbanized pleasures."[8]

Olmsted is noted as the *Father of American Landscape* for his innovative designs with neighborhoods constructed around a *common* or *green* space designed for communal activities. These open spaces were used as local hubs for outdoor activities. Olmsted's design of *Riverside*, for example, was considered the first suburb of Chicago. The 1869 plan indicated an organized community with curved drives rather than a street grid system with all utilities designed according to both ecological and functional usage.[9]

catalogue 41

Not only was nature thus *physically* manipulated by humans in pursuit of aesthetic pleasure, it was also captured in many Impressionist works. Charles Baudelaire (catalogue 41) was an influential figure during the rise of Realism and Impressionism. He encouraged artists to focus on everyday life rather than exotic or historical subjects dripping with symbolism and manipulated nature. As he stated: "He shall be the true painter who can pull out of everyday life its epic side and make us understand just how great and poetic we are in our neckties and polished boots."[10]

Dabour captured such instant views and thus led his audience to believe that the figure in *Child on a Second Empire Balcony* was observing the elaborate gardens beyond the viewer. The young child's attention is fully devoted to something past the viewer toward the landscape beyond. Could it be younger children playing with hoops or the secrecy of a whisper as observed in Ruff's paintings? The very suggestive nature of the composition invites audience response. Such ideas of painting people looking out onto urban landscapes can be seen in other Impressionist works.

During this period, many artists changed their points of view toward their subjects. They often combined portraiture and genre scenes with an emphasis on nature. Portraits no longer were stiff in appearance, but instead depicted people in relaxed positions on balconies. Comfortable, yet often psychologically removed or at least interrupted. Even in the early Romantic period, Goya painted *Majas on a Balcony* (1810-12), presenting two women dressed as lower class performers, relaxed on a balcony that overlooked an urban landscape. Strong *chiaroscuro* allows the figures to stand out against the dark background. A mysterious light illuminates the *majas* and at the same time creates a focus on the wrought iron railing. Many historians claim that this is one of the earliest images depicting a balcony scene. Compared to Dabour's, it is much darker, with more penetrating psychological content in keeping with Goya's Romantic aims. Both works share the wrought iron railing in the foreground with figures posed gazing outward.

catalogue 48

Artwork depicting balcony scenes of this time include Edouard Manet's *The Balcony* (1869) and Berthe Morisot's *On the Balcony* (1871-72). These two images are similar in that the relaxed figures pose as they gaze over railings within their defined urban spaces. Manet depicted three figures looking outward from a balcony,

behind an iron railing and elevated above street level. Similar to Dabour's piece, these females lounge while observing the activities below. Again, a wrought iron railing indicates the new elevated viewpoint established for selected urban landscapes and genre scenes.

Each image has figures that appear to be emotionally contained by the balconies on which they stand. Physically congested, yet socially isolated; this common theme unites all these modernist images. Such depictions encouraged viewers to become more aware of their environment, using balconies to bring urban dwellers closer to nature. The young girl in Morisot's image has similar characteristics to both the child in Dabour's work as well Manet's *Railway*. Again the viewer's focus is channeled toward the young girl gripping the iron pickets and staring out past the cage-like railing. Yet in this example, the mother (or nursemaid) joins the child in observing the view.

On the Balcony, 1871–72
Berthe Morisot (watercolor, with touches of gouache, over graphite, on off-white wove paper)
20.6x17.3cm, Gift of Charles Netcher in memory of Charles Netcher II, Photography © The Art Institute of Chicago

In *Child on a Second Empire Balcony*, Dabour represented a fresh approach toward the dynamics of an expanding bourgeoisie interacting within landscaped urban spaces. He effectively brought the exterior world to people in their apartments by selecting a balcony as his stage. The artist historically bridged Impressionism with modernism, not only within the context of art, but geographically as well. He represented influences from Paris, center of the western art world, moving westward to America, the new world of discovery, but ironically behind the times in terms of artistic development. His use of an elevated vantage point and incorporation of wrought iron helped establish modern emotional connections with viewers. Such techniques and interpretations placed Dabour on the cutting-edge of the Impressionist movements in both France and America. At the same time, through them, he created a whimsical pause in an otherwise busy world, as he captivated viewers with a lovely child who seems to pluck a blossom from a foliated railing, symbolizing the advent and bloom of modernity.

catalogue 48

[1] Dr. David Ellis, Augustana College, 1 May 2005, e-mail interview: "It is difficult to attach exact dates to the IR [Industrial Revolution], and I am less familiar with the IR to the late 1700's (many say around 1770s) in northern England, and the IR spread (again, rather modestly) from there to certain parts of northwestern Europe, including northeastern France, by around 1830s. Some current scholarship claims that the IR was more gradual (and therefore less revolutionary) in France than in Britain. The IR also continued to unfold and enter new phases, too. Some claim we are now in a fourth phase of the IR, characterized by the electronic manipulation of information."

[2] La Tribune de l'Art, "Philippe-Auguste Jeanron, peintre, dessinateur et graveur," *L'actualité de l'Histoire de l'Art Occidental du Moyen-Age au 19e siècle*, 2005, http://www.latribunedelart.com/expositions_2004/Philippe_Auguste_Jeanron.htm(May 1, 2005).

[3] Clara Waters, Erskine Clement and Laura Hutton, *Artists of the Nineteenth Century and Their Works* (New York: Arno Press, 1969), 178.

[4] Ibid.

[5] E. Bénézit, *Dictionnaire Critique et documentaire des peintres, sculpteurs, dessinateurs et graveurs de tous les temps et de tous les pays par un groupe d'écrivains specialists français et étrangers*, vol. 4 (Paris: Gründ, 1999), 170.

[6] "Painted Grant and Sherman," *New York Times,* 26 March 1905, 9.

[7] Michael Boyler, owner, *Boyler's Ornamental Iron* (Bettendorf, IA), interview on 12 April 2005, provided information on the history and technical process of creating wrought iron. He stated the guild is still around to this day and is considered the highest quality of craftmanship in the world.

[8] Frederick Law Olmsted, *Forty Years of Landscape Architecture: Central Park* (London: The MIT Press, 1973), 3-4. "When Mr. Olmsted used the term in his address 'The Justifying Value of a Public Park' in 1870, he considered that he was entitled to restrict the meaning to a large tract of land set apart by the public for the enjoyment of rural landscape, as distinguished from a public square, a public garden, or a promenade, fit only for more urbanized pleasures."

[9] "Frederick Law Olmsted Society of Riverside," *LandscapeOnline.com,* 2004, http://www.landscapeonline.com/research/article/4090 (19 April 2005). "Frederick Law Olmsted, the renaissance man: voyager, writer, publisher, gold miner, abolitionist, preservationist, father of American landscape architecture. In 1868, eastern businessmen wanted to develop a countryside community near Chicago. Land by the Des Plaines River, nine miles from Chicago, was selected, and the Riverside Improvement Company (RIC) founded. That same year, RIC hired Frederick Law Olmsted and his partner, Calvert Vaux, to plan the community, based on their reputations for developing New York City's Central Park and Brooklyn's Prospect Park. Olmsted wanted to create a community that combined rural with urban advantages. Olmsted and Vaux set out to create one of the first modern American suburbs. In 1869, the plan was unveiled, which including divided roads to the city and curved roadways, eschewing a traditional grid of streets. The streets had drainage, too (cobblestone gutters), and the modern conveniences of sewers, water and gas lines, and gas street lamps. To keep it rural, half the land was set aside for public use, two large common areas and river frontage. Large residential lots were plotted, with two trees in each front yard. In 1968, 100 years after Olmsted began planning the community, the Frederick Law Olmsted Society of Riverside wad founded and Riverside became a National Historic Landscape District in 1970. The society promotes the preservation of Riverside's heritage and actively supports historical studies within the village. Olmsted, of course, is considered the father of American landscape architecture, and like many great figures of the 19th century, he was a renaissance man."

[10] www.kirjasto.sci.fi/baudelai.htm. (10 May 2005) Among Baudelaire's friends was Edouard Manet (1832–83), whose works were frequently rejected by the *salon*. After the Salon of 1845, Baudelaire prophesized: "He shall be the true painter who can pull out of the everyday life its epic side and make us understand just how great and poetic we are in our neckties and polished boots." Manet and Baudelaire were both influenced by Romantic artist, Francisco Goya; "Goya," Baudelaire wrote in *The Painter of Modern Life* (1863), "is always a great and often a terrifying artist." Goya's etchings inspired some of Manet's subjects as well as Baudelaire's poems in *Les fleurs du mal*.

Moulin Rouge - La Goulue
Henri de Toulouse-Lautrec (catalogue 69) 1896

Intimacy and Perspective:

Toulouse-Lautrec and Scenes of Montmartre

Dana Kau

Allure. There is something in the nature of artists that draws our attention to them. Throughout history, many have been known as much for their charm, wit, eccentricities and actions as they have for their artwork. Henri de Toulouse-Lautrec is no exception. He undoubtedly redefined what was acceptable in the art world through his choice of decadent lower class subject matter. From cabaret stars to brothel madams, he depicted a subculture of Paris that was considered taboo, yet predictably irresistible. No matter what subject he chose to represent or in what medium, he always provided the viewer with an intimate look into the world he portrayed. As both a product of and a participant in late nineteenth-century Parisian culture, Lautrec's artwork explored the distinctly visual environments of the city's nighttime cafés, theatres and brothels, both with a rather close,

personal touch, as well as a distant, spectator's view. His own persona was forged within this atmosphere, profoundly affected by a tumultuous family history combined with his fin-de-siècle lifestyle. It is this combination which will be explored through his decisively intimate portraits of life at the famous nightclub, the *Moulin Rouge*. His posters and sketches reveal to us a seemingly contradictory combination of intimacy mixed with distance, as well as pleasure clouded by decadence.

At the Moulin Rouge, 1892/1895
Henri de Toulouse-Lautrec, (oil on canvas)
123x141cm, Helen Birch Bartlett Memorial Collection,
Photography © The Art Institute of Chicago

To understand and explore this intimacy and distance in the works of Lautrec, we must place them within the context of a broader understanding of his childhood, family life and ultimately his years in the Parisian art district of Montmartre. Furthermore, the socioeconomic context of the late nineteenth-century art world in Paris will be explored. Finally, the artistic influences of new viewpoints offered through photography and *Japonisme*[1] will be examined. The approach for this research will be multidisciplinary, exploring Lautrec's works both through their historical context within traditional art historical methodology and through the rhetoric created by these pieces as studied through the discipline of communication.

Before tracking the life and development of Lautrec's works we must examine the meaning of intimacy. This research will consider several meanings for intimacy, which will then be applied to the artwork of Lautrec. We have interpersonal intimacy which will be explored through *dialectics*, sexual intimacy and spatial intimacy, or *proxemics*. A key aspect of interpersonal relationships is the theory of relational dialectics, a term referring to the inherent polarity of all relationships. Dialectics refer to forces that are contradictory in nature. Internal dialectics express a desire to be connected and separate, certain and uncertain, and open and closed all in one.[2] A related set of dialectical tensions can be applied to works in which Lautrec included self-portraits. Inclusion-seclusion, conventionality-uniqueness and revelation-concealment are the inherent tensions between people and their community, referred to as external dialectics.[3]

Since such push-and-pull forces are present, for better or worse, relational theorists argue people should value the struggle. These constantly changing dynamics work to create dialogue, while maintaining individuality.[4] Dialectical tensions are a crucial psychological aspect of our understanding of intimate relationships, but we do not want to neglect the physical aspects as well. Intimacy in relationships is often read through proxemics, or the physical distance of a person or a group to another person or group.[5] With these terms guiding our ability to contextualize intimacy in the works of Lautrec, we can now examine how the dialectics of intimacy had troubled him since childhood.

Texts that explore the works of Lautrec unavoidably include a rich biography on the artist, an exploration into his personal history which was definitive in shaping his artistic creations. Who was Lautrec before he was shaped by Montmartre? The idea of intimacy for the artist was certainly one of mixed character as defined through the great polarity between his parents. Lautrec's mother, Adèle, was of fine breeding and like most upper class women of the period, carried herself with a sense of typical nineteenth-century propriety and decorum. Her husband (and first cousin) Comte Alphonse de Toulouse-Lautrec, was a descendant of an aristocratic family that had ruled France for one thousand years, their infamy and fortune rivaled nearly any monarch. The privilege that distinguished them for so long, however, diminished as inbreeding led to a weakening of family genes, creating eccentricities in family personalities.

The Comte was legendary for his self-indulgent hunting escapades. It was rumored that he neglected to show up for his own honeymoon, an action which established a precedent for further neglect throughout their unhappy marriage. It was not unusual for the couple to take residence at separate châteaux, Alphonse often relocating according to gaming seasons and Adèle preferring to stay near her extended family. Even when Alphonse chose to summon Adèle, by the time she arrived he had often moved on to yet another locale. The result was that Henri spent the first few years of his life virtually fatherless. This pattern doubtless established a great polarity in familial intimacy between the certainty that Lautrec associated with his mother and the uncertainty that he felt toward his father.

With her husband absent, Adèle's focus was on Henri. And with the death of the Lautrec's second son, Alphonse redirected some of his attention to Henri. These affections were brief, since as the boy continued to grow, it became clear that his health was tenuous. Without the potential of his being a sportsman like his father, the young Lautrec began to turn to his other passion, drawing. The subjects of his artistic interests, however, revolved around the preoccupations of his father (game birds, horses and other animals), perhaps in an attempt to partake in his lifestyle the only way he could.

Lautrec's legs were both broken as a child, and many texts cite his mother's letters referencing a horseback riding accident. As scholars we see here only a certain degree of integrity in these correspondences as primary documents. Lautrec actually fell at two points in his youth and neither fall included a horse. At age thirteen, he broke his left femur when his cane slipped out from his body as he attempted to push himself out of a chair, and at age fourteen, he broke his right femur by falling into a shallow ditch.[6] His legs never recovered, despite the finest medical care, leaving him to mature with the torso of an adult and the stumped legs of a dwarf. At maturity his body only reached the height of four feet eleven inches. His physical deformity and his exposure to struggling male-female relations with his parents are themes that will be explored.

To appease her son's only pleasure, Adèle actively sought out the highest artistic training for Lautrec, and settled on the "favorite of millionaires," Léon Bonnat. Harshly critical of Lautrec's work, Bonnat pushed him as an artist to be self-evaluating and to reject the judgmental nature of public audiences.[7] Perhaps the greatest skill Lautrec gained in training under Bonnat was dedication to rigorous formal study and draftsmanship, which enabled him to perfectly adapt reality into glorious abstract representations.

Lautrec by all accounts was a gentle man and a loyal friend. He dedicated his waking hours to his extraordinarily productive working career, yet was as integral a fixture in the nightclubs as the performers themselves. A great deal of his world view came from his lifestyle as an observer. Charles Baudelaire's[8]

(catalogue 41) quote about painter Constantine Guys directly relates to Lautrec: "The crowd is his domain, as air is for the bird and water for the fish. His passion and his vocation is to become a part of the crowd. It is an immense pleasure for the perfect flaneur, for the passionate observer, to take up his abode in the multitude, in the undulating and moving, in the fugitive and the infinite."[9]

This comment reflects how strongly the internal dialectic of connectedness-separateness played in the role of this artist-as-commentator. The poet Paul Leclercq recalled this dialectic specifically in Lautrec's relationship to women: "The feeling he experienced with his women friends was a curious mixture of jovial comradeship and restrained desire. And he was fully conscious of his physical inferiority…."[10] Such aspects of his personal life would continue to impact his works.

catalogue 41

As a master spectator, there was no better role model for Lautrec than the brilliant Impressionist Edgar Degas (catalogue 56 and 58), who was "unquestionably Lautrec's most important artistic idol, and this is confirmed by numerous formal and iconographic similarities."[11] Both Lautrec and Degas valued characterization within their works. They aimed to be typological, producing images that were anecdotal in nature, and therefore social, yet still retained qualities that were unique to the observed subject. Post-Impressionist images were successors to generations of meticulously constructed academic works. These artists aimed to be original and *modern*, yet they did not want to be recorded as artistic *dilettantes* who would have no lasting effect on the great Parisian salons. The lives and artwork of this generation of new masters reflect the external dialectical tension between the desire for both conventionality and originality.

catalogue 58

They were charged with the task of forging the raw emotional power of Impressionism, arrived through color and setting, while maintaining the intellect of the great masters who carefully constructed the canvas as a narrative. Degas used strong lighting and photographs to model his studies in order to capture the scene as a slice of life that existed only for an instant. His *Absinthe Drinkers* (1876), for example, portrayed in dreary earthtones, are lost in a world of absinthe and opium-infused alcohol. Degas chose to show women living and working within a reality that was largely avoided by most Impressionists. Lautrec took that reality a step further, moving the experience from the unique to the anecdotal, with brutal honesty that at times bordered on ugliness. Critic Gustave Geffroy aptly noted in 1893: "Lautrec lends himself to cruel mockery, as he makes us visit dance halls, bordellos, and unnatural couplings. But he retains his integrity as an artist; his power of observation and his refusal to see his subjects as pitiful support the beauty of life."[12]

As the great observers of their century, Degas and Lautrec placed themselves deeply within their Parisian milieu. There are very few documented surviving self-portraits of Lautrec. Our readings of the dichotomous balance of intimate closeness in combination with distance can perhaps be best understood by looking at how Lautrec positioned himself in the world of Montmartre. *At the Moulin Rouge* (1892-95) is a meticulous catalogue of the key players at the concert ball, including a self-portrait of Lautrec. This piece moves our reading of Lautrec's work into the realm of the *archetypal*.[13]

At the Moulin Rouge (detail), 1892/1895
Henri de Toulouse-Lautrec,
Helen Birch Bartlett Memorial Collection,
Photography © The Art Institute of Chicago

Lautrec had been working as a commercial artist and had become a master of rendering characters as *types*. The element of *type*, in this sense referring to a caricatured person, was crucial to Lautrec's sketches because his figures could be assessed instantly on a cognitive level. The viewer did not need to perform in-depth analysis of who was in Lautrec's work, but could quickly sum up the characters within a scene toward overall effect.[14] Why is this so important in the creation of intimacy? If figures are instantly recognizable, we as viewers feel immediately closer to their world. During his working career, Lautrec saw the relaxation of censorship that encouraged further caricature in public media such as periodicals and newspapers.[15] Typology became an appropriate medium for the lower and middle classes because of its ease in comprehension. Satire via caricature was in vogue and *At the Moulin Rouge* was Lautrec's perfect vehicle for portraying the world of Montmartre, through anecdotal yet personal experience.

Like the dancer Valentin de Désossé in *Moulin Rouge-La Goulue* (1896, catalogue 69) the figure of May Milton in green in the immediate foreground of *At the Moulin Rouge*, appears to be within our own space, expressing an aspect of connectedness. Yet her distant stare brings in the internal dialectic of separateness. Like la Goulue in *Moulin Rouge-La Goulue*, her eyes appear tired and worn. The dialectic between figures at the table suggests inclusion as they are seated close together in a circle. Yet, they seem as individuals, psychologically secluded by the lack of eye contact between them, suggesting boredom, avoidance and lack of attention.[17]

catalogue 69

We also cannot neglect Lautrec's own caricatured figure in the upper left region of the canvas walking next to his lanky cousin, Gabriel Tapié. His self-positioning perhaps represents how he felt about his own relationship to the great personalities of the Moulin Rouge. Studies of communication and our proxemics to others note that public distance, our perceived least intimate space, is created with twelve or more feet between us and the other.[18] He would repeat this same position with his cousin, in the background of *Cha-U-Kao* (published in *Le Rire* in 1896), observing the circus performer as

Au Moulin-Rouge: Entrée de Cha-U-Kao
Henri de Toulouse-Lautrec, *Le Rire,* 1895 (lithograph)
Paul A. Anderson Art History Collection

she enters the great hall of the Moulin Rouge. In this depiction, however, Lautrec quizzically turns his head toward the performer and consequently, the viewer. This is where dialectics play into Lautrec's personal life. He was a part of the Moulin Rouge, yet an outsider. He drew himself as distant from the main characters in the scene, and perhaps more essential to his legacy, furthest away from his audience. His *voyeuristic* relationship to the scene is ironically mirrored by our own.

Contemporary theorists of Lautrec's era, particularly Hippolyte Taine, argued that the individual "is unvaryingly the product of three factors: his heredity, his surroundings, and the historical moment at which he lives."[19] Historically, Lautrec lived and worked in the era known as the *belle époque.*[20] Post-Industrial Revolution Europe saw a great deal of social change.

catalogue 42

The mechanization and industrialization of France afforded the burgeoning bourgeoisie the financial resources for partaking in leisure. The last quarter of the century was heralded by the *joie de vivre*, joy of living, represented by Impressionists such as Louis-Eugène Boudin (catalogue 42).

Artists were encouraged by critics and theorists like Baudelaire, to be *of their time*. For Lautrec, *his* time and place was Montmartre, the artists' district of Paris. This outer borough was incorporated into the city limits during the 1860s. Upon its inclusion, entrepreneurs capitalized on the complementary dynamics of cheap property and increased demand for leisurely locales. The café-concert was born. Early Montmartre attractions included *les Ambassadeurs, le Moulin Rouge* and *le Chat Noir*. The café culture rapidly evolved from late afternoon luncheons to all night affairs with cancan dancers and prostitutes. The Impressionist *joie de vivre*, as recorded by Pierre Auguste Renoir in his *Moulin de la Galette* (1876), was eclipsed by the decadence of the Post-Impressionist café-concert.

catalogue 45

Lautrec's visualizations of such locations were forged through a combination of diverse elements ranging from photography and *Japonisme* to psychology and contemporary art criticism. By looking at these factors one can better understand how such elements synthesized in his works. Photography was initially used to create portable portraits for the middle and lower classes (catalogue 45) who could not afford hand-painted miniatures. This new medium thus made art more accessible, and its potential toward recording instantaneous records and new approaches (catalogue 44) was soon grasped. Japanese prints also served to inspire new viewpoints. With the reopening of trade with the East, porcelain vases were shipped to Europe, wrapped in woodblock prints (catalogue 57). These *ukiyo-e* (scenes from the *floating world*) prints, like photographs, were dramatically *cropped* and focused on refreshing new subjects, consisting of genres scenes ranging from mothers with their children to performers and prostitutes. Such imagery influenced Lautrec and his contemporaries to experiment with flat planes of color, bordered by strong outlines, which created rich patterns while rejecting traditional Renaissance linear perspective. New subjects appeared as well, often enriched through greater psychological insight.

catalogue 57

The stylistic and iconographic aspects of photography and Japanese prints can clearly be seen in the greater body of works by Lautrec. In particular, *Moulin Rouge-La Goulue* is generally considered his masterpiece for its adaptation of such diverse elements into one lithograph. When it was first exhibited in 1891, it clearly established his reputation. Requiring three sheets of paper to print the massive poster (measuring 192 x 117 cm.) it overwhelmed all printed rivals glued to the walls and streets of Paris. With little historical documentation as to its origins and development, we are left only with the masterwork and smaller versions.

catalogue 69

Artists like Jules Cheret and Lautrec, who pioneered the medium, furthered their own publicity by marketing such prints as *fine* art. *Moulin Rouge-La Goulue* (catalogue 69) is an important example of Lautrec's capitalizing on his popularity by creating sizable and affordable reproductions for galleries and collectors. Lautrec promoted his scaled down versions, as he was aware of the fragility of full-scale versions, which were designed to advertise, and so were exposed to the elements as well as the general wear and tear resulting from their size. This collector's scale version was a modified rendition, published in 1896 as *Les Affiches Illustrées*, and is also considered an original Lautrec poster.

The artist's choice of figural positioning here presents a guidebook of sorts for our reading of intimacy. Perhaps there is not one overall feeling we can discern from such work, since Lautrec wrote into his anecdotes a dichotomy of intimacy and distance through his distinct placement of figures and figural groups in the foreground, middle ground and background. Sometimes he arranged a composition that allows access to his figures, and other times the arrangement communicates intimacy from a distance. There are four positions created in the Moulin Rouge poster, which suggest this odd tension so typical of Lautrec: the Moulin Rouge choreographer Valentin (the *boneless* one), cabaret star *la Goulue*, the spectators in the background and perhaps most importantly, the intended positioning of the viewer to the print itself.

Subtle sexual gestures in this work suggest intimacy. In the foreground, Valentin's long left arm extends down his side until our eye reaches his wrist, which is upturned in phallic form. Similarly, his right hand is raised just inches from his mouth, his thumb arching away from him and directly pointing to La Goulue's skirt, billowing and receptively lifted for her cancan dance. She is the center of the composition, wearing her signature scarlet stockings and standing firmly on her right foot as her left leg kicks towards her spectators, caricaturing her celebrated ability to kick the top hats off the heads of gentlemen. Her audience is painted as a silhouette backdrop of black forms.

Contrasting Lautrec's poster with similar works by Jules Cheret, the so-called *father of the modern poster*, we see drastic differences in interpretation of the same scene. Cheret's Moulin Rouge poster is littered with figures and details to the point of being visually cluttered. Many of his lines are harsh and somewhat geometric. Lautrec's, in contrast, are curvilinear and simple, more modernist and *Art Nouveau* in style. In rejecting the individuality of *every* character in the scene, Lautrec allows his viewers to become visually engaged in the scene, since they are less distracted by superfluous details that might dilute the legibility inherent in advertising.

While rich in intimacy via sexual references, *emotional* connectedness is lost in Lautrec's *Moulin Rouge-La Goulue*. The image consists of three figural groups, each visually distant from the other. Lautrec may have used this technique, however, to imbue his four-color lithograph with an illusion of depth. The printing techniques for color lithographs at the time were somewhat limited. Valentin's purple shadowy figure, for example, was created through the overlapping of the red and blue stones, in order to "create broad areas of one color, so that the overall result is a rhythmic pattern of flat colors."[21]

While the total effect perfectly imitates the broad, flat colors and strong geometry of Japanese prints, there is something lost in its character. Valentin and the audience are one broad mass, rather than defined individual characters. His eyes are closed, and la Goulue neglects to smile as she stares past the border of the stage that her designer created for her. Lautrec was a master at "contrasting the public face of stardom with the day-to-day weariness performance entails: he understood that celebrity was a construction, a superficial masquerade."[22]

What then, were Lautrec's intentions? The era of the Moulin Rouge was not unlike the celebrity culture of modern America with its accompanying frenzy for collectibles and clippings related to star performers. Perhaps Lautrec wanted to contribute a piece of work that was a combination of sexual exploitation, humor and the tired reality of stardom. A further reading might suggest that such facial expressions were observed through Lautrec's constant presence at the Moulin Rouge, his hand reacting to whatever he observed on a daily basis. La Goulue was a part of his life, not a model for a few hours in the studio, and was thus rendered with an understanding eye. Leclercq related that Lautrec "in the middle of a walk, or of a conversation, wherever he might be, at the theatre or elsewhere, if something in casually passing happened to catch his eye, would quickly take a notebook out of his pocket, make a rapid sketch and promptly replace the book—all in the space of a few seconds."[23]

A second lithograph depicts *La Goulue and Valentin Dancing*. This print was produced in black with text for a music book cover. A limited edition of fifty lithographs in olive green was reproduced without text for collectors.[24] This image is a wonderful advancement from *Moulin Rouge-La Goulue* in terms of depicting intimacy. Here, Lautrec omitted extraneous details, focusing in on the action of the two dancers engaged in the moment. The scene is highly cropped and immediately inviting to viewers, bringing them nearer to the action.

A second monochromatic green lithograph is a music sheet cover for *Repertoire de Jane Avril* (catalogue 70), published by A. Bosc in 1893. Lautrec was famous for his somewhat obsessive focus on his subjects. Although he drew the performers of the Moulin Rouge often throughout his career, his eye shifted from one woman to another, as he seemingly exhausted his need to capture each on paper. Perhaps he was searching for a subject with which he could achieve intimacy that went beyond a mere model.

La Goulue and Valentin Dancing
Toulouse-Lautrec, 1894 (lithograph)
Private Collection

catalogue 70

In Lautrec's world, "…women are never portrayed as dependant on men for their status and support…[Lautrec] was perfectly aware that…his [physical] handicap was too great a deterrent, that in general he would never be loved for his qualities and that he would have to pay for sexual favors. Perhaps it gave him some satisfaction to see that women also suffered from lack of love."[25] This comment directly supports the suggestion that dialectical tensions in Lautrec's own life were expressed in his work. The lack of intimate relationships in his reality was perhaps balanced by the openness and accessibility he gave viewers to the women in his artwork. And no figure was given a more sympathetic and intimate treatment than Jane Avril.

Avril was another showcased star at the Moulin Rouge and an elegant foil to the more boisterous la Goulue. In his array of sketches, lithographs and paintings of Avril, the exploration of intimacy was not limited to one perspective, but enriched through examining her from multiple viewpoints. Accounts by her contemporaries recorded her personality as strikingly different from that of la Goulue. Arsène Alexandre described her as "a very graceful filiform person, with her delicate goat-face, her wondrous urge to dance, the truly original, instinctively artistic agility and elegance of all her movements and techniques."[26]

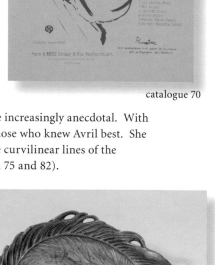

catalogue 70

catalogue 71

One biographer cites that Avril claimed that Lautrec had asked her to sleep with him, a request to which she acquiesced, but only once, to humor him.[27] Perhaps the intimacy of carnal knowledge, as well as constant friendship, led Lautrec to paint her with the same scientific intensity that characterized his childhood animal sketches. He had a clear mastery of the concept of advertising as his work became increasingly anecdotal. With this image he achieved a likeness to match the comments of those who knew Avril best. She bends gracefully, with a voluminous skirt that emphasized the curvilinear lines of the international *Art Nouveau* movement (catalogue 71, 72, 73, 74, 75 and 82).

In an era before artistic copyright became standard practice, Lautrec astutely managed the rights to his imagery. By allowing an unlimited number of reproductions, as long as they included text as in the case of *Repertoire de Jane Avril*, he further stimulated public interest in his works. The reproductions retain less value than the limited edition prints, but are crucial to our understanding of how Lautrec viewed artistic license and direction. He astutely perceived the value of mass production for self-promotion. Such effective blending of commercial and fine art would perhaps not occur again until the 1960s with Andy Warhol's pervasive *Pop* imagery.

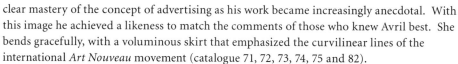

catalogue 72

From cafés to brothels, Lautrec painted women with intimate honesty within their world of Montmartre. He was able to caricature fantastic celebrity personalities as archetypal personae, immortalizing the aura of fin-de-siècle Paris. Lautrec was a master observer, dividing his waking hours between his studio and the cabaret scene, becoming a signature celebrity himself. His intimate relationship to the Moulin Rouge and its performers was formulated through his ability to remain a voyeur amongst the crowd.

Lautrec ultimately, however, became an unfortunate victim of the decadent lifestyle that he portrayed, as his friend, Alexandre wrote: "Visibly before the very eyes of his friends, he began to burn himself out, slowly at first, then with ever-increasing speed. Much as we deplored his fabrication of his ruin, we lacked the courage to admonish him. He was one of those who shorten their life by its very intensity and who rarely survive to old age."[28] Understanding the opposing forces that Lautrec portrayed within his vignettes of intimacy, we can appreciate the feelings of lust, loss, connection and distance that he encapsulated into each image and into his all too brief life as well.

[1] *Japonisme*: a type of western art impacted by Japanese stylistic elements such as flat planes of color and bold, cropped images, particularly in vogue during the Impressionist and Post-Impressionist movements.

[2] Em Griffin, *A First Look at Communication Theory* (New York: McGraw-Hill, 1997), 180-1.

[3] Ibid., 182. The text refers to these tensions as those of the couple to a community, but they can also be applied to the individual and community.

[4] Ibid., 181-2.

[5] Ibid., 98-99.

[6] W. Wittrock and R. Castleman, *Henri de Toulouse Lautrec, Images of the 1890's* (Boston: Little, Brown and Company, 1985), 24.

[7] Ibid., 26.

[8] Charles Baudelaire was a highly influential poet and theorist who helped to frame Realism, Impressionism and Post-Impressionism.

[9] Charles Baudelaire, *The Painter of Modern Life* (1863), quoted in Wittrock and Castleman, 42.

[10] Julia Frey, *Toulouse-Lautrec: A Life* (New York: Viking, 1994), 330.

[11] Wittrock and Castleman, 45.

[12] Frey, 321.

[13] *Archetypal*: an idea, thought or personality that is so engrained into our cultural consciousness that it becomes typological.

[14] See mere exposure effect, in Brehm, Miller, Perlman, and Campbell, *Intimate Relationships* (New York: McGraw-Hill, 2002), 70.

[15] Richard Thomson, Phillip Dennis Cate and Mary Weaver Chapin, *Toulouse-Lautrec and Montmartre* (Princeton: Princeton University Press, 2005), 15.

[16] There has been debate as to the identity of this figure, but most recent research identifies her as May Milton. Thomson, Cate and Chapin, 58.

[17] Joseph DeVito, *Messages: Building Interpersonal Communication Skills* (Boston: Allyon and Bacon, 2002), 158.

[18] Ibid., 158-9. This distance however, was created in studying Americans in the 20th century, and may therefore be somewhat different when applied to the French in the 19th century. Griffin, 99.

[19] Wittrock and Castleman, 45.

[20] "The beautiful era" (literal), referring to joy and beauty in the period leading up to World War I.

[21] Wittrock and Castleman, 81.

[22] Thomson, Cate and Chapin, 58.

[23] Huisman and Dortu, 204.

[24] *Toulouse-Lautrec* (New Haven and London: Yale University Press, 1991), 258.

[25] Frey, 252.

[26] Ibid., 272.

[27] Ibid., 274.

[28] Huisman and Dortu, 196.

"*To be truly immortal a work of art must escape all human limits: logic and common sense will only interfere. But once these barriers are broken, it will enter the regions of childhood vision and dream.*"

Giorgio de Chirico *(1888-1974)*

Exhibition Checklist and Catalogue Entries

All measurements are listed in centimeters (cm.) and inches ("), height by width, and, if applicable, by depth. Key abbreviations are as follows: n.d. is not dated; ca. is circa; b. is bottom; l. is left; c. is center; r. is right; a slash (/) indicates copy moved down a line. This list is in general chronological order. When titles have been assigned to untitled pieces for the purpose of writing references in the catalogue annotations, this has been designated by *ascribed title*. Attributing scholars are listed in brackets. The Augustana College Art Museum gratefully acknowledges the many donors, lenders and contributors whose generosity is reflected in the exhibition checklist.

1

Artist unknown, attributed to the "Class of the Top-Band Stemlesses" (Greek) [D. Caccioli]
Attic Black-figure *Kylix*, ascribed title, ca. 520–500 B.C.E.
Interior: small medallion with gorgoneion
A: lion between palmettes and eyes
B: lion between palmettes and eyes
Ceramic
Unsigned
7.8 x 23.8 x 17.3 cm., 3-1/8 x 9-3/8 x 6-7/8"
Paul A. Anderson Chair in the Arts Purchase, Augustana College Art Collection, 2000.54

The *kylix* was a popular drinking cup in ancient Greece. Such vessels were often used at all-male drinking parties called *symposia*. These recreational activities were restricted to wealthy aristocrats who indulged in the pleasures life could offer (and their class could afford)—particularly related to wine, sex and music. As all of these elements were inherently tied to symposia, artists often depicted them on drinking cups.[1]

This particular kylix was created in the black-figure style, which entailed painting figures in black slip over the natural terracotta-colored clay. Details were added either by incising lines into the black slip to reveal the body color beneath or by painting red or white decorations over the black pattern.[2] Pots were fired using a three-step process that produced the well-known red and black coloring noted here. After allowing pieces to air-dry, *slip* (liquid black clay) was applied to form the design. The pots were then placed in a kiln where they went through the steps of oxidation, reduction, and re-oxidation.

During *oxidation*, the kiln was heated by a fire built beneath it, as air was allowed in through a vent at the top. The oxygen would bond with the clay, turning both the slip covered area and the exposed natural clay different shades of red. The temperature would then be increased and air flow cut off during the *reduction* phase. Moisture was added by placing damp fuel on the fire, producing carbon monoxide that would bond with the clay in place of the oxygen. This temperature would turn the slip a dark, shiny black color. The uncovered clay, which became matte gray during the reduction phase, would revert to its reddish hue during *re-oxidation* when the vent was again opened. The more porous, untouched clay would bond with the oxygen, while the glaze retained its reductive black coloring.[3]

The exterior of this *kylix* is separated into black and red bands. The top one depicts a centered lion framed by two eyes between the handles on both sides,

further enclosed by two *palmettes* (stylized leaf patterns) placed next to the handles. The interior is painted entirely black except for the circular mask of a *gorgon* (called a *gorgoneion*), which stands out in red relief.[4] The *gorgons* were three hideously ugly mythological sisters who were said to have had snakes for hair. According to the legends, they turned men who looked at them to stone. The eldest sister was Medusa, whom Perseus beheaded with the help of the goddess, Athena. Incised lines articulate the muscles and faces of the lions as well as the circular eyes and hair of the gorgon. Additional decoration was applied with red paint to the lion's mane and the gorgon's hair.

The large eyes on the exterior of the cup were not an uncommon addition, especially in kylikes of this style with a shallow bowl atop a short foot (Type A). Given the title *eye-cups*, these kylikes generally depicted large staring eyes on their sides. They were usually male eyes, as with this particular kylix, which is evident by the stylized tear ducts at the corners. Female eyes, as with the gorgon, were symbolized as having an almond shape and no tear ducts.[5] The symbolism behind these eyes often depending on the particular vase, from an *apotropaic*, or protective, function, to being merely decorative. Another theory, perhaps more fitting to this particular kylix, is that they are the eyes of the wine god Dionysus, or one of his fellow drunken friends, comically watching as the drinkers approach their same fate.[6] The humor of this piece is seen both in the *gorgoneion* inside the cup and the face that is formed by flipping the cup upside down. After draining one's cup, the patron would be confronted with the comical face of a staring gorgon. Though originally serving a protective function, the purpose of gorgons over time became diluted to one of general amusement. While drinking, the *kylix* would be tipped upward to reveal to one's companions, a humorous face on the bottom as well. With eyes in the top band, the handles could then take on the shape of ears and the circular foot becomes a mouth.[7] Such imagination combined with skillful technique reflects the extraordinary creativity of the ancient Greeks.

[Errin Copple, *Class of 2005*]

[1] A drinking game they used to play with kylikes was *kottabos*, where an individual would fling the dregs from his cup and try to hit a target. Andrew J. Clark, Maya Elston and Mary Louise Hart, *Understanding Greek Vases: A Guide to Terms, Styles, and Techniques* (Los Angeles: The J. Paul Getty Museum, 2002), 2.

[2] John Boardman, *Athenian Black Figure Vases: A Handbook* (New York: Thames & Hudson Ltd., 2000), 9.

[3] Clark, Elston and Hart, 17.

[4] David Caccioli, *The Paul A. Anderson Art History Collection*, ed. Catherine Carter Goebel (Rock Island: Augustana College, 2001), 16.

[5] Boardman, 107.

[6] Clark, Elston and Hart, 91.

[7] Caccioli, 16.

2

Attributed to the Middle Apulian "Milan Orpheus Group" (South Italian)
[D. Caccioli]
Red-figure Dish with Running Female Figure with Wreath and Ivy-garnished *Phiale*, ascribed title, ca. 340–330 B.C.E.
Ceramic
Unsigned
5.8 x 24.9 x 24.9 cm., 2-3/8 x 9-7/8 x 9-7/8"
Paul A. Anderson Chair in the Arts Purchase, Augustana College Art Collection, 2000.55

This piece provides an illustration of the need to understand conventional cultural symbols—the code each time and place creates for itself—if one is to make sense of an event from that context. Events a society considers perfectly natural become revealed as social creations. In its revelation, this pot seems to anticipate a poetic form soon to be created by Theocritus (about 300–260 B.C.E.), the *eidyllon*: an idyll or snapshot-like image of a unique personality caught unawares while engaged in an archetypal event of life. Theocritus' verbal portraits deliberately evoke and riddle more than they explain, suggesting the unique within the archetypal. Of course a contemporary of the painter might have recognized a precise occasion depicted here. But, in Theocritus' practice, we have a guide to how the Hellenistic artist looks for the common state that adds transcendence to the particular. As in an idyll, the pot guides us by presenting a few select pieces of a puzzle and inviting us to imagine how they might fit together.

Before imagining, let us observe the pieces. The artifact as a whole is of red-figured pottery. That ceramic technique, whereby major shapes were left undecorated to acquire the distinctive red color of the unpainted, fired clay against a painted black background, flourished in Greece and Greek colonies from around 530 to 300 B.C.E.[1] The date of this particular pot is placed more precisely at 340–330 B.C.E.[2] It is found to accord with the production of the Middle Apulian "Milan Orpheus Group."[3] The pot comes from Apulia, the southeastern region of Italy. (On a map, begin with the spur on the Italian "boot," across the Adriatic from mainland Greece.) Apulia was a key portion of what Romans called "Magna Graecia"—Large Greece—, a burgeoning network of Greek colonies whose establishment began in the eighth century B.C.E. in the southern half of Italy.[4] South Italian red-figure work is thought by some to have developed with an imagination and verve that had faded in the homeland of Attica (around Athens) during the fourth century.[5]

The shape of this pot is that of a *phiale*, a shallow, dish-like, handleless cup. Its function par excellence was for libation: that is, the pouring of liquid offerings to divinities and the spirits of the dead. Some recipients were accorded wine; for others it was olive oil or milk. Occasions especially suitable for libations would be ones of transition in life: weddings, for instance, or funerals, or travel.[6]

Our focus will be on the interior of the pot. On the rim is painted a wreath of laurel. As laurels were conventionally an award for victory, that plant would be suggestive of use at a festivity involving contests of some sort, though not definitively so. In the tondo—the inner circle, double-banded—is centered the figure of a young woman in haste. Here is where the pieces of the puzzle are laid out.

Although she is clearly doing a task, her apparel makes it certain that she is no servant or slave, and that the task is not routine. Her headband is decorated, not utilitarian. Her necklace is brightly evident, as are the broaches at the shoulders of her dress. She has sizeable bracelets on both arms. She wears sandals, and they are brightly decorated as well. Her dress is not casual. It is a *chiton* (i.e., a light-weight but full gown), sleeveless, pleated, properly ankle-length. The painter gives it the conventional appearance of thin cloth, wind-blown by her rapid movement, so that it will show the contour of the legs. The chiton is, as often, tied at the waist with a blousing of the upper gown.

Her haste is evident in details other than the wind-blown chiton, too. Her hair is spun outwards, as her head has turned quickly to her right and to the back. The pose itself is of running, but of running carefully: there is her phiale to balance. She balances a large phiale (proportionately much larger than the phiale on which it is painted) like a tray with the palm of the right hand, looking back as if to keep it from spilling. She tilts the phiale slightly downward in the direction of her running, again to forestall a spill. Like the pot we hold, her phiale is decorated with a spray of greenery. The greenery, identified as ivy,[7] would suggest an occasion for Dionysus—that is to say, for wine and conviviality, not the victory honors that the laurel on the rim of the actual vessel would intimate.

The figure grasps in the left hand, extended ahead for balance, a decorated garland. Jane Borelli identifies this as a myrtle garland,[8] a plant associated with Aphrodite.

This would put in place a second suggestion (after her phiale itself) of a festive or ritual occasion. Garlands would be worn by human participants and placed on divine images as well. Reinforcing that suggestion is the scarf-like "fillet" (*tainia*, ritual ribbon) seeming to hang in the air behind the figure. The invisible means of suspension for a draped tainia is a frequently-seen feature of pots that indicate some approach to divinity.[9] The unnaturalness of the convention surely marks it a "code" feature, an announcement of cultural function.

Similarly floating free are, to the right of the figure, two small shapes, roughly circular but markedly different from each other—the lower one of rounded, spotted circles, the upper one cruciform or rayed. Shapes of this sort are generally described as flowers.[10] The assumption seems to be that they are decorative only, with no function as "code." That assumption may well be correct, but a recent study of analogous free-floating shapes (albeit Minoan) has argued for an astronomical symbolism in some seen in that tradition.[11] Speaking specifically of Apulian symbolism, H. R. W. Smith has seen one such rayed shape as the evening star Hesperus, the harbinger of the wedding night.[12]

The figure, however, is not left free-floating. Beneath her feet is the stylized *cymation* (wavelet) ornamentation as a ground.[13] Although such a line is conventional, its placement (bisecting the lower portion of the circles surrounding the figure) seems to draw a line between the ground upon which she stands and the undecorated void beneath it, quietly calling attention to the fact of a beneath.

What, then, is the task that inspires such animated haste? We have noted items the painter has made salient: a young woman, her fine attire, the phiale and myrtle garland readied for an occasion, a fillet to honor divinity, perhaps a flower at her feet, perhaps the evening star rising at her shoulder, and the ground. Since such a large proportion of Apulian ceramics were given as funeral offerings,[14] and since the theme of the young woman who dies on the brink of her wedding is so recurrent in Hellenistic literature,[15] it is tempting to see that theme here. If so, this would surely be the bride. She would be hastening in preparation for the wedding that would not take place in life, hastening poignantly to a premature death and a symbolic wedding to the god of the underworld.[16]

[Thomas R. Banks, *Professor of Classics, Dorothy Parkander Professor of Literature*]

[1] For a description of the technique, see Andrew J. Clark, Maya Elston, and Mary Louise Hart, *Understanding Greek Vases: A Guide to Terms, Styles, and Techniques* (Los Angeles: The J. Paul Getty Museum, 2002), 138-39.

[2] David Caccioli, *The Paul A. Anderson Art History Collection*, ed. Catherine Carter Goebel (Rock Island: Augustana College, 2001), 18.

[3] Caccioli, 18.

[4] Cumae, for example, was founded near Naples as early as 750 B.C.E. See *Cumae* in Simon Hornblower and Anthony Spawforth, eds., *Oxford Classical Dictionary*, 3rd ed. (Oxford: Oxford University Press, 1996), 412.

[5] Martin Robertson, *The Art of Vase-painting in Classical Athens* (Cambridge: Cambridge University Press, 1992), 267.

[6] See a scene of a libation from a phiale for a travel departure in Dyfri Williams, *Greek Vases* (Cambridge: Harvard U. Press, 1985), 57, figure 61.

[7] Caccioli, 18.

[8] Jane Borelli, *The Paul A. Anderson Art History Collection*, ed. Catherine Carter Goebel (Rock Island: Augustana College, 2001), 18.

[9] Compare, to choose almost at random, plates 116, 118, 162, 166, and 169 in A. D. Trendall, *Red Figure Vases of South Italy and Sicily: A Handbook* (London: Thames and Hudson, 1989).

[10] For this piece, cf. Borelli, 18, and Caccioli, 18.

[11] E. Kyriakidis, "Unidentified Floating Objects on Minoan Seals," *American Journal of Archaeology* 109, no. 2 (April 2005): 137-154.

[12] H. R. W. Smith, *Funerary Symbolism in Apulean Vase-painting*, ed. by J. K. Anderson (Berkeley, Los Angeles, London: University of California Press, 1976), 260. For the convention of the evening star as the seal of the marriage day, the *locus classicus* is Catullus' wedding poem, #62. See, e.g., lines 26-27: "Hesperus, what flame shines more merrily in the sky? You confirm wedding vows with your blaze...."

[13] Clark et al., *Understanding Greek Vases*, 121, fig. 8.

[14] J. K. Anderson relates the assumption by H. W. R. Smith that "[a]ll Apulian red-figured vases are funerary." See Smith, 3.

[15] For instance, from the woman poet, Anyte: "Instead of a solemn wedding and marriage-bed / your mother gave you for a statue for your tomb, / Thersis. It stands life-size, it has your beauty / so, although you are dead, we can speak to you." Book 7.649, Sally Purcell, trans., in Peter Jay, ed., *The Greek Anthology* (Middlesex, England: Penguin Books, 1981), 76, #104.

[16] On the wedding to Death, cf. also the comments of David Caccioli, 18.

3A

Attributed to a Roman workshop (Eastern Mediterranean) [D. Caccioli]
Double Cosmetic Tube, ascribed title, 4th century C.E.
Free-blown glass
Unsigned
13.6 x 6.7 x 3.3 cm., 5-3/8 x 2-11/16 x 1-5/16"
Gift of Estate of Paul A. Anderson, Augustana College Art Collection, 2001.9

3B

Attributed to a Roman workshop (West Roman) [D. Caccioli]
Bowl, ascribed title, 4th–early 5th century C.E.
Free-blown glass
Unsigned
6.5 x 7.2 x 7.2 cm., 2-1/2 x 2-7/8 x 2-7/8"
Gift of Estate of Paul A. Anderson, Augustana College Art Collection, 2001.8

The two examples of Roman glassware in the Paul A. Anderson collection offer a number of connections between the ancient and the modern world. Not the least of these is the material itself: glass. Wherever you are as you read this, you are almost certainly surrounded by glass; indeed, glass is such a common part of our lives we tend to take it for granted.

We naturally think of Roman glass as being ancient, but the story of glass begins long before Rome. It was during the sixteenth century B.C.E. that the peoples of northern Mesopotamia (modern Iraq) first discovered how to make vessels out of glass using what is known as the *core-forming* technique.[1] In this process a solid core of clay mixed with dung is dipped in molten glass to form the vessel; once the glass has cooled the core is removed, leaving a hollow glass container.[2] The core-forming technique remained the most common means of producing glass vessels for nearly 1500 years.

The technology of making glassware spread quickly from Mesopotamia to Syria and Palestine on the eastern coast of the Mediterranean, and from there to Egypt. Syria, Palestine and Egypt remained important centers of glass production throughout antiquity, so it is not surprising that the next great breakthrough in the technology of glass making, the art of blowing glass, appears to have been made in this area. The earliest evidence of glassblowing comes from a small workshop, dated to around 50 B.C.E., recently discovered in the Jewish Quarter of the Old City of Jerusalem.[3] Blown glass is made by inflating a globule of molten glass attached to a tube; the inflated globule can then be shaped with the help of gravity and various hand-working techniques.[4]

The invention of glassblowing was significant because glass vessels could now be produced more quickly and cheaply than previous techniques had allowed. Since by this time all roads did indeed lead to Rome, the art of glassblowing was already well established in Italy by the end of the first century B.C.E. From Italy the technology spread north into Gaul (modern France and western Germany), where important centers of production took root in the bustling cities that grew up around the Roman legionary bases along the Rhine river.[5]

The two pieces of Roman glass in our collection wonderfully reflect the story of glass itself, and also reveal some of the many links between antiquity and our present day. Indeed, the first of these (item A, opposite), stunningly links ancient Egypt with the cosmetics counter at your local department store. What you are viewing is an ancient eyeliner kit. The basic design of the kit, double tubes to hold the components of the eyeliner[6] and an applicator (missing in our piece), seems to have developed in Egypt during the period of the New Kingdom (c. 1587–1085 B.C.E.).[7] Remarkably, the design remained essentially the same into the later Roman Empire (200–400 C.E), the period in which blown glass versions of the kit appear to have become popular—a span of almost 2000 years.[8]

Kits of this sort would have been used to make *Egyptian eyes*.[9] Surviving applicators are similar to those in modern eyeliner kits: one end was broad and flat, the other pointed.[10] The flat end was used to make a broad stripe around the bottom of the lower eyelid, while the pointed end was used to make a thinner stripe under the eyelashes on the upper eyelid. The Egyptian fashion (for both men and women[11]) was to begin both stripes near the edge of the nose and extend them all the way to the edge of the forehead, a technique that created the highly exaggerated eyes characteristic of all Egyptian portraits. The fashion was probably similar throughout the near East, but apparently never caught on elsewhere; kits of this sort are found commonly only in Egypt, Israel, Palestine, Syria, and on the island of Cyprus.[12]

The tubes of our piece were blown out of what was originally a greenish yellow glass common throughout the Roman world. The handles and the decorative thin glass trails were attached after the tubes were blown. The flared mouths of the tubes and the twining glass trails, a characteristic feature of these kits, may represent an artistic memory of very early Egyptian kits whose design was based on the Egyptian *palm column*; the upper series of trails would reflect the bindings immediately below the capital, in the shape of expanding palm fronds, of the architectural prototype.[13]

The handles on these kits suggest that they were meant to be hung, but from what is not entirely clear. While it is possible that men and women carried kits such as this on their persons, perhaps by means of a cord attached to the side handles,[14] this seems unlikely given the fragile nature of the kit. A painting from an Egyptian tomb depicting a servant applying eyeliner to a man shows in the background a double tube kit which is apparently hanging by its handles on a wall.[15] This is probably a more realistic explanation for the use of the handles, which would have been useful also for holding the kit in one's hands while applying eyeliner.

The other example of Roman glass in the Paul A. Anderson Collection (item B,

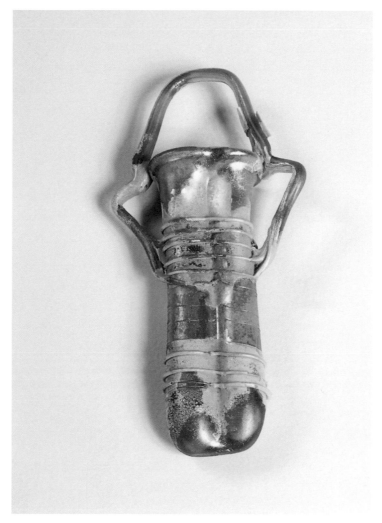

3A

opposite) carries us across the Mediterranean and into the northernmost reaches of the western Roman Empire where important centers of glass production had grown up around the Roman legionary bases along the Rhine river.[16] Hardly as enigmatic as the eyeliner kit in our collection, this diminutive blown glass bowl[17] would be at home in any kitchen or on any table, ancient or modern.

The fragile nature of this piece at first seems to belie the context of its origins. Bowls of this sort were manufactured primarily in cities along the Rhine river during the later Roman Empire (from the late 3rd through the 5th century C.E.),[18] a time when Rome was frequently challenged by incursions of Germanic tribes across the Rhine and Danube rivers which marked the northern frontiers of the empire. But as pleasing as the simple design of this bowl is, such pieces were easily and cheaply produced.[19] Despite its fragile appearance and nature, this beautiful glass bowl was perfectly suited to the troubled times in which it was made and used: though remarkably it stands before us today,[20] this bowl was not made to last.

Both of the pieces of Roman glass in our collection—and most examples of Roman glass—are striking for their bright and iridescent colors. Ironically, the remarkable colors that make these pieces so distinctive are accidents of time; both of our pieces were originally a uniform yellowish-green color. The present appearance of the pieces is the result of weathering over the last 1500 years. When glass is exposed alternately to wet and dry conditions over such a span of time, the surface of the glass begins to break down chemically.[21] This process ultimately produced the varied hues of bright green, gold, and blue evident on the eyeliner kit, and the shimmering iridescent patina of the bowl. These transformations serve as a reminder that artifacts of antiquity—material and also literary—sometimes acquire meaning and significance never envisioned by their creators.

[Emil A. Kramer, *Assistant Professor of Classics*]

[1] V. Tatton-Brown and C. Andrew, "Before the Invention of Glassblowing," in *Five Thousand Years of Glass*, ed. by H. Tait (London: British Museum Press, 1991), 22-23; the technology for making glass itself dates back to around 4000 B.C.E.

[2] For the technique see W. Gudenrath, "Techniques of Glassmaking and Decoration," in *Five Thousand Years of Glass*, 214-215.

[3] For the evidence and the argument see Y. Israeli, "The Invention of Blowing," in *Roman Glass: Two Centuries of Art and Invention* (London: The Society of Antiquaries, 1991), 46-55; the "invention" of glassblowing appears to have been accidental.

[4] For the techniques, see Gudenrath, 223-225.

[5] C. Isings, *Roman Glass from Dated Finds* (Groningen: J.B. Wolters, 1957), 4-13; V. Tatton-Brown, "The Roman Empire," in *Five Thousand Years of Glass*, 64-66.

[6] It is not clear why these kits generally contained two tubes. M. Dayagi-Mendels, *Perfumes and Cosmetics in the Ancient World* (Jerusalem: The Israel Museum, 1989), 40-42, suggests that each tube contained a different color of eyeliner. Many early examples, however, consist

of only one tube (for examples see Tatton-Brown and Andrews, 31-32), and later glass versions similar to that in our collection sometimes have four tubes (for examples see Dayagi-Mendels, 49). An alternative explanation for the multiple tube kits is that one tube contained the dry powder of the kohl, and the other water or perfumed oil with which it was mixed (for the technique see Dayagi-Mendels, 36-37). If this explanation is correct, the double tube kit would have developed as a convenience for applying one color, and the four tube kit that developed later would have been for two colors (presumably one would want to have a separate liquid tube for each dry color in order to avoid mixing the colors). I have found no examples of odd numbers of multiple glass tubes.

[7] Dayagi-Mendels, 44; evidence for the use of eyeliner in Egypt dates back to at least 4000 B.C.E. Early kits were made of many different materials, including wood, pottery, ivory, stone, bronze (see Dayagi-Mendels, 42-48) and core-formed glass (see Tatton-Brown and Andrews, 32).

[8] Our kit is most similar to examples dating to the 4th century (300s C.E.); for the dating see D. Caccioli, "Double Cosmetics Tube," in *The Paul A. Anderson Art History Collection*, ed. Catherine Carter Goebel (Rock Island: Augustana College, 2001), 20.

[9] I like to call these *Egyptian eyes*.

[10] Applicators were made of many different materials, including wood, bone, ivory, glass, and bronze (Dayagi-Mendels, 36).

[11] The use of eyeliner had both functional and decorative purposes (compare modern football players who use what is in effect eyeliner to lessen the glare from the sun). Early Egyptian kits often have inscriptions touting the health benefits of the cosmetics (see Dayagi-Mendels, 44, for examples); one suspects that a certain degree of "snake oil salesmanship" was involved here.

[12] Dayagi-Mendels, 58; S. Fleming, *Roman Glass: Reflections of Everyday Life* (Philadelphia: The University of Pennsylvania Museum, 1997), 9.

[13] For examples of the design on these 14th–13th century B.C.E. kits and the argument for its interpretation, see Tatton-Brown and Andrews, 31-33.

[14] See Caccioli, "Double Cosmetics Tube," 20.

[15] In Dayagi-Mendels, 38.

[16] C. Isings, 4-13.

[17] The dimensions of the bowl are a mere 6.5 x 7.2 x 7.2 centimeters. According to Caccioli ("Bowl," 22), a label attached to this piece at some time in its afterlife identified it as a wine cup. As Caccioli points out (ibid.), this is unlikely given that the edges of the rim are unfinished. Bowls of this sort with unfinished edges may have originally have had lids (for an identical bowl with a surviving lid see Tatton-Brown, 86); another possibility is that such bowls were intended to serve as oil lamps (for the references see Caccioli, ibid., notes 4 and 5).

[18] For origins and the dating see Isings, 113-114; Caccioli ("Bowl," 22) provides some additional comparanda for dating.

[19] The glass was originally of the same greenish-yellow variety used in the eyeliner kit and common throughout the Roman world. A four step process (five if the edges were finished) produced such bowls: a globule of molten glass was blown into a simple sphere; its bottom was then flattened and the flare around the lip created with pincers ("jacks"); finally, using a technique known as "cracking off," the top of the globule was removed from what would become the edge or lip of the bowl. The edge could then be finished or, as in our piece, not. For the techniques, see Gudenrath, 223-227.

[20] Though we do not know the provenance of this bowl, it was almost certainly taken from a burial where it was deposited as a grave gift for its humble owner.

[21] For those interested in the scientific details of the weathering process, see Fleming, 61.

3B

4

Attributed to a Parisian workshop (French)
Book of Hours: Crucifixion Scene Opening the Hours of the Cross,
ascribed title, ca. 1425–1450
Hand-painted with gold leaf on vellum
Unsigned
15.5 x 11.6 cm., 6-1/8 x 4-1/16"
Paul A. Anderson Chair in the Arts Purchase, Augustana College Art
Collection, 2000.13

This is a single leaf that has been cut out of a medieval book of prayers, called a Book of Hours; that book was likely produced in Paris sometime in the early 15th century. Because we do not have the rest of this hand-made book, or manuscript, we do not have a physical context by which we can readily interpret the image's meanings and uses. There are, however, a few things the image itself tells us and we can infer much information from this. We know from the text below the image, and its continuation on the back, that this page comes from a Book of Hours, a book used by clergy and lay alike to guide them in a series of prayers and contemplations that were practiced throughout the day.[1] The text comes from the Hours of the Cross—prayers said in contemplation of Christ's death—and the image was used to aid in that contemplation. Books of Hours were increasingly popular in the late medieval era and were themselves based upon previously established monastic practices. The way the figures are drawn and the rich decoration along the borders look like other manuscript pages made in Paris in the early 15th century, especially those of the so-called Boucicaut Master. This page is not by him, but by an artist who copied elements of the Boucicaut Master's style.[2]

Since manuscripts were made from the skin of a lamb or calf (called vellum), they often have irregular edges and uneven textures. This leaf, however, is of a very fine quality and, along with the plethora of gold and exquisite design, indicate a wealthy patron, likely of the newly emergent merchant class in 15th-century Paris. We can tell also that the page has been trimmed or cut down from its original size—the edges are too straight and regular. This often happens to manuscripts over the centuries to make the edges more uniform. As well, there is usually a little more blank or unpainted space between the richly painted borders and the edge of the page (so that the book's users could handle and turn the page without rubbing off the paint and gold leaf). Despite the trimming, we can see that the vellum along the right edge of the leaf is a little darker in tone than the left edge, indicating that the page was handled and turned from this edge; the image of the Crucifixion, then, was on the recto or right hand side when the book was opened to this leaf (as opposed to the text, which is on the back of the leaf, its verso). This arrangement, to have images lay on the right hand side as you turn through the pages, was quite common in the Middle Ages. And because we also know the most common sequence of prayers in these Books of Hours, we can even suppose that there followed an image of the Pentecost, which often accompanied the Hours of the Holy Spirit, the next set of prayers in a Book of Hours.[3]

The decoration of this leaf is interesting and unusual in a number of ways. First, it was relatively uncommon for extra scenes to accompany the Crucifixion.[4] At the bottom of the page, on the left, an Angel kneels in a landscape while praying and gazing up at the image of the crucified Christ. On the right, a narrative element is added to the scene as a grotesquely drawn man, whose tongue hangs out of his mouth, pulls Christ along the path of His passion. Jews were often depicted as grotesque figures in medieval art in the belief that the exterior appearance of people was a reflection of their interior, spiritual state. And so because medieval people commonly blamed the Jews for the death of Christ, they depicted them as grotesques.[5] Up above, however, are two unidentified figures who seem to gesture in opposite directions, even as they both gaze down at Christ. They are set in different kinds of landscapes and are dressed quite distinctly. Although some might suppose they are angels, because of their backgrounds, they are more likely personifications of Day and Night.

In the main scene, Christ is shown dead upon the cross, with a great deal of blood and pathos that emphasize his suffering; he is mourned by his companions, Mary, the mother of Christ, and John the Evangelist on the left and Joseph of Arimathea and an unknown man on the right. In the late medieval devotional culture, there was an increasing emphasis on the body of Christ, especially its suffering during the Passion, both as the locus for the contemplation of that suffering, and ultimately as a vehicle for divine salvation.[6] The skin of Christ naturally played a key role in this signification and the image of a blood-soaked Christ is truly compelling of the more affective contemplation that had become more popular in the later Middle Ages.[7] As well, the scale of the figures differ from each other. Christ's body is smaller, certainly more vulnerable and exposed. We might be tempted to say he is set further back in the landscape than the mourners, except that at the bottom of the image, the cross and the other figures all line up in the same space. The body of Christ appears then somewhat removed and distant. The object of everyone's gaze and prayers, it may have reminded the fifteenth-century viewer less of any realistic image of the event, and more of a picture of a Crucifix, a ubiquitous piece of sculpture that also made present Christ's suffering and death on the cross. Crucifixes, as objects of intense personal devotion, were becoming more and more prevalent in late medieval visual culture. In our image, then, the ravaged body of Christ is blood soaked and punctured with wounds that actively spew blood and, in the case of the wounds at his feet and side, form the odd, yet distinct and purposeful decorative patterns of a star-burst and crescent moon. More than a decorative fancy, these cosmic shapes may in fact suggest the sun and moon that had traditionally been depicted above the Crucifixion as a way to represent the sympathetic reaction of the cosmos to the death of its creator—Christ Logos.[8] In this image, then, Christ's body, that is the Word made flesh in the world and simultaneously the creator of that world, draws the universe into itself, enfolds creation into this sight of contemplation as the viewer joins Mary, John and attendants in gazing upon and contemplating the passing of the Son of God.

[Daniel K. Connolly, *Assistant Professor of Art History*]

[1] For an account of the Book of Hours and this image's place in its sequence of prayers, see the catalogue entry by Mary Em Kirn in *The Paul A. Anderson Art History Collection*, ed. Catherine Carter Goebel, (Rock Island: Augustana College, 2001), 30, no. 7.

[2] Augustana correspondence with the seller of this leaf, Dr. Sandra Hindman, a specialist in medieval manuscripts, dated May 15, 2000. Art Museum files.

[3] Roger Wieck, *Painted Prayers: The Book of Hours in Medieval and Renaissance Art* (New York: Braziller, 1997), 140.

[4] Augustana correspondence with Sandra Hindman.

[5] Michael Camille, *The Gothic Idol: Ideology and Image-making in Medieval Art* (Cambridge: Cambridge University Press, 1990), 180–94.

[6] Caroline Walker Bynum, "The Body of Christ in the Later Middle Ages," in *Fragmentation and Redemption: Essays on Gender and the Human Body in Medieval Religion* (New York: Zone Books, 1991), 79–117.

[7] Jeffrey F. Hamburger, *Nuns as Artists: The Visual Culture of a Medieval Convent* (Berkeley: University of California Press, 1997), *passim*.

[8] Gertrud Schiller, *Iconography of Christian Art*, trans. Janet Seligman (New York: Graphic Society, 1971), 88–117.

5

Giorgio (Mantovano) Ghisi (Italian 1520–1582) after Michelangelo (Italian 1475–1564)
The Erythraean Sibyl, early 1570s
Engraving, five known states
Signed b.c. in image "*Georgius Mantuanus Fecit*" and "*Michael Angelus Invent et Pinxit Georgius Mantuanus Fecit Nii Van Alst Formis Romae*"
56.6 x 43.3 cm., 22-1/4 x 17-1/8" image and sheet
Gift of Thomas E. Rassieur, Augustana College Art Collection, 96.8.4

Giorgio Ghisi, also known as Giorgio Mantovano, was primarily an engraver of prints. Born in Mantua, Italy, around 1520, he was the brother of the painter Teodoro Ghisi.[1] Very few documents survive related to this artist (other than his impressive prints) making it difficult to establish a complete biography. For the last few years before his death in 1582, however, it is recorded that he worked for Guglielmo Gonzaga, the Duke of Mantua,[2] for whom he served as guardian of precious metals and jewels. This employment is logical considering his exceptional reputation as a metalworker, both in engraving and *damascening* (the art of decorating metal).[3]

Ghisi's engraving of the *Erythraean Sibyl* is a copy after Michelangelo's figure of the same name, one of twelve seers painted in the famous Sistine Chapel from 1508 to 1512 at the Vatican in Rome. The seers were sibyls and prophets, individuals who were said to be inspired by the gods or God.[4] Although such images were quite popular, as were all the paintings in the chapel, one could only see them in the Sistine Chapel itself since the original artist, Michelangelo, never made copies of his art. Ghisi, realizing this, shrewdly determined to make prints of many popular images within the chapel, including a series of six seers. He thus enabled people to own the artwork themselves and ponder it at their own convenience—many could now essentially have the Sistine Chapel within their own homes. Artists, as well, benefited from such imaging of major works of art in prints. It was much easier for them to study portable versions in their own studios, freeing them from the burden and expense of traveling to various sites in order to see them in person. Since copying the masters before them was considered one of the best methods for learning art techniques, such multiple images were crucial toward artists' proper education.

By the turn of the sixteenth century, the output of engravings increased dramatically. Like many engravers of his time, Ghisi was considered a reproductive engraver, copying other artists' works and reproducing them so they could reach a wider audience.[5] *The Erythraean Sibyl* was one such print.

The term, *sibyl*, comes from the ancient Greek word *sibylla* which means "prophetess." Sibyls were often isolated from society so that they could receive new prophecies which they would then share with the people. The *Erythraean Sibyl*, was so named because she prophesied from a cave in the town of Erythrae. At the end of the Middle Ages, the Catholic Church adapted these Classical sibyls by accepting them as twelve pagan prophets who foretold the coming of Christ, counterparts to the Old Testament Prophets. They thus linked the ancient Greco-Roman world with the Christian era.

The Erythraean Sibyl is said to have prophesied many important Christian events, such as the *Annunciation*, Christ's *Presentation in the Temple*, the *Apocalypse* and the *Last Judgment*.[6] Michelangelo portrayed her as a young, idealized and somewhat masculine woman, typical of High Renaissance standards combined with the artist's own style. Ghisi, in this engraving, exaggerated the sibyl's muscular definition even further than Michelangelo's original fresco.

In Ghisi's engraving, Erythraea is half-dressed in fine clothing that fits loosely, yet suggests the body beneath, as in classical wet drapery. She has opened a book, one of the *Sibylline* Books which recorded her prophecies, as two *genii* frame her head. *Genii*, plural for *genius*, originated in Roman mythology and were guardian spirits of a person or place, in this case, Erythraea. One of the genii holds a torch in order to light a lamp by her head, representing divine illumination.[7] There are a total of fourteen characters, the main one being Erythraea, and all are appropriately idealized.

In this engraving, many of the faces appear wistful and it is hard to determine exactly what they are thinking. The original painting was vibrantly colored in bright green, orange-yellow, pink and purple, whereas the print is reduced to black and white, with modulation created through further linear definition. Yet it is effective and dramatic in its reductive coloring. The piece is symmetrical and balanced with an evenly distributed number of males and females. What makes this print appear so remarkable is all the detail that was put into it, not to mention how three-dimensional it looks, similar to the Sistine Chapel.

Such reverence for masters like Michelangelo, so soon after his death, demonstrates the sixteenth-century elevation of the position of artists. Michelangelo, as a High Renaissance artist, enjoyed acclaim and was considered a genius in his own lifetime. Unlike the generally subservient roles for medieval craftsmen, artists were now appreciated as educated and talented individuals, well-versed in such fields as anatomy, theology and science, as well as artistic techniques. Michelangelo was a poet as well, illustrating the new concept of the *Renaissance* man, a genius with expertise in many fields. Artists like Ghisi effectively furthered Michelangelo's position for history by making his masterpieces from the Sistine Chapel more accessible to the public and future generations.

[Amanda Nordstrom, *Class of 2008*]

---

[1] Suzanne Boorsch, *The Engravings of Giorgio Ghisi* (New York: The Metropolitan Museum of Art, 1985), 16.

[2] Ibid., 22.

[3] Unlike engraving where the artist incises the metal plate, in damascening an object is cut into and a thin wire of precious metal is laid inside the cut. Ibid., 22–23.

[4] Michelangelo painted five Sibyls and seven Prophets on the pendentives, where the ceiling meets the wall. Ibid., 164.

[5] David Landau and Peter Parshall, *The Renaissance Print*, 1470–1550 (New Haven: Yale University Press, 1994), 167.

[6] Loren Partridge, *Michelangelo: The Sistine Chapel Ceiling, Rome* (New York: George Braziller, Inc., 1996), 82.

[7] Carlo Pietrangeli, et al., ed. Pierluigi de Vecchi, *The Sistine Chapel: A Glorious Restoration* (New York: Harry N. Abrams, Inc., 1994), 139.

MICHAEL ANGELVS INVENT ET PINXIT GEORGIVS MANTVANVS FECIT Nil Van all formis Roma

6

Albrecht Dürer (German 1471–1528)
Death of the Virgin from **Life of the Virgin**, 1510
Woodcut
Signed b.r. in image with monogram "A D"
29.3 x 23.3 cm., 11-1/2 x 8-1/4" image and sheet
Purchase with Gift of Augustana College Art History
Alumni in Honor of Dr. Mary Em Kirn, 2003.7

Albrecht Dürer, the Nuremberg painter and printmaker, enjoyed international status as one of the most innovative and forward-looking Renaissance artists of his time.[1] Even today as we view his *Death of the Virgin* woodcut (1510), Dürer's modernity is readily apparent in his painterly approach to narrative in the graphic arts. Here he combined his personal interest in exploring the temporal and psychological aspects of narrative imagery with the use of one-point perspective, more naturalistic and dramatic light effects, and other established pictorial devices intended to create the illusion of a realistic, three-dimensional space on a two-dimensional surface, and did so in a manner that few, if any, had ever attempted outside the medium of painting. His success in this regard won him immediate recognition throughout northern Europe and Italy, while his printmaking challenged his fellow artists to test the thematic and expressive limits of the various print media.[2]

The 1510 *Death of the Virgin* was one of twenty woodcuts in Dürer's *The Life of the Virgin*, which he published in book form for the first time in 1511. Benedictus Chelidonius, a Benedictine monk and member of the Nuremberg society of humanist scholars, joined Dürer in this enterprising venture, providing poems in classical Latin verse to accompany the nineteen narrative images in the series. At the time of their collaboration, Chelidonius was serving as a teacher at the monastery of St. Giles in Nuremberg.[3] Dürer intended that his woodcut books be viewed by a learned audience is evidenced in his dedication of *The Life of the Virgin* to Caritas Pirckheimer, Abbess of St. Clara's Franciscan convent in Nuremberg and a gifted Latinist, whose scholarly acumen was praised by the German arch-humanist Konrad Celtis. It has been noted that the large, folio format with text and image opposite each other across the binding, as well as the high quality of Dürer's *The Life of the Virgin* series and other religious prints would have made them an excellent means for classroom instruction, or for private devotional use.[4] Regarding the latter, on the eve of the Protestant Reformation the popularity of the cult of the Virgin Mary was second only to that of the Holy Sacrament, the Body of Christ, among the Christian faithful. Dürer was certainly aware of this dynamic when he published his three great woodcut books of 1511, any of which would have made suitable visual aids for those reciting the rosary, or any number of other prayers associated with worship and veneration of the Virgin Mary and Christ.[5]

The legendary account of the Virgin Mary's death and subsequent Assumption is drawn from various apocryphal books dating to the 2nd and 5th centuries. These earlier sources were condensed and popularized in the thirteenth century by a Dominican friar, Jacobus de Voragine, in his so-called *Golden Legend*. The story of Mary's death is included in the *Golden Legend* as part of the reading intended for the feast of the Assumption of the Blessed Virgin Mary (15 August). From this text we learn that Mary, twelve years after Christ's Crucifixion desired to be reunited with Jesus and prayed that she might be delivered from her earthly life. Her prayer was answered by an angel, who at Mary's bidding miraculously transported first John the Evangelist, and then the remaining Apostles,[6] all of whom were engaged in missionary work around the world, to her doorstep. Once inside Mary's house, they held vigil around her bed and joined in the singing and reciting of the funeral service until the third hour of the night, when Christ suddenly appeared in the room accompanied by a heavenly host of angels and saints, all of whom joined the Apostles in celebrating the *obsequies* (funeral rites). Later, around daybreak, Jesus took possession of Mary's soul and departed heavenward.[7]

By Dürer's time, it was no longer customary for *Death of the Virgin* imagery to include Christ and the heavenly host at her bedside. In Northern Renaissance art, the Virgin Mary is generally shown holding a candle, in accordance with established Christian death ritual,[8] which recommended placing a candle in the

hands of a dying person as a symbol of his or her faith, as she rests on a canopied bed set within a domestic interior. Several of the Apostles, who appear gathered at either side of her bed, hold liturgical books (possibly Books of Hours) and other liturgical equipment, and they are frequently assigned specific tasks associated with the priestly administration of last rites and the celebration of the Office of the Dead. All of these features were employed by artists to psychologically engage the viewer, to humanize this sacred event believed to have taken place in the distant past and to relate it to the viewer's common, everyday experience by setting the narrative within real, historical space and time. Dürer's woodcut rendering of the theme, which owes much to Martin Schongauer's pre-1481 *Death of the Virgin* engraving, an enormously popular and widely copied work, contains all of these traditional pictorial elements and more.

What set Dürer's composition apart from those of his predecessors was his innovative narrative style—in particular, his sophisticated use of one-point perspective (invented in the previous century) to draw in the viewer, to focus the eye on the central figure of Mary, and to map out the interior space in a clearly legible, realistic manner. We, the viewers, stand on the threshold of Mary's bedroom as she expires. Two *repoussoir* figures—one standing in near profile holding a *thurible* for incense, and the other with his back turned to us as he kneels, holding a processional cross erect—appear in the lower-left corner on a raised landing set just inside the picture plane, inviting us into their world. The space at the foot of the stairs has been left open, offering us a clear field of vision as we look down upon the foreshortened figure of Mary, who is in the act of receiving a candle from John the Evangelist. The orthogonal lines of the foreground stairs, of the ribs of the canopy, and of the monumental framing arch direct our vision toward the vanishing point, the middle console supporting the shelf that is situated directly above and slightly behind Mary on the headboard of the bed. Immediately to the left of this point in space, we encounter St. Peter, dressed in bishop's garb and holding an *aspergillum* in his extended right hand as he sprinkles Mary with holy water. To Peter's right (our left), another apostle assists him by holding the bucket containing the holy water while reading a book, presumably a breviary containing the funeral service, the Office of the Dead. This figure is positioned in such a way that he directs our eye to the opposite side of the bed, where the remaining apostles are shown praying and keeping vigil. Following his return from his second Italian sojourn in 1507, Dürer began employing a more sophisticated tonal system in his woodcuts, which included a middle gray tone, allowing him to impart an even greater sense of naturalistic light and shadow to the final three prints of his *The Life of the Virgin* series, as we see here.[9] All things considered, Dürer's *Death of the Virgin* was as innovative and thoroughly modern as any woodcut of its day and age.

[Paul Bacon, *Class of 1990*]

---

[1] Regarding Dürer's international reputation both during and after his lifetime, see Jane C. Hutchison, *Albrecht Dürer: A Biography* (Princeton: Princeton University Press, 1990), 187-206.

[2] For a brief overview of Dürer's personal achievements and impact on his artistic contemporaries in the print media of woodcut, engraving, and etching, see David Landau and Peter Parshall, *The Renaissance Print, 1470-1550* (New Haven: Yale University Press, 1994), 170-74, 309-20, and 327-29.

[3] David Hotchkiss Price, *Albrecht Dürer's Renaissance: Humanism, Renaissance, and the Art of Faith* (Ann Arbor: University of Michigan Press, 2003), 137-47, provides this biographical information concerning Benedictus Chelidonius and further elaborates upon the humanist monk's poetic contributions to Dürer's three woodcut books of 1511: *The Large Passion*, *The Life of the Virgin*, and the *Small Passion*.

[4] Hutchison, 54.

[5] Robert N. Swanson, *Religion and Devotion in Europe, c. 1215-c. 1515* (New York: Cambridge University Press, 1997), 136-90; and Anne Winston-Allen, *Stories of the Rose: The Making of the Rosary in the Middle Ages* (University Park: The Pennsylvania State University Press, 1997), 70.

[6] Once Christ's remaining disciples went their separate ways to preach the Gospel following Pentecost, they were traditionally referred to as the Apostles, as in the Acts of the Apostles.

[7] Jacobus de Voragine, *The Golden Legend: Readings on the Saints, 2 vols.*, trans. William Granger Ryan (Princeton: Princeton University Press, 1993), II: 77-79

[8] Regarding late-Medieval and early-Renaissance Christian death rituals and their representation in art, see Paul Binski, *Medieval Death: Ritual and Representation* (Ithaca: Cornell University Press, 1996), 33-47; and Rogers S. Wieck, *Time Sanctified: The Book of Hours in Medieval Art and Life* (New York: George Braziller, Inc., 2001), 124-36, figs. 109-119.

[9] Liz Gunter, "Dürer's Narrative Style," in David R. Smith and Liz Guenther, *Realism and Invention in the Prints of Albrecht Dürer* (Durham: The Art Gallery, University of New Hampshire, 1995), 13.

7

Hans Holbein the Younger (German 1498–1543)
recto: **The Child** [Job xiv, 1 and 2] from **Dance of Death**, published 1538
Les simulachres et historiees faces de la mort, autant elegammet pourtraictes, que artificellement imaginées [sic, Images and illustrated facets of death, as elegantly depicted as they are artfully conceived], later edition
Woodcut
Unsigned
6.5 x 4.9 cm., 2-5/8 x 1-15/16" image
13.9 x 8.6 cm., 5-1/2 x 3-3/8" sheet
Augustana College Art Exhibits Purchase, 91.72 a and b

Hans Holbein the Younger's woodcut entitled *The Child* is one of several prints published in 1538 in the book *Les simulachres & histories faces de la mort*. In order to understand the context for this print, one must first grasp the central idea of the book which focuses on the medieval theme known as the *Dance of Death*. The *Dance of Death* shows the encounter of Death, in the form of a skeleton, with representatives from all varieties of human life. These scenes are meant to mirror society and the various states and social strata in which people live. While those being led away possess little emotion, Death itself dances mockingly, as if ridiculing the hopeless yet continuous striving of humans after things of this world.[1] The idea of a world beyond death was prevalent in the Christian mindset, especially within the context of the medieval period.[2] Death worked as an unbiased equalizer, coming to this temporal world to visit all humans regardless of gender, age, status or wealth.

Holbein was born around 1497 in Augsburg, Germany, where he likely first confronted this subject in a well-known wall painting entitled the *Dance of Death*. At the age of seventeen, he moved to Basel, an important printing center that boasted two fifteenth-century wall paintings which illustrated variations on the *Dance of Death*. The designs found in the Basel paintings seem to stylistically bridge earlier medieval examples and Holbein's later interpretation.[3] By exposing Holbein to various illustrations of this subject, these cities played an important role in the creation of his most famous work.

In his fascinating and imaginative *Dance of Death* woodcuts, Holbein transformed a traditionally well-known medieval art form to a new vehicle for his own Renaissance time period. Previously the theme had always represented *Death's* arrival as a punishment for a person's sins. It was during the Renaissance period that the *Dance of Death* moved away from this theme of retribution to focus instead on the state of humankind, frequently with mocking undertones.[4] A *memento mori* (reminder of death) generally appeared as the familiar skeletal form of Death, who served to remind people of the frailty of their passing life in comparison to the eternal life for which their soul was destined. People of the time believed that after death all would be judged by God, and thus what they did in their lifetime determined their soul's future. Due to significantly shortened life expectancy because of war, disease and food shortages, death was indeed a grim and constant reality, regardless of social position. This fact, combined

with the belief in an afterlife, made Holbein's *Dance of Death* woodcuts in *Les simulachres & histories faces de la mort* take on a special significance.

With the woodcut of *The Child*, Holbein depicted a living drama, showing Death's sudden intrusion into everyday life. An inscription beneath it reads, "Man that is born of woman has/ Few days, made difficult with woes;/ He passes, even as flowers pass;/ He comes, and like a shadow goes."[5] This monochromatic woodcut shows Death, in the form of a skeleton, leading a young child away from his mother while she prepares dinner over an open fire. With one hand, the mother clutches her cooking pan and with the other holds her head in horror. Another child behind her also grabs at his hair as he watches, with panicked eyes, his younger sibling being wrenched away from his home. By placing this scene in a common house with a family performing the familiar task of preparing a meal, Holbein creates a picture of an immediate reality, of an innocent child being taken away by death from a mother who, contrary to her maternal instincts, cannot save him. It serves as a *memento mori*, reminding all that life is fleeting and *Death* is inescapable, sparing not even the young and innocent.

The Child was first published as part of *Les simulachres & histories faces de la mort* in 1538, a book containing forty-one of Holbein's woodcuts.[6] With the Renaissance invention of the printing press and its facility to produce multiple copies of books, rather than the medieval tradition of the handmade illuminated manuscript (catalogue 4), books became more accessible to larger audiences. Woodcuts developed as an excellent parallel medium for advancing multiple images of art as well, since many copies could be made from a single block and thus the cost was much lower than a one-of-a-kind drawing or painting. Holbein sketched the designs for the woodcuts that craftsman Hans Lützelburger carved into wood. Lützelburger then sold the woodcarvings to the Trechsel printing firm in Basel.[7]

Holbein's *Dance of Death* works are probably his best known, most imaginative and original woodcuts. He adapted medieval iconography to make it relevant to Renaissance ideas. This series of woodcuts communicates the necessity for readiness. People must be prepared to leave behind their earthly life, to die and to be judged according to their deeds, since everyone, rich or poor, young or old, weak or powerful, is destined for an inevitable encounter with Death.[8]

[Jessica Feinman, *Class of 2008*]

[1] Marsha Collins, *The Dance of Death in Book Illustration* (Columbia: University of Missouri, 1978), 14.

[2] James M. Clark, *The Dance of Death in the Middle Ages and the Renaissance* (Glasgow: Jackson, Son & Company, 1950), 5.

[3] Collins, 29-30.

[4] Ibid., 29.

[5] Hans Holbein the Younger, *The Dance of Death: A Complete Facsimile of the Original 1538 Edition of Les simulachres & histories faces de la mort,* Introduction by Werner L. Gundersheimer (New York: Dover Publications, Inc., 1971), 144.

[6] Clark, 71.

[7] Oskar Bätschmann and Pascal Griener, *Hans Holbein* (Princeton: Princeton University Press, 1997), 56.

[8] Hans Holbein the Younger, Introduction by Gundersheimer, xi.

8

Attributed to Antonio Allegri da Correggio (Italian ca. 1489–1534)
Woman with a Book, ascribed title, n.d.
Oil on canvas
Signed verso, not yet verified
101.5 x 75.4 cm., 40 x 29-3/4"
Lent by Barbara Bradac in Memory of Hubert A. and Ruth E. Boisvert

In the elegant painting *Woman with a Book*, a richly and simply dressed woman sits in a landscape, her arm resting on a pedestal, one hand holding an open book on her lap, the other pointing toward it. Her glance is aimed away from the volume, looking down demurely in thoughtful, somber reflection. The text on the page of the tome reads, *Ut non confundar* (literally, "That I am not confounded"), and probably refers to the longer passage in Psalms 118, verse 80, that in the Vulgate translation reads: "Let my heart be undefiled in thy justifications, that I may not be confounded."[1]

At some point, this painting was attributed to Antonio Allegri da Correggio (ca. 1489–1534), the great Renaissance painter. Indeed, the signature on the verso could be interpreted as stating that name, although it is not completely legible, and does not appear to match any of the various signatures this artist was known to have used.[2] Correggio, whose genius has been equated with High Renaissance masters Michelangelo Buonarroti and Raphael Sanzio, is less known today, but remains a vibrant, original painter who influenced subsequent artists such as Gianlorenzo Bernini and Sir Joshua Reynolds.[3] If not an original work by this painter, it is likely a copy of an untraced masterpiece by another artist, learning from the *master* through imitation.

Looking at this image alongside Correggio's authenticated works, it seems unlikely that his hand was directly involved in this painting. His female figures, mostly consisting of Madonnas, are generally deeply engaged with their world. Their expressions are typically warm, intimate and charming.[4] This woman is neither maternal nor sacred. Perhaps she represents a type rather than an actual person. Her features are generalized in a classical profile, a beauty standard based on ancient Greek statuary (catalogue 21). She seems more like an alabaster statue than an actual woman with daily concerns and passions. Whereas Correggio's females are expressive and revealing, this figure appears serious and remote, her eyes are downcast and lost in shadow.

The only known portrait painted by Correggio, aside from one that includes a donor, is the *Portrait of a Gentlewoman* (Leningrad, Hermitage), and it is very unlike this piece.[5] Although the gentlewoman similarly sits in a landscape and presents a large triangular pose, her bosom the center of the painting, it is the gentlewoman's face we first notice. She looks directly at the viewer—modest, curious and seemingly amused. The goals of the two paintings are entirely different; one imparts a moral and the other introduces us to a real person.

The two works are different also in their styles. *Woman* is painted with rather broad brushstrokes, whereas Correggio used a finer stroke in *Gentlewoman*, in which the gold chain, the headdress, the gathered ruffles along the bodice and the sheen of the sleeves were all carefully rendered. In contrast to Correggio's articulated naturalistic landscape, the background in *Woman* is rather flat and static.[6] An abstracted billow of clouds or trees stands before a blank sky, bordered on the left by dark, barely discernible leaves.

Those of us who live in the Midwest have an opportunity to view a Correggio, *Madonna and Child and the Giovannino*, at the Art Institute in Chicago. *Woman* and this *Madonna* make a good comparison because the latter also shows a demure woman in a landscape setting. Correggio's *Madonna* sits against a trellis laden with golden fruit, delicate green sprigs of grass at her knee. In the distance lie a lake, castle and mountains. As noted above, the background in *Woman* reveals no corresponding interest in such landscape details. Although the directional gaze of the figures in the two paintings is similar, the *Madonna* is livelier and more realistic. She smiles slightly, revealing a shyness and quiet pleasure in the little boys in her lap.

Although *Woman* may not be a Correggio, we can admire it. The woman's triangular pose is just asymmetrical enough to make us look again. We follow her tilted glance as it leads us to the lower left. There, her bent arm and pointing hand direct our eyes to the lower right, to the book where we read the inscription: *Ut non confundar*. The painter seems to say, this resting place for the eye is the moral center of the painting.

The *physical* center of painting, however, is not the book but the woman's expansive white bosom. Although the viewer's eye follows her glance around the painting to the book, it also jumps to the center of the canvas where her breasts seem almost illuminated. Satin-like chemise creases and folds of the robe draw even more attention. The stately formality of the face, drapery and pose contrasts sharply with this sensuality. Whereas the outer margins of the canvas are formal and static, the center is informal and lively, perhaps acknowledging her nurturing and sensual center.

What is the viewer to make of this contradiction? This painting is not, after all, a rendering of a specific woman with friends and family, tasks and responsibilities, but of a female who is meant to represent all women who are religious, good and follow the rules. She is a model for others of her time. Perhaps it was the artist who inserted his own view of the world: that living a moral life is all well and good, but as sensate beings, we must also take into account everyday life, including the beauty of the body and its passions. Whether Correggio painted this work or not, he would likely have agreed with the subtle message sent by this image because, of all the concerns he revealed in his paintings, the intensity of a life fully lived was most prominent.

[Margi Rogal, *Reference Librarian, Liaison to the Fine and Performing Arts Division*]

---

[1] Emil Kramer, Classics Department, kindly helped with the Biblical translations.

[2] E. Bénézit, *Dictionnaire Critique et documentaire des peintures, sculpteur, dessinateurs at graveurs* (Paris: Grund, 1999), s.v. "Corregio, Allegri Antonio," and John Denison Champlin, *Cyclopedia of Painters and Painting* (New York: Scribner's, 1913-15), s.v. "Correggio." In December 1933, the painting was borrowed by The Los Angeles Museum of History, Science, and Art, identified as "attributed to Correggio."

[3] David Ekserdjian, "Correggio," in Jane Turner, ed., *The Dictionary of Art*, vol.7 (London: Macmillan Publishers,), 893. Limited, 1996

[4] Lucia Fornari Schianchi, *Correggio* (Florence: SCALA, 1994), 40-53.

[5] Cecil Gould, *The Paintings of Correggio* (Ithaca: Cornell University Press, 1976), 59.

[6] Schianchi, 12.

9

Philip Galle after Pieter Bruegel (the Elder, Flemish 1537–1612)
Justicia [Justice], 1559
Engraving, Gothic "P" watermark
Unsigned
22.6 x 29.2 cm., 8-15/16 x 11-1/2" cut to plate mark edges
Purchase Made Possible by Sonja Knudsen, George and Pat Olson, and Paul
A. Anderson Chair in the Arts, with Courtesy of Mr. Harris Schrank,
Augustana College Art Collection, 2005.10

Pieter Bruegel's complementary sets of drawings, *The Seven Deadly Sins* (anger, sloth, lust, gluttony, avarice, pride and envy) and *The Virtues* (prudence, charity, justice, faith, hope, temperance and fortitude), became models for his two most popular series of engraved prints. In both series, a central allegorical figure is surrounded by other characters in a way designed to cause the viewer to think more deeply about sin and virtue.

The allegorical figure at the base of the landscape in *Justicia* is Iusticia. She is the Roman equivalent of Hellenic Themis. The imageries of Iusticia and Themis have been combined to create a symbol familiar to all, Lady Justice, who hovers over scores of courthouses around the United States.

Symbolism is rich whenever Iusticia or Themis is artistically represented. But true to form, Bruegel packs symbolism into every corner of his *Justicia*, from the aloof feminine figure that provides the work's focal point, to each nook and cranny of the frenetic scene that surrounds her. Bruegel's manner of rewarding the viewer for a close and patient appreciation is easily seen in such great works as *The Blue Cloak*, *The Battle between Carnival and Lent*, and *The Tower of Babel*. Each of these, and many others, can be broken into subordinate pictures that merit independent consideration, while adding to the larger message of which they are part.

Around the pedestal which elevates Iusticia a mere step above her surroundings, a riot of official violence is being played out: a tortuous rack, a beheading, a flogging and a hand being cut off are sufficiently graphic that gallows and torture wheels on the horizon seem somehow less chilling by comparison. Each of these acts is committed by self-righteous persons, seemingly in the name of justice. Iusticia is oblivious to the world around her. Aloof and blindfolded, she stands as a statuesque symbol of justice, who neither sees nor understands the horrors done in her name. That Bruegel would surround Iusticia with such horrors is not surprising given the artist's time. *Justicia* was completed in about 1560. It was in 1547 that Henry II, King of France, tried heresy cases by setting up special courts, colloquially called "Burning Chambers." In 1555, Philip became King of Spain and reinstituted the Inquisition. During that time, the justice dispensed with such horrific results was influenced by religious fervor. A careful examination of *Justicia* makes it clear that the persecution surrounding Iusticia was religious persecution. The peasant holding the cross before the court in the lower right corner is sure to receive Inquisition-style justice, without any mercy from Iusticia.

Bruegel clearly did not mean to suggest that the "virtues" of justice related to the horrific way in which justice was dispensed. But is *Justicia* an attack on how justice was dispensed at the time? Alexander Wied, a curator at the Kunsthistorisches Museum in Vienna, wrote that the drawing cannot "be seen as an attack on Justice," since, he observes, "the artist's attitude remains cold and distant."[1] But Bruegel is not neutral. Art historian Timothy Foote views it a bit differently. He notes that the self-righteous figures who are dispensing justice in Iusticia are "paragons" that "carry virtue to the point of foolish excess." He views all of this as "a canny moral commentary" where Bruegel "shows some of them behaving with so fanatical a zeal that it amounts to sinfulness."[2] That Iusticia stands on a pedestal with the power of the sword and the ability to weigh what is equitable with her scales, but does not remove her blindfold to use those tools, is surely an intentional statement indicting how justice was dispensed at the time. Iusticia is not unaccountable for the suffering around her; instead she is duplicitous through her failure to see what is done in her name.

Though Bruegel might have seen Iusticia's blindfold as allowing her to turn such a "blind eye" to the horrors wrought in her name, contemporary notions of Lady Justice view the blindfold more positively. Today, "Justice is blind" has a positive connotation, indicating that neither worldly wealth nor position can create advantage in her presence. Likewise neither race, gender nor creed should put one at a disadvantage when justice is blind.

If Bruegel lived in contemporary America, would he view the blindfold in the more positive light that we see it? Given that justice in America is not dispensed in the horrific way that it was in Bruegel's time, would he take a less cynical view of Iusticia? Or would he find that Lady Justice, hovering above American courthouses, is duplicitous in turning a blind eye to what is done in her name? Instead of the horrors of the Inquisition, would he surround Themis with prisoners, disproportionately persons of color, who have little chance for rehabilitation in our prisons? Would he depict children being sentenced to life in prison as adults? Would he depict inordinately long sentences for relatively minor offenses, all as part of the *war on drugs*? Would he draw Guantanamo Bay, to depict eroded civil rights guarantees made in the name of the *war on terror*?

Not all depictions of Iusticia and Themis are blindfolded. In fact, the blindfold did not appear until the 16th century, about the time Bruegel completed *Justicia*. The oldest depictions of Themis are quite different from Bruegel's vision. Rather than a youthful, athletic figure, Themis is a mature woman; rather than a blindfold, she is possessed of a calm and steady gaze. According to various strands of Greek mythology, Themis was the daughter of Heaven and Earth, and became the consort of Zeus and mother to the Hora, the goddesses of natural order and the seasons. Not only did she have sight, some sources indicated she was gifted with foresight, able to see things of which not even Zeus was aware. Similarly, early depictions of Iusticia incorporated an olive twig as a symbol of peace and a *patera*, a vessel of libation.

How did the gifts of an olive branch and libation regress into blindness? Why didn't Bruegel use the more classic view of Iusticia, common less than a century before? The blindfolded Iusticia graphically shows what justice can be like without mercy. Justice without mercy was dispensed in the name of the church, ironically ignoring the Biblical injunction in Micah 6:8, "to act justly, and to love mercy, and to walk humbly with your God." Had Iusticia not been blinded, might there have been some mercy?

There is a ray of hope imbedded here. At the upper left corner of Bruegel's *Justicia*, on a hill rising above the agony below, is a lone cross of crucifixion, attended by two watchers. It is uncertain if much could be made of who the watchers might be, and whether the implied crucifixion has occurred or is about to occur. A fascinating aspect of the cross is the movement that Bruegel invests in the slopes of the hill on which it stands. The overhanging brow of the hill appears to be in motion – almost suggesting a wave about to crest over the horrors below. Might this be an allusion to the Pauline notion that because of grace, the sacrifice of Jesus accomplishes what the law could not, a washing away of sin?

[Steven C. Bahls, *President*]

[1] Alexander Wied, *Bruegel* (New York: Macmillan Publishing, 1980), 60

[2] Timothy Foote, *The World of Bruegel* (New York: Time-Life Books, 1968), 80

SCOPVS LEGIS EST, AVT VT EV QVE PVNIT EMENDET, AVT POENA
EIVS CAETEROS MELIORES REDDET AVT SVBLATIS MALIS CAETERI SECVRIORES VIVAT.

10

Willem Pietersz De Leeuw (Flemish ca. 1603–1665) after Pieter Paul Rubens (Flemish 1577–1640)
The Hunt of the Hippopotamus and the Crocodile, ca. 1650
Engraving after **The Hunt**, 1615–1616
Signed in print b.r. in plate below image "*WP Leeuw fecit.*" and b.l. in image: "*P.P. Rubens invent. C. Dankertz excudit*"
45.3 x 63.5 cm., 17-13/16 x 25" image
46.7 x 64.2 cm., 18-3/8 x 25-1/4" sheet
Augustana College Art and Art History Department Purchase, 95.10

Peter Paul Rubens is generally regarded as one of the greatest and most influential artists in history. High Renaissance masters of the sixteenth century such as Raphael Sanzio and Michelangelo Buonarroti, in their late Mannerist style, only hinted at the emotional qualities for which seventeenth-century Europeans were yearning. This intricate Mannerist style was replaced around 1600 by the less symbolic and more realistic pieces of the emotionally charged Baroque era. The Roman Catholic Church, one of the most powerful sources of patronage at the time, utilized this dynamic style as a rallying force for the Counter-Reformation. Catholic clergy realized the power of art's persuasive appeal to the senses and emotions,[1] replacing the more intellectual focus common in Renaissance works of the previous century. Developed by Caravaggio and Gian Lorenzo Bernini in Italy, the international Baroque inspired artists from many countries, including the Dutch Rembrandt Van Rijn, Spanish Diego Velasquez and the Flemish Rubens.

Rubens was born in 1577 in Siegen, Germany.[2] His precocious intelligence and talent early distinguished him in school. As a young boy, he convinced his mother to allow him to apprentice to a painter and as a young man, he joined the painter's Guild of St. Luke in 1598.[3] Like many aspiring artists of the day, he traveled to Italy, the major European art center at the time, to complete his education by copying and learning from the great masters of the past. From works of Classical artists to those of the Renaissance, the art of Italy continued to inspire him throughout his life.[4] His illustrious career included a period of time as a court painter to the Duke of Mantua and later to the royal courts of Spain, England and France.[5] Beyond his artistic genius, Rubens was fluent in many languages, facilitating his parallel career as a diplomat, wherein he was instrumental in international relations such as the peace agreement between Spain and England in the 1620s.[6]

Rubens' artistic popularity grew immensely while he produced many religious masterpieces, landscapes and secular hunting scenes including *The Hunt of the Hippopotamus and the Crocodile*. These highly emotional and intense subjects in nature appealed to his audience who sought empathetic, rather than thoughtful, responses. The majority of these pieces were massive in scale, often covering entire walls. The compositions, already visually overwhelming, were made even more immediate through the use of life-sized figures.

This print after Rubens' famous painting *The Hunt* (1615–16), was engraved a few years after the artist's death, attesting to the continued popularity of the painter and this particular piece. Like other highly successful artists of the time, Rubens completed the sizeable number of large-scale commissions he received by overseeing a huge workshop with many assistants. The actual effort that the master contributed to an individual painting varied greatly, from making sketches and adding final touches with his assistants carrying out the middle steps, to Rubens himself completing the entire painting.[7] Most pieces fell somewhere in the middle of these two extremes.

Rubens' *The Hunt of the Hippopotamus and the Crocodile* captures the spirit of the Baroque era with its fascination for exotic cultures. The observer is taken to the climax of struggle between five men, a crocodile and a hippopotamus, the moment before the prey is stabbed to death by three of the men on horseback. These turbaned and bearded men were considered *exotic* by their European audience, as were the crocodile, hippopotamus, and location, which included a palm tree in the background. The figures are draped in various fabrics and armed with spears and swords. Rubens did an exquisite job of shading their rippling muscles, as well as modeling the anatomy of the horses and dogs that have their jaws clenched on the enormous hippopotamus.

The foreshortening effect on the hippopotamus and crocodile make them appear to be leaping out of the marshy tropical environment and into the viewers' space. *The Hunt* captures intellectual and emotional tensions. Viewers are left in suspense, not knowing the fate of the man lying on the ground, perhaps about to be devoured by the lunging crocodile. Our eyes are carefully guided full circle in a pinwheel motion, starting from the center with the juxtaposition of the hippopotamus' teeth, the straining dogs and the jabbing spears. This active overall composition is characteristic of Rubens' distinctive style, effectively capturing all of the climactic action that occurs throughout the piece. Such masterpieces as this validate Rubens' popularity during his lifetime, both with the masses as well as elitist artistic groups and patrons, and demonstrate why he is still today considered one of the greatest artists of all time.

[Kaitlin Bradley, *Class of 2008*]

---

[1] Following the Protestant Reformation, the idea of converting people back to the Catholic Church through artistic means was, in fact, ruled by the Council of Trent in 1563. Roger Kimball, "The Gallery: Rubens and His Circle in a Fresh Light," *The Wall Street Journal* (12 October 1993), Eastern ed., sec. A: 18, ProQuest (11 January 2005).

[2] Christopher White, *Peter Paul Rubens: Man and Artist* (New Haven: Yale University Press, 1987), 2.

[3] Ibid., 8.

[4] Ibid., 13.

[5] Ibid., 11.

[6] Kerry Downes, *Rubens* (London: Jupiter Books Limited, 1980), 15.

[7] Kimball, A18.

P. P. Rubens invent.   C. Danckerts excudit.   Wtewael fecit

11

Anton (Anthony) Van Dyck (Flemish 1599–1641)
Grisaille portrait of **Marie de' Medici**, 1631
Oil on oak panel
Unsigned
25.4 x 19.8 cm., 10 x 7-3/4"
Gift of Professor Irma Adelman, Augustana College Art Collection, 2004.25

Marie de' Medici (1573–1642) gazes stolidly at us from this small oil sketch.[1] The 58-year-old Queen Mother of France wears a black oval cap preferred by widows (her husband Henri IV was assassinated in 1610).[2] Her dress, with its stiffly starched white band collar, features fashionably slashed, wide puffed sleeves that end in double cuffs at her wrist.[3] The tight bodice is held together with pearl buttons and adorned with a brooch, her only jewelry. Cupped in her hand are flowers similar to those held by women in van Dyck portraits. Marie's features are not idealized as evidenced by her prominent nose, pursed lips and jowly jaw. On a shelf, next to Marie, rests a crown topped with a *fleur-de-lis* design that references her relationship to the French royal family. Although this oil sketch is not signed by the artist, the thick impasto dots and small slashes of white paint evident on the curtain and Marie's right sleeve and bodice are visual signatures of van Dyck's painting style.

Marie de' Medici and her younger son, Gaston, the Duke of Orleans, met Anthony van Dyck in the artist's studio in Antwerp sometime between September 4th and October 16th, 1631.[4] Documented by her personal secretary, Jean de la Serre, this visit resulted in a large, full-length oil portrait of Marie now in the collection of the Musée des Beaux-Arts, Bordeaux of which, at least, one other variation exists.[5]

Certainly, the early 1630s were major watershed years for both Marie and Anthony van Dyck. In 1631, Marie and her son Gaston had been expelled from the French court by her oldest son King Louis XIII for plotting to overthrow his major advisor, the Cardinal Richelieu and initially they had taken refuge in Antwerp.[6] Just five months after Marie's visit to van Dyck's studio, van Dyck moved permanently to England and by July 1632 had become the principal painter to King Charles I and his wife Henrietta, one of Marie's daughters.[7] Some scholars have even speculated that van Dyck's move to England could have been facilitated by Marie, who might have recommended van Dyck to her daughter Henrietta.[8]

Also in the early 1630s, van Dyck initiated a project known posthumously as the *Iconography*. It appears that van Dyck intended to create an engraved series of portraits—a contemporary "who's who" of artists, printmakers, art collectors, princes, politicians, soldiers and scholars.[9] He involved at least nine printmakers and their engraved portraits were based on charcoal drawings and grisaille oil sketches supplied by van Dyck. Apparently van Dyck never formally named this project and some scholars believe that his intent probably shifted from its initial conception.[10] However, by 1641, sufficient engravings existed for an edition marketed by Martin van den Enden and in 1645, a posthumous edition was published by Gillis Hendricx.[11] The arrangement and number of engraved portraits significantly changed between the two versions.

Because of Marie de' Medici's status as a patron of the arts, her engraved portrait is included in both early editions of the *Iconography*. This portrait was engraved by Paulus Pontius, who probably based the image on a black chalk drawing and a *grisaille* oil sketch of Marie supplied by van Dyck.[12] Unfortunately, the chalk drawing no longer survives, but two *grisaille* oil sketches of Marie still exist, one in the Augustana College Permanent Art Collection and one in the Bavarian State Painting Collection in Munich.[13]

In all, van Dyck is associated with over sixty small, grisaille oil sketches that were apparently used by engravers as models for the *Iconography*.[14] *Grisaille* refers to images dominated by tonal ranges from white to black. This technique was not invented by the artist, but can be traced back to medieval manuscripts and Renaissance panel paintings.[15] Scholars disagree about the level of van Dyck's direct participation in the creation of these small oil portrait sketches and many believe that at least some of these images were done by pupils in van Dyck's

workshop.[16] Certainly, van Dyck portraits were highly valued by art collectors and artists from the 17th century on, and preliminary drawings and oil sketches of a particular sitter are common.

Why then is a *grisaille* oil sketch from the 17th century included in an exhibition focusing on the development of modernism? Since the 17th century, oil sketches have been appreciated by other artists and art connoisseurs because they were thought to be the purest and closest means to understand the artist's conception of an image.[17] These connoisseurs believed that if you truly wanted to understand an artist, you would need to understand the person's drawings and oil sketches since finished paintings or engravings masked the immediacy of the initial artistic ideas. Since the 19th century, this fascination with the artistic process, not just the finished painting, broadened to an even wider audience. During the 20th century, German Expressionist painters like Vassily Kandinsky and Abstract Expressionist action painters like Jackson Pollock took the importance of the artist's gesture or movement to its logical conclusion in their search for personal expression.

Clearly, the spontaneity of the paint application is evident in this *grisaille* oil sketch of Marie de' Medici. This feeling of spontaneity allows us not only to see an image of the sitter, but also to comprehend how the artist created that image through a variety of brushstrokes. Stepping away from this oil sketch allows the individual brushstrokes to coalesce into more solid forms. Thus, the process of *how* the paint is applied becomes as important as the subject the artist painted, an element present in many modern images. The incompleteness of the sketch results in forms that are suggested and surfaces that are not precisely delineated. As in some *modern* paintings, we have to use our imagination to fill in these surface details. In this oil portrait sketch of Marie de' Medici painted over 370 years ago, we are still able to envision the creative skill of the artist.

[Mary Em Kirn, *Professor Emerita of Art History*]

1 The faculty of the Art History Department would like to express their gratitude to Professor Irma Adelman for her generous gift of this oil sketch from her personal collection to the Augustana College Permanent Art Collection. In addition, it should be noted that on the back of the panel is a tag that states "2 May 1896. Bought at the sale of Miss Euphemia Laing's pictures." Although the name of the person who purchased this panel in 1896 remains unknown, we do know that Euphemia Laing (1808-1896) was the sister of David Laing (1793-1878), the well-known Scottish antiquarian, bookseller and librarian of the Signet Library. Their father, William (1764-1832), a bookseller in Edinburgh, was a noted collector and connoisseur. Refer to "David Laing," Edinburgh University Library, Gallery of Benefactors, http://www.lib.ed.ac.uk/about/bgallery/Gallery/records/eighteen/laing.html (17 February 2005).

2 Susan Saward, *The Golden Age of Marie de' Medici* (Ann Arbor: UMI Research Press, 1982), 98-99.

3 Emilie Gordenker, *Anthony van Dyck and the Representation of Dress in Seventeenth-Century Portraiture* (Turnhout: Brepols, 2001), 83.

4 Arthur K. Wheelock, Jr., et al., *Anthony van Dyck* (Washington, D.C.: National Gallery of Art, 1990), 76.

5 Erik Larsen, *L'opera completa di Van Dyck*, vol. 2 (Milan: Rizzoli, 1980), 105-106. I would like to thank Professor *Emerita* Sonja Knudsen for her willingness to provide important Italian translations.

6 Suan Barners, et al., *Van Dyck: A Complete Catalogue of the Paintings* (New Haven: Yale University Press), 332-333.

7 Wheelock, 76.

8 Ibid., 246.

9 Carl Depauw and Ger Luijten, *Anthony van Dyck as a Printmaker* (Antwerp: Open, 1999), 75.

10 Joaneath A. Spicer, "Anthony van Dyck's Iconography: An Overview of its Preparation," in *Van Dyck 350*, ed. Susan J. Barnes and Arthur Wheelock, Jr. (Washington, D.C.: National Gallery of Art, 1994), 327.

11 Ibid., 328.

12 A biography of Paulus Pontius is found in Depauw and Luijten, 381-383. For some examples of black chalk portraits by van Dyck that have been associated with engravings in the *Iconography*, refer to Christopher Brown, *The Drawings of Anthony van Dyck* (New York: Pierpont Morgan Library, 1991), 190-213.

13 Spicer, 359. Refer to Larsen, 105, for an illustration of the Munich panel.

14 Ibid., 357-363.

15 Ronni Baer, "Rembrandt's Oil Sketches," in *Rembrandt's Journey*, ed. Clifford S. Ackley (Boston: Museum of Fine Arts, 2003), 32.

16 Depauw and Luijten, 81-82.

17 Baer, 39-41, surveys the critical reception of oil sketches from the 16th to the 20th centuries.

12

Rembrandt Harmensz Van Rijn (Dutch 1606–1669)
Christ Preaching, or *La Petite tombe*, ca. 1652
Etching and drypoint
Unsigned, Strasburg Lily Watermark
15.4 x 20.7 cm., 6-1/8 x 8-1/8" image
17.6 x 22.4 cm., 6-15/16 x 8-3/4" sheet
Paul A. Anderson Chair in the Arts Purchase, Augustana College Art
Collection, 2001.12

Rembrandt Van Rijn is generally regarded as the most significant printmaker of all time. He grew up in Holland during the seventeenth century, the era of the Dutch Baroque, which represented a great change from the established Italian Baroque style. The Dutch began to create more secular works of art in response to the taste of the growing middle class, who wanted more comprehensible themes.

Most of the art created during the Baroque era, particularly in Italy, was stylistically excessive in adornment. The eminent contemporary philosopher, Rene Descartes, in criticizing the lifestyle that accompanied this context, asserted, "Everyone is so engrossed in furthering their own interests that I could spend the whole of my life there without being noticed by a soul."[1] Rembrandt, working in the Dutch Baroque style, changed this self-preoccupation that Descartes described. Within his art, Rembrandt took on a more humanistic perspective that greatly appealed to the middle class. By creating etchings, such as *Christ Preaching (La Petite tombe)* circa 1652, he enabled his art to be mass-produced, which consequently also made it more affordable to the public, and caused his name to become instantly recognizable.

Rembrandt was an extremely religious man, reflected in his preference for Biblical themes. Mirroring Mennonite beliefs of his time, the theme of Rembrandt's work often focused on the "poor in spirit" over "the worldly wise and learned."[2] His imagery is filled with ordinary people expressing sorrow and joy; characters with whom everyone can relate. He even took the faces of common folk as his models when depicting esteemed powerful or religious figures.[3] By doing this he made revered religious events seem like everyday life. It was as if each of these people could be someone standing next to you. This made Rembrandt distinctly different from other artists of his day such as Pieter Paul Rubens (catalogue 10) and Gian Lorenzo Bernini. Unlike their complex and explosive imagery, he chose to depict the simple aspects of life. Although some of his art shows slight influences of Italian Baroque and Renaissance classicism, these were never seen to the extent that would place him within either of these movements.

The Baroque era was slow to accept etching as a respectable medium. Patrons largely preferred oil paintings that were grand, gaudy and ornate rather than simple black-and-white etchings.[4] Rembrandt revealed much of himself in his prints. He believed that art should be accessible to all. His response to the growing middle class led to his humanistic approach to art, clearly visible in his etching of *Christ Preaching*.

According to the gospels, Jesus spent the last three years of his life traveling from city to city, teaching people and preaching the good news of the kingdom of heaven. Christ in this etching is seen speaking to the poor in a small, yet comfortable area that appears similar to seventeenth-century neighborhoods found in modern Holland, in order to help his audience relate to the idea. The viewer's focus is drawn to Christ since He is the central and brightest figure in the print. Only the faint halo above His head, symbolizing religious light, distinguishes His holy lineage. Christ stands upon a small platform separating Him from the rest of the public. This example of hierarchic scale enables the viewer to understand the importance of the figure, not in a symbolic, but in a more human manner. Christ is preaching with his hand upward in the traditional position for oration, stemming back to classical tradition. He is revealed as a gentle and approachable man who is simply spreading the word of the gospel to those who need it most. Visible to the left are a few wealthier men, probably Pharisees, with finer clothing and hats, however, Jesus is focusing his attention on the poor and sick, grouped to the right in the print. Everyone is captivated by what he is saying. People are leaning forward as if straining to make sure they do not miss a single word.[5] Particularly noteworthy are the man with his hand to his face in deep thought while listening to the gospel and the small boy who stops playing to set down his spinning top to write quietly on the ground.[6] All of these people are genuinely interested in what Christ communicates. This etching is considered one of Rembrandt's greatest masterpieces.

Rembrandt clearly defined the rules of etching. He was able to bring to life such etchings by using chiaroscuro, a sharp contrast between light and shadow, very difficult to achieve with prints. In order to accomplish this technique, he painted an acid-resist over the metal plate then etched into the resist with a sharp tool called a stylus. The plate was then dipped in acid which ate away the metal where lines were exposed.[7] When inked, the lines held the ink as the paper was pressed for multiple images. Etching was a difficult process and had an element of surprise because the artist never knew exactly how a print would appear as it was put on paper.[8] It took great patience and a lot of imagination and talent to create such works of art and to predict the right outcome for the finished piece. The artist used short lines, as in sketching, in order to create movement, detail and emotion within the etching.

Rembrandt helped change the world of art. During a time when oil painting was predominant, he established etching as a rich new medium with infinite possibility. He also demonstrated that one could create magnificent works of art even when portraying the simpler and humbler aspects of life. Through the print medium he reached a vast new audience with a quiet but powerful religious message.

[Cristy Martinez, *Class of 2008*]

[1] Quoted in Christopher White, *Rembrandt and His World* (New York: The Viking Press, 1964), 22.

[2] Ibid., 41.

[3] Guy Hubbard, "About This Self-Portrait," *Arts & Activities* (2004): 25-27, EBSCOhost (2005).

[4] K. G. Boon, trans. by Elizabeth Willems-Treeman, *Rembrandt: The Complete Etchings* (Secaucus: The Wellfleet Press, 1962), v.

[5] Boon, xxxiii.

[6] Mary Em Kirn, *The Paul A. Anderson Art History Collection*, ed. Catherine Carter Goebel (Rock Island: Augustana College, 2001), 40.

[7] Kirn, 40.

[8] Christopher White, *Rembrandt as an Etcher: A Study of the Artist at Work*, vol. 1 (University Park: The Pennsylvania State University Press, 1969), 7.

13

Artist unknown
Hebe, attributed to mid-18th century
Oil on canvas
Unsigned
38.3 x 32.9 cm., 15-1/16 x 13"
Paul A. Anderson Chair in the Arts Purchase, Augustana College Art Collection, 2004.10

In the eighteenth century, French art evolved through various styles to gradually meet new demands. Painters began to depict the elitist pleasures found within the sumptuous lifestyle of the French aristocrats during this period. The *Rococo* style, in fact, was based upon the priorities of royalty and the aristocratic class in France, molded by eighteenth-century *feminine* taste and influence.

Hebe is a French Rococo painting created within this context. In reaction to the previous Baroque style, Rococo taste shifted from *masculine* pieces based on the past, to lighter subjects that were tasteful to the eighteenth-century female eye. Common characteristics of paintings of the time were light and playful themes, graceful compositions and delicate coloring, as well as elegant figures and clothing.[1] Many Rococo subjects focused on mythological characters. Portrait painters even depicted modern patrons in the guise of classical gods and goddesses, thus obliquely attributing their flattering characteristics, such as immortality, beauty, youth and strength, to the sitters.[2]

In this particular painting, the female subject is portrayed as the beautiful *Hebe*, the mythological goddess of youth and the cupbearer to the gods.[3] Although the identity of the artist remains unknown, it is most likely based on Jean-Marc Nattier's *Madame de Caumartin as Hebe* from 1753, although the female sitter is different. Similar to Nattier's piece, the woman holds a pitcher and cup in her hands in order to serve the gods. The vessel's form resembles, and was probably inspired by, the ancient cups that were unearthed at the excavations of the lost Roman city of Pompeii, rediscovered in the early eighteenth century after long being buried beneath the erupted rubble of Mt. Vesuvius.[4] Hebe was the daughter of Jupiter and Juno, the king and queen of the gods, and was said to have married the great Hercules when he ascended to Mount Olympus. The bird flying through the pastel sky is either Jupiter's attribute or the personification of the god himself, disguised as an eagle.

This painting carefully balances its dual purpose of depicting an actual portrait of a Rococo woman and illustrating a classical goddess. The pastel colors of light pinks and blues, representing delicacy and feminine taste, are typical of the Rococo style. Attention is drawn to Hebe's face through minute detail and brilliant lighting. The artist likely tried to portray her as ideal. She sits in an informal pose, reflecting an intimate, and perhaps even seductive, mood. Surrounded by delicate atmosphere, she wears typical clothing and hair decorations for the time period. Rather than showing her rank or position, the artist concentrated more on the subject's expression, gesture and individual personality, inviting the viewer to consider her thoughts. She is portrayed as a sophisticated individual who is caught in a brief and intriguing moment of contemplation.

This pampered mood, however, was soon to end as the Rococo style fell into disfavor. Following the focus on high ideals and intellectual freedom fostered by the Enlightenment and the subsequent French Revolution, the Rococo was consequently decried as frivolous and decadent. The Revolution resulted from many factors, perhaps most pertinent to this painting, the pampered lifestyle reflected in this portrait that hints at the enormous class discrepancies of the time. Jean Honoré Fragonard was the last noteworthy painter of the Rococo and continued to paint in this style, even while younger and more innovative artists like Jacques Louis David defined new Neoclassical history paintings. Like *Hebe*, these were largely based in classicism, but unlike this light and playful interpretive view, Neoclassicists sought moral lessons from the ancients that were applicable to the present. The coy charm of the woman who posed for *Hebe* would soon be replaced by grander and idealistic visions for the future, ironically framed in the past.

[Erin Reeverts, *Class of 2008*]

[1] Julius S. Held and Donald Posner, *17th and 18th Century Art: Baroque Painting, Sculpture, Architecture* (New York: Harry N. Adams, Inc. Publishers, 1971), 302-308.

[2] Held and Posner, 318.

[3] Jane Davidson Reid, "Hebe," *The Oxford Guide to Classical Mythology in the Arts, 1300–1990s*, vol. 1 (New York: Oxford University Press, 1993), 490.

[4] "From the Tour: 18th-Century France — Chardin and Portraiture," *National Gallery of Art*, 2005, http://www.nga.gov/collection/gallery/gg53/gg53-32707.0.html (11 January 2005).

14

William Hogarth (English/British 1697–1764)
Marriage a-la-Mode, Plate I, 1745, Series of six plates, fourth state of seven
Etching with engraving
Signed in printed text below image in plate margin at b.l. "Invented Painted & Published by Wm. Hogarth" and b.r. "Engraved by G. Scotin, /According to Act of Parliament April 1st 1745"
38.4 x 46.8 cm., 15-1/8 x 18-1/2" image
46.3 x 56.1 cm., 18-3/16 x 22-1/16" sheet
Paul A. Anderson Chair in the Arts Purchase, Augustana College Art Collection, 2000.22

William Hogarth was born in England in 1697. His father, a schoolmaster and an author, had a long history of financial problems, so severe that he landed in debtors' prison on several occasions. Many believe that Hogarth's embarrassment over his father's misfortune followed him throughout his life and influenced his works,[1] which as in the case of *Marriage-a- la-Mode*, often reflected his contempt for the upper classes who inherited title and position and yet squandered such privilege.

Hogarth originally planned to be a silversmith, even becoming an apprentice in 1714. He eventually abandoned this career in favor of painting portraits and, in 1720, he enrolled in a new academy of art started by John Vanderbank.[2] He also learned the technique of engraving, related to his early training as a silversmith, which became an important medium to make his art more accessible.

Hogarth's general philosophy was that art should not be extremely fancy. He rebelled against the feminine frills and idyllic scenes of the contemporary French Rococo style. He believed paintings should instead be didactic and deliver a message, often deeming that several moralistic scenes would more accurately tell the story, rather than limiting himself to just one. For instance, *Marriage-a-la-Mode* (1743), a series of six images, makes a mockery of the wealthy upper class and their extravagant lifestyle. In traditional English manner he advanced the storytelling potential of his art. Hogarth drew the faces of the characters in the original painted scenes himself, both since he was an experienced portrait painter and also because he understood, like a novelist, that proper character sketches made the scene palpable. However, for the engraved versions he called in French engravers to finish the background and prepare the different plates.[3]

The Marriage Contract is the first of the six plates in this series. The setting is the home of Lord Earl Squanderfield, who is the father of the groom. He is seated to the left and holds a document containing a family tree which traces his family's aristocratic lineage back several generations. At the beginning, at the tree's base, is William the Conqueror, thus attesting to the Earl's long line of royal blood. Hogarth also depicted Lord Squanderfield with his foot in a bandage and crutches nearby, representing his affliction with gout. At the time medical experts believed that eating too much fancy food and being sexually indiscreet caused gout,[4] making for a fairly unsympathetic view of this character and the class he represents. Also seated at the table is the father of the bride, a middle class merchant who can be identified by his plain clothing. He carefully examines the contract, going over the details related to the legalities of the marriage.

In the background, through the window, a large building is under construction. This palace alludes to the reason why the marriage is taking place. Lord Earl Squanderfield is building a new home with such extravagant plans that it has put him into debt. He has no money left, only his noble title. The father of the bride, however, has made a great deal of money from his employment as a merchant, yet he is still not considered a member of the socially elite. Through this union, Lord Earl Squanderfield will acquire needed funds and the father of the bride will elevate his family's status through his daughter's new position.[5]

The prospective bride and groom are located on the right side of the engraving. Although physically seated together, they display absolutely no psychological interest in one another. The groom is shown admiring his reflection while he takes a pinch of snuff and the bride is looking in an entirely different direction as she weeps and is comforted by the attentive Lawyer Silvertongue, who will figure largely in the ultimate tragic downfall of this arranged marriage. The groom wears elaborate clothing and has a dark spot on his neck, most likely suggesting that the young man has a sexually transmitted disease.[6] The bride seems depressed and preoccupied with the ring on her handkerchief, trying to ignore the advances of the lawyer Counsellor Silvertongue, who is clearly not discouraged and continues his overtures.

In the foreground there are two dogs of different genders chained together, representing the unfortunate loveless union between this hapless couple. Copies of famous works of art hang on the walls in the background (with Hogarth's intended barbs and lessons inferred) as does a pompous portrait, perhaps of the vain earl himself, always conscious of his position. Through these paintings, Hogarth further forewarns his viewers of the ridiculousness of this marriage and its impending consequences.[7]

Hogarth did not sell nearly as many copies of *Marriage a-la-Mode* as he had of previous print series, probably because the target for this satire, the wealthy and upper middle classes, was the same as the audience who could afford the prints.[8] Nevertheless, it proved to be an overall success, both then and now, and furthered Hogarth's reputation throughout England as an artist and satirist. He skillfully combined didactic art with entertaining stories, which advanced not only a rejection of arranged marriages in particular, but of French Rococo aristocratic frivolity in general. In this manner, Hogarth predicted in England the direction toward didactic art that France would soon follow with the Neoclassical movement.

[Kristin McLinden, *Class of 2008*]

[1] Ronald Paulson, *Hogarth: His Life, Art, and Times*, vol. 1 (New Haven: Yale University Press, 1971) 38.

[2] Paulson, 80.

[3] Robert L. S. Cowley, *Hogarth's Marriage a-la-Mode* (Ithaca: Cornell University Press, 1983), 8-9.

[4] Ibid., 28.

[5] Ibid., 29-30.

[6] Florence Staelens, "Marriage a-la-Mode," *The Paul A. Anderson Art History Collection*, ed. Catherine Carter Goebel (Rock Island: Augustana College, 2001), 46.

[7] Cowley, 42.

[8] Ibid., 12.

Marriage-A-la-Mode, (Plate I)

Invented Painted & Published by W. Hogarth

According to Act of Parliament April 1. 1745

15A

Engraving by Robert Benard (French b. 1734, fl. 1750–1785)
Antiquités, Planche IV [Antiquities, Plate IV] from **Encyclopédie**… of
Denis Diderot and Jean d'Alembert, Published Paris, 1751–1772
Engraving
Signed b.r. below image in plate *"Benard Fecit"*
Inscribed in plate at top left "Figure 1ere" and center left "Fig. 2" and at
bottom left "Fig. 3"
35.9 x 22.8 cm., 14-3/16 x 9" image
40.2 x 25.8 cm., 15-3/4 x 10-1/8" sheet
Purchase with Gift of Elizabeth and John Ducey, Augustana College Art
Collection, 2001.35.c

Note: The original 1750 full title was *Encyclopédie, ou Dictionnaire raisonné des sciences, des arts et des métiers, par une société de gens de lettres, mis en ordre par M. Diderot de l'Académie des Sciences et Belles-Lettres de Prusse, et quant à la partie mathématique, par M. d'Alembert de l'Académie Royale des Sciences de Paris, de celle de Prusse et de la Société Royale de Londres.* The title is now abbreviated to *Encyclopédie, ou Dictionnaire raisonné des sciences, des arts et des métiers, par une société de gens de lettres,* or *Encyclopedia, Reasoned Dictionary of the Sciences, Arts and Crafts.* The title-page was amended as d'Alembert acquired more titles. There were 28 volumes. Because d'Alembert quit before the project was completed, Diderot was the sole editor for the final volumes.

Diderot's *Encyclopédie ou Dictionnaire raisonné des sciences, des arts et des métiers, par une société de gens de letters,* is a massive compilation of information. Seventeen volumes of text and eleven volumes of illustrations were published in Paris between 1751 and 1772 by Denis Diderot and Jean d'Alembert. A typical entry included the word, its gender and part of speech, the category (sculpture, history, etc.) and the defining text, which could be anywhere from one sentence to twenty-eight pages in length.[1]

The encyclopedia reflected the basic philosophy of the European Enlightenment and the growing interest in intellectual pursuits, especially in the arts and sciences which are referenced within. The point of this work was to summarize contemporary knowledge and offer people a new way to look at the world. It was written by more than 140 contributors, many of them the *great thinkers* of the Enlightenment, with some of the more famous names being Jean-Jacques Rousseau, François-Marie Arouet de Voltaire, and Jean-François Marmontel.[2]

[Katie Otter, *Class of 2008*]

This engraving, *Antiquities Planche IV,* was done by Robert Benard, a prolific engraver who was most active during the 1770s and 1780s. Although this piece is not dated, it can be assumed it was created during this time. Most of his work was engraved after sketches done by other artists. Ancient architecture as is depicted on this page, *Antiquités,* was extremely influential both culturally and artistically as the modern European world looked to its enlightened past for inspiration. As Pompeii and Herculaneum were being unearthed, students completed their Grand Tour and intellectuals fawned over the grandeur of the past. The architectural wonders of Rome particularly attracted many admirers. This specific engraving depicts three ancient structures in Rome, the Circus of Caracalla (or Circus of Maxentius), the Theater of Marcellus and the Forum Nerva.[3]

The top image is the *Circus of Maxentius* (previously called the *Circus of Caracalla* because of an unearthed statue of this emperor that was found nearby). It was renamed in 1825 after the emperor responsible for its construction as well as the attached housing complex.[4] This is an ancient Roman structure located outside of the city on the *Via Appia.* The circus was a

place for Roman chariot and horse races and was the largest structure of this type used for entertainment, reaching between 400-650 meters with seats lining the longer walls and circular end.[5] The bird's-eye viewpoint of the sketch reveals the interior of the track, which is illuminated, while the columns and surrounding walls are shaded.[6] In this detailed etching, there is a large Egyptian obelisk in the center of the circus, later moved to Rome by Baroque sculptor, Gian Lorenzo Bernini, to be incorporated into his *Fontana dei Quattro Fiumi* (Fountain of the Four Rivers) when the Circus was unearthed in 1647.[7]

The middle building is the *Theater of Marcellus,* constructed for mass entertainment by Emperor Augustus in honor of his nephew Marcellus. The theater was begun by Caesar, and then dedicated in 13 or 11 B.C.E. by Augustus.[8] This monument was viewed from a distance, at a slightly elevated angle. Cross-hatching creates a strong chiaroscuro between the lighter and darker areas of the structure. With the bottom level of Doric columns, the middle Ionic and the top most likely Corinthian[9], the exterior likely influenced the Colosseum built almost a century later in Rome. The numerous pillars lining the theater consisted of half columns laid between the arches, a design that became popular for theaters after its use here.

The bottom structure is the *Forum Nerva,* also known as *Forum Transitorium* (the passageway forum), since it connected the Forum of Augustus and the Temple of Peace. It was built in the center of the city by the emperor Domitian and finished by his successor Nerva in 96-97 C.E.[10] In this sketch, there are two columned structures already in ruins on the left, and a bridge over a pathway on the right. The pathway is accentuated with the light before the bridge, drawing attention to its function as a passageway. Three people stand in the foreground of the composition, further focusing our attention toward the bridge.

These three ancient structures, among others, are in the *Encyclopédie* as a reference source for classical architecture. This work allowed people to access knowledge not previously available to them, including the architecture of the past, in a well-organized and structured manner. It helped transcend boundaries, its editors believing that human reason and intellect could redeem the world. All three images relate directly to an emperor, and they all remain standing today. The third engraving of the Forum Nerva is the most aesthetically pleasing and picturesque, with the use of depth and shading to make viewers feel as if they were in the picture. The etchings themselves are very detailed. Such imagery inspired many enthusiasts of antiquity to take the Grand Tour and visit these sites in person (catalogue 20) in order to experience firsthand the wonders of ancient Rome.[11]

[Andrea Ritchie, *Class of 2008*]

[1] The article on Anatomie was a full 28 pages. *"Encyclopédie ou Dictionnaire raisonné des sciences, des arts et des métiers, par une société de gens de lettres,"* The ARTFL Project, University of Chicago, http://lib.uchicago.edu/efts/ARTFL/projects/encyc/ (2005).

[2] Ibid.

[3] Ibid.

[4] John B. Ward-Perkins, *Roman Architecture* (New York: Harry N. Abrams, Inc., Publishers, 1977), 317.

[5] Frank Sear, *Roman Architecture* (Ithaca: Cornell University Press, 1983), 38.

[6] Interestingly, during its construction, hollow jars were added to the walls to relieve weight. Ward-Perkins, 152.

[7] Marco Bussagli, ed., *Rome: Art & Architecture* (Slovenia: Könemann, 1999), 540.

[8] Sear, 52.

[9] The top portion has been destroyed. Sear, 53.

[10] Bussagli, 32.

[11] All Encyclopédie essays were written by students in the LS112: Modern Scientific Thought Class (2004-05) of Dell Jensen, Chemistry Department.

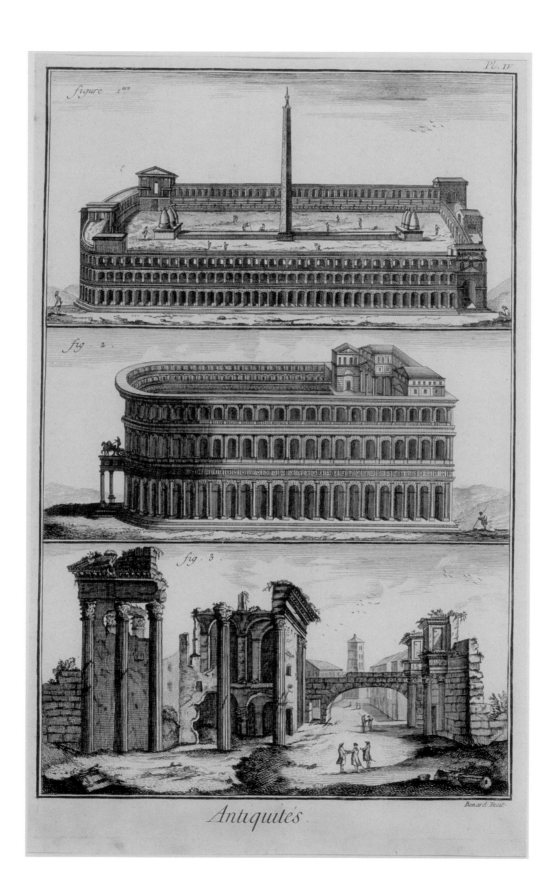

figure 1.re

fig. 2.

fig. 3.

Benard Fecit.

Antiquités.

Pl. IV

15B

Drawing by Bourgeois, engraving by Robert Benard (French b. 1734, fl. 1750–1785)

Sculpture, l'opération d'élever un bloc de marbre et outils, Planche 1ère
[Sculpture, Operation to Lift a Block of Marble and Tools. Plate One] from ***Encyclopédie…*** of Denis Diderot and Jean d'Alembert, Published Paris, 1751–1772
Engraving
Signed b.r. below image in plate "*Benard Fecit.*" and b.l. below image in plate "*Bourgeois Del.*" and t.c. in image in plate "*P. Falconet Fil. Inv.*"
Inscribed in plate at top "Fig. 1" through "Fig. 5" and at bottom "Fig. 1" through "Fig. 4"
35.8 x 22.7 cm., 14-1/16 x 9" image
40.0 x 25.7 cm., 15-3/4 x 10-1/8" sheet
Purchase with Gift of Elizabeth and John Ducey, Augustana College Art Collection, 2001.35.k

Diderot's *Encyclopédie* was developed by a large variety of contributors from many different backgrounds, from doctors and priests to nobility and merchants. Containing 72,000 articles, it represents one of the most important historical artifacts toward technology education.[1] The *Encyclopédie*, with its detailed illustrations of the mechanical arts, allowed industrial knowledge to be available to many people. This created a potential shift towards a liberal economic strength based more on the individual's self-interest. It also created a shift that minimized the amount of control the state and government had on industrial aspects. This particular plate, engraved on laid paper, introduced a jack mechanism used for lifting marble blocks (*L'operation d'elever un bloc de marbre, & outils*).[2]

Featured at the top of the plate is a diagram (top Figures 1-5) that illustrates a situation where this tool would most commonly be used. Figure 1 displays an uncut block of marble to be lifted with a jack and pulley system. Notice the action of the individuals and their purpose in representing the amount of work needed to lift the marble upright. They do not appear to be full-grown adults, which helps to emphasize the capabilities of the tool to lift extreme amounts of mass. Figure 2 shows a sculpted statue that represents a final construction in marble. Figure 3 illustrates two young men using the jack in its correct

position with proper technique. This illustrative approach was a very important contribution to the *Encyclopédie*, because it informed its audience about essential operations in a straightforward manner in order to make it comprehensible to a wide audience. Figure 4 depicts an individual using a large wooden bar to help position the marble in an upright angle. And finally, Figure 5 illustrates the block of marble, being raised to a vertical position, before the sculpting begins.[3]

At the bottom of the plate (Figures 1-4), the tool is depicted in four different views in order to communicate its constructive attributes. Figures 1 and 3 are similar in the sense that they are both seen from the front. The first figure illustrates the jack in its full state, while the third figure cuts away the exterior to give the reader a view of the interior in order to depict how the tool functions with a gear system. Figure 2 illustrates the back of the tool on which is positioned a gripping hook that helps lift the blocks of marble. To finalize the depiction, Figure 4 presents a side view of the instrument, completing the viewer's perceptual needs toward comprehending how the tool works.

As seen in this particular plate, the *Encyclopédie* introduced many mechanical tools and how they were used in the technological industry. In this massive compilation, both the theoretical and the practical were treated with the same degree of seriousness. One could read about the practical business of making stockings by machine then flip forward to a discussion on the soul.[4] The publication explained, through text and illustrations, the workmanship, tools and physical operations that were needed to use the displayed mechanism to its full capability. The manner in which knowledge was conveyed through this approach advanced understanding without much prior knowledge. The contributors to the *Encyclopédie* developed an accurate integrated language that could be digested by the largest variety of people and paved the way towards approaches used in modern education.

[Jeffrey Weiland, *Class of 2008*]

[1] Robert Wernick, "Declaring an Open Season on the Wisdom of the Ages," *Smithsonian*, vol. 28, iss. 2 (1997): 72-80.

[2] "*Encyclopédie ou Dictionnaire raisonné des sciences, des arts et des métiers, par une société de gens de letters: Sculpture en tous genres, Elevation du marbre: Planche Iere,*" *The ARTFL Project, University of Chicago,* http://lib.uchicago.edu/efts/ARTFL/projects/encyc/ (2005).

[3] Ibid.

[4] Wernick, 73.

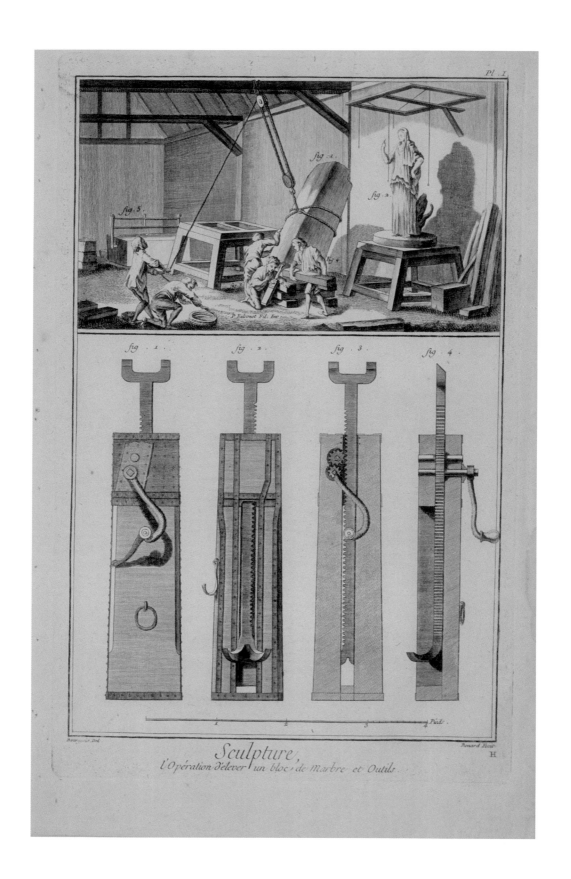

Sculpture,
l'Opération d'élever un bloc de Marbre et Outils.

16

Attributed to John Hesselius (American 1728–1778) [Carlton Neville and Stephanie Strass]
Portrait of a Lady in a Blue Gown, ascribed title, ca. 1748
Oil on canvas
Unsigned
119.9 x 89.5 cm., 47-1/4 x 35-1/4"
Gift of Neville-Strass Collection to Augustana College; Conservation Funding Assisted by George and Pat Olson, Mr. Dan Churchill, and Mr. Barry Bauman, 2004. 4

In eighteenth-century American portraiture, definitive attributions are rare. Such is the case with this portrait of a lady in a blue gown. Although the attribution to John Hesselius remains tentative, it is extremely persuasive.[1] It was first suggested when the painting was sold at auction in 1988. Since that time the donors, Carlton Neville and Stephanie Strass, have conducted extensive research and located two very similar portraits. The more relevant of the two is a portrait of a female member of the Byrd family, currently in a Philadelphia private collection. That painting has likewise been attributed provisionally to John Hesselius.[2] As in Augustana's painting, the woman in the Philadelphia picture is wearing an almost identical blue gown with white trim and a cord tied loosely around her waist. Both women have silk drapes, loosely slung around their backs, folded in identical patterns. The compositions are also similar. Several elements are quoted nearly verbatim, such as the pose of the women, the placement of the pedestals and the backgrounds. Since the two portraits appear to be by the same artist and the Philadelphia work has been attributed to Hesselius, we can likewise consider this painting to also be by John Hesselius.

Hesselius was one of the first successful native-born American portrait painters.[3] He most likely received his earliest training from his father, the Swedish born painter, Gustavus Hesselius (1682–1755), known principally for church painting. Like most colonial artists of the time, the younger Hesselius absorbed influences from a variety of sources, such as fellow native-born artist Robert Feke (1707–1752), who was active in Philadelphia in 1746 and 1750 and the English artist John Wollaston (ca. 1710–ca. 1775), who painted in Maryland from 1753–1754.[4] If this picture is indeed the work of John Hesselius, then it may date from the early 1750s, when he first began mimicking Wollaston's emphasis on luxurious fabrics with rich folds, while simplifying decorative patterns. It was not until the late 1750s that Hesselius was able to blend Wollaston's approach with Feke's interest in fabric detailing into his own signature style.[5] An example of Hesselius's mature approach is *Mrs. William Carmichael* (1764–1778) in The Art Institute of Chicago.[6] Augustana's painting differs markedly from *Mrs. William Carmichael* in the simple elegance of her attire, thereby placing this unidentified work earlier in Hesselius's career. Finally, Augustana's portrait foreshadows the impact Hesselius would have on the younger generation of American colonial portraitists. For example, the woman's solid mass, inescapable presence and direct gaze are traits that Hesselius's student, Charles Willson Peale (1741–1827), would incorporate into his own portraits.[7]

Because Hesselius was one of the most mobile colonial portraitists, the identity of the woman depicted remains a mystery. Hesselius traveled to Philadelphia, to Maryland and to Virginia, fulfilling commissions until he finally settled in Maryland in 1759. As a result, the woman depicted could be from any of those cities or any community in between.[8] Although her costume clearly indicates she hails from a wealthy family, there is nothing shown in the painting that could elucidate her identity. She is not wearing jewelry. Nor is she holding a book or musical instrument and is not wearing a specific uniform. The absence of these details maintains this woman's anonymity.[9]

Despite the fact that this painting perhaps encourages more questions than it answers, it is an example of a particularly dynamic period in American history. It illustrates the emergence of a powerful middle class that is simultaneously exuding its British colonial pride, while creating strong, independent communities, economic markets and individual identities. Moreover, this portrait was created when the status of painters was shifting from practical craftsmen to learned gentlemen. The work of Hesselius and this painting specifically embody this new American spirit.[10]

[Emily Vokt Ziemba, *Class of 1998*]

---

[1] The painting was sold at auction by Sloan's, New York, November 11–13, 1988, lot 2515, as by John Hesselius. Additionally, Ellen G. Miles, a curator at the National Portrait Gallery, viewed the painting in 2002 and initially believed it to be by John Hesselius. I am grateful to Carlton Neville for sharing all of this research.

[2] *Antiques* (June 1962): 582 (ill.).

[3] According to Ellen Miles, Hesselius's training and career took place entirely in America. See: Richard H. Saunders and Ellen G. Miles, *American Colonial Portraits, 1700–1776*, exh. cat. (Washington D.C.: The National Gallery of Art, 1987), 251, cat. 81.

[4] It should be noted that the second painting that Neville and Strass discovered has been attributed to Feke.

[5] Saunders and Miles, 251, cat. 81. Another point should be made about the importance of textiles in American colonial portraits. According to T. H. Breen, the colonists were obsessed with fabric and when they viewed a portrait painting, they were immediately drawn to the costume, before the facial features of the subject. See: T. H. Breen, "The Meaning of 'Likeness': Portrait Painting in an Eighteenth-Century Consumer Society," in *The Portrait in Eighteenth-Century America*, ed. by Ellen G. Miles (Newark: University of Delaware Press, 1993), 44–49. Therefore, in order to be a successful portraitist in the American colonial market, the artist had to be skilled at depicting all the nuances of fine fabrics.

[6] That painting was previously attributed to Jeremiah Theus. It is number 1967.177 in the Art Institute's collection.

[7] Saunders and Miles, 253, cat. 82. The similarity in Hesselius's and the young Peale's styles explains the misattribution of the portrait of *John Paca* in the collection of The Peabody Institute of Johns Hopkins University. The painting had long been considered a work by Charles Wilson Peale, until a cleaning in 1973 revealed Hesselius's signature. On this, see Saunders and Miles, 1987, 253, cat. 82 (ill.).

[8] To make matters even more difficult, the background of this painting is non-specific. There are no geographic markers included.

[9] On the importance of props in portraiture, particularly of this period, see: Wayne Craven, "Colonial American Portraiture: Iconography and Methodology," in *The Portrait in Eighteenth-Century America*, ed. Ellen G. Miles (1993), 102–115.

[10] On these points see: T. H. Breen, op. cit., Arlene Katz Nichols, "Biography as History: Making and Shaping American Art in the Eighteenth Century," in *Likeness & Landskips: A Portrait of the Eighteenth Century*, exh. cat. (New York: Hirschl & Adler Galleries, 2002), 9–23, and Ellen G. Miles, "The Portrait in America, 1750–1776," in Saunders and Miles, 1987, 28–76.

17

Engraved by Illman and Pilbrow (firm active circa 1829–1836) after John Trumbull (American 1756–1843)
Declaration of Independence, published in Hartford by H. and F.J. Huntington, ca. 1832, after ca. 1786–1794 original painting
Hand colored engraving
Signed in printed text below image at b.l. "Painted by Trumbull" and b.c. "Hartford, Published by Messrs. H. & F.J. Huntington" and b.r. "Engraved by Illman & Pilbrow"
13.0 x 19.9 cm., 5-1/8 x 7-7/8" image
13.2 x 22.3 cm., 5-3/16 x 8-13/16" sheet
Purchase with Gift of Adam J. DeSimone and David A. DeSimone, Augustana College Art Collection, SDC2005.19

Napoleon's loss at Waterloo began to mark the end of the European epic tradition in painting. The glory of one man's triumph over the world was coming to an end. Napoleon Bonaparte aimed to depict himself as a great warrior with victory after victory. However, as this great general began to dwindle in his own passion, or rage, and was exiled from France, the age of the European heroic conqueror began to die out, thus paving the way for a new type of history painting, in a more realistic style.

In 1817, President James Madison was given the authority by the United States Congress to hire an artist to create four paintings for the Rotunda of the Capitol Building in Washington D.C. President Madison designated John Trumbull to carry out this first official art commission awarded by the government. Together they envisioned many different subjects from American history. Following much discussion, they settled upon four important events from the American Revolution: *The Surrender of General Burgoyne, The Surrender of Lord Cornwallis at Yorktown, The Resignation of Washington*, and most importantly, *The Declaration of Independence*.

Trumbull decided to portray *The Declaration of Independence*, along with the three other paintings, in a factual manner. Rather than fictionalizing and dramatizing the stories surrounding these events, he created a straightforward American rendition. The men in the scene were not dressed in elegant clothing fit for a royal ceremony or papal benediction, or even in the classical drapery currently in vogue, they were instead represented in authentic American fashion. The room was decorated in plain, Classic Ionic form, providing the painting with a true sense of American simplicity and realism compared to the old traditions of European artists who generally represented lavish scenes of luxury and decadence for such important historical events.

The large painting for the Rotunda was actually based on a study that Trumbull had begun in 1786, at the suggestion of Thomas Jefferson, while both were in Paris.[1] The nineteenth-century hand-colored engraving illustrated here, like the public Capitol commission, reinforced the democratic nature of the country, allowing further image accessibility to its citizens. Most of the portraits for the original smaller version were drawn from life between 1790 and 1793.[2] As the chief framer for this pivotal document and a true child of the Enlightenment, Jefferson correctly perceived the need to record this moment for posterity. And Trumbull, the son of an American patriot and governor of Connecticut, firmly embraced his role as the painter who would "preserve and diffuse the memory of the noblest series of actions which have ever presented themselves to the history of man."[3]

Trumbull's own proficiency in map-making had earlier brought him to the attention of George Washington (catalogue 18), Commander-in-Chief of the American Revolutionary Army, who appointed him his aide-de-camp. After graduating from Harvard, Trumbull trained in London under American expatriate, Benjamin West, who pioneered modern history painting and encouraged his precocious student to do the same. During this period of study in England, Trumbull was imprisoned as an American spy, perhaps in retaliation for the execution of British Major John André.[4] Thus from these

beginnings to his consummate illustration of *The Declaration of Independence*, Trumbull aptly summarized that "The Military and political circumstances of my Life are so interwoven with the…years which I have devoted to the arts that they cannot be separated."[5]

The brave men involved in signing *The Declaration of Independence* were not depicted as idealized warriors, but as real life farmers and lawyers of the Revolution. The understated *heroes*, according to Trumbull, were Thomas Jefferson, John Adams and Benjamin Franklin. Jefferson, the tallest member standing in the center of the group, presents the document to the President of the Continental Congress, John Hancock,[6] who would release it with his signature on July 4, 1776. As the chair of the committee charged with drafting the *Declaration*, Jefferson actually wrote the first draft. In time, he would go on to become vice president under John Adams and third president of the United States of America. John Adams, a lawyer from Massachusetts who helped with the drafting, appears to Jefferson's right. Adams would be George Washington's vice president and the country's second president. Benjamin Franklin, standing to Jefferson's left, is depicted as older and perhaps more weathered than the other members of the Continental Congress. Franklin, a representative from Pennsylvania, was also instrumental in constructing *The Declaration of Independence*.

Trumbull distinguished these men by placing them in the center of the painting. The other forty-seven members of the Continental Congress surround them in parabolic formation, sitting or standing in various groups. There is a mood of somber purpose as they reflect upon the historical significance of this event. Their faces reveal no emotion, suggesting a reverential silence in anticipation of this important moment.

Unlike many traditional history paintings, *The Declaration of Independence* did not present one grand person who solely carried the burden or the glory, rather Trumbull portrayed a large solemn group, aware of their determined purpose: "…We hold these truths to be self-evident, that all men are created equal, that they are endowed by their Creator with certain unalienable Rights, that among these are Life, Liberty and the pursuit of Happiness…."[7] Adams, Jefferson and Trumbull had convened and discussed how the event should be portrayed and all agreed upon a realistic and authentic depiction. No *Founding Father* should be falsely sketched, as Trumbull said, "lest it being known that some were to be found in the painting, a doubt of the truth of others should be excited in the minds of posterity."[8]

Trumbull's realistic representation was conceived during a time of transition from the propagandistic European tradition to the modern American hero. Trumbull presented his champions as common working men who came together for the greater good rather than for the promotion of any single person. The painting suggests a true sense of *republic* in the art of many men working together for a common purpose. It thus provided the United States of America with a realistic sense of its own heroism. As Irma Jaffe stated, "Trumbull's painting is not grand, but achieves grandeur….The painting, like the Declaration that inspired it, American to the core, may be said to be the ultimate statement of European Enlightenment."[9]

[Thomas J. Goebel, *Class of 2008*]

[1] Irma B. Jaffe, "John Trumbull Views the French Revolution: An Unpublished Letter by the 'Patriot-Artist' of the American Revolution," *Bulletin of Research in the Humanities* (1979): 450.

[2] Irma B. Jaffe, *Trumbull: The Declaration of Independence* (New York: The Viking Press, 1976), 6.

[3] John Trumbull, "Letter to Thomas Jefferson, 1789," in John W. McCoubrey, *American Art: Sources and Documents: 1700-1960* (Englewood Cliffs: Prentice-Hall, 1965), 40-41.

[4] John Trumbull, *Autobiography of Col. John Trumbull Patriot-Artist*, ed. Theodore Sizer (New Haven: Yale University Press, 1953), 70.

[5] Jaffe, *Declaration*, 19.

[6] Ibid., 77-78.

[7] Benson John Lossing, *The Declaration of Independence with Short Biographies of Its Signers* (Bedford: Applewood Books, 1996), 3.

[8] Jaffe, *Independence*, 78-79.

[9] Ibid., 78.

Painted by Trumbull

DECLARATION OF INDEPENDENCE.

Engraved by Illman & Pilbrow

HARTFORD, Published by Messrs H. & F.J.Huntington

18

Engraved by Thomas B. Welch (American 1814–1874) after Gilbert Stuart
(American 1755–1828)
Washington, 1852, published by George W. Childs, Philadelphia, after 1796
original painting
Engraving
Signed at b.l. in image "Stuart" and b.r. in image "Welch" and inscribed in
printed text below image in plate at b.c. "Engraved by Thomas B. Welch (by
permission) from the original portrait by Gilbert Stuart, in the Athenaeum,
Boston./ Washington./ Published by George W. Childs Philadelphia./ Entered
according to the Act of Congress in the year 1852 by George W. Childs in the
Clerk's Office of the District Court of the Eastern District of Pennsylvania."
and b.l. "Proof" and b.r. "Printed by A.E. Lent & Co. Phil.a"
67.2 x 50.6 cm., 26-1/2 x 19-7/8" image
71.7 x 53.6 cm., 28-3/16 x 21-1/8" sheet
Purchase with Gift of Adam J. DeSimone and David A. DeSimone, Augustana
College Art Collection, SDC2005.23

When asked his profession, American portrait painter Gilbert Stuart wryly
replied: "I get my bread from making faces."[1] This witty response was actually
true: clearly Stuart's greatest talent was in *pinning* a likeness to a canvas. Raised
in Newport and trained in London, Stuart fled Great Britain in order to avoid
debtors' prison and aptly perceived the growing art market in post-Revolutionary
America. In particular, he realized the seemingly limitless potential for painting
portraits of the first president of the United States, George Washington, as he
predicted: "I expect to make a fortune by Washington alone."[2]

This particular nineteenth-century engraving of Washington is based on Stuart's
most famous portrait of the *father of our country*. The so-called *Athenaeum
Portrait* was known during Stuart's lifetime as one of a pair of *Mount Vernon
Portraits*[3] commissioned by Martha Washington to be hung at Mount Vernon in
commemoration of Washington's retirement from public life. Unfortunately,
however, Stuart never delivered the promised works, and instead kept them,
making multiple copies of George's likeness for an endless number of responsive
patrons. In fact, this painting remained in Stuart's studio until his death in 1828,
when it was acquired for the Boston Athenaeum where it remains today.[4]

Fellow artist Rembrandt Peale later recalled that this version was "painted I
believe in 1796,"[5] the second and most successful of Stuart's three portraits of
Washington. Many contemporaries described the reluctance on Washington's
part to pose for such images, since keeping his attention was difficult as he often
drifted into deeper thoughts. One such writer related Stuart's dilemma in an
1829 lecture: "The best portrait painter of the age, was now to take the likeness of
the greatest man of all ages; and the artists and the patriots of all countries were
interested in it. To have failed in getting a good likeness would have been death
to the artist's fame, and a perpetual source of mortification to the people of the
country…[Stuart however succeeded in capturing] the martial air of the warrior
chief…admirably mingled with the dignity and majesty of the statesman and
sage."[6]

Washington himself described the tedium of posing for the many portraitists who
demanded his presence for such studies: "In for a penny, in for a pound is an old
adage. I am so hackneyed to the touches of the painter's pencil that I am now
altogether at their beck, and sit like Patience on a monument, whilst they are
delineating the lines of my face."[7] Stuart described the challenge in effectively
capturing Washington's complex nature and characteristics: "There were features
in his face totally different from what I have observed in any other human
being…All his features were indicative of the strongest passions; yet like Socrates
his judgment and self-command made him appear a man of different case in the
eyes of the world."[8]

Stuart however rose to this challenge and effectively captured a straightforward
depiction of the former general and statesman. The dark background, contrasted
against the warm flesh tones, blue eyes and simple powdered hair, lent an air of
intimacy and dignity to the composition. In this particular likeness, Washington
posed to face the viewer's left, in order to balance Martha's mirrored position to
the viewer's right, as it was anticipated that the two would ultimately hang
together. The squared jaw and bulge around Washington's mouth in this version

were likely owing to a new set of dentures that the president complained to his
dentist sat "uneasy in my mouth."[9]

The real genius in this work rests in its balance of portraiture, a popular type of
painting in America since Colonial times, and history painting, considered the
most elevated form according to European academic standards. Artists like John
Trumbull, one of Stuart's competitors, actively pursued history painting in the
wake of the American Revolution, as in his famous image of the *Declaration of
Independence* (catalogue 17). Although this work hung in the Capitol Rotunda,
the market for large, expensive history paintings was more problematic in this
new republic than in the traditional patronage system of European popes and
monarchs. Stuart, on the other hand, shrewdly perceived that just the *right*
portrait of the first American president could astutely blend the popularity of
portraiture with the elitist status of history painting. In the *Atheneaeum Portrait*,
he thus successfully combined the two in order to create an icon for American
history.

Under the influence of the Enlightenment, Stuart aimed to portray Washington as
a "morally sublime person."[10] Within the current context of reviving Classical
texts, third-century Cassius Longinus was first described by Alexander Pope as
sublime. Longinus himself had "defined the sublime as an expression of elevated
thought and greatness of soul."[11] In his contemporary English translation of
Longinus' text, William Smith suggested that portraiture could play an important
role in bringing such characteristics to life. Fellow American artist, Washington
Allston, recognized these qualities in this portrait when he described it as
"sublime," and concluded that "a nobler personification of wisdom and goodness,
reposing in the majesty of a serene conscience, is not to be found on canvas."[12]

Stuart's greatest achievement in this image, as read by his contemporaries, was
that he depicted a "multifaceted moral ideal that could be linked to the noblest
characters of antiquity."[13] Critics appropriately responded with *awe* at his ability
to portray Washington as "the gentleman and the sage, the hero and the
Christian," yet some criticized that in achieving this goal he perhaps rendered
"too much sublimity in the face."[14] Although Stuart ridiculed Johann Caspar
Lavater's *Essays on Physiognomy (1775-78)*, like most of his contemporaries, he was
influenced by Lavater's theory that a direct connection existed between a person's
inner character and outward appearance. Washington's "indomitable will" was
described as his "most sublime aspect,"[15] as Stuart illustrated here.

This image of Washington, arguably the most famous portrait in American art,
effectively combined portraiture with history painting, all within the visage of a
great man. The sublime nature of Classical theorists was ably blended with
Yankee pride in straightforward realism. The unfinished quality of the face
enables it to be completed to satisfaction within the eye of each admirer. This
engraving, similar to those hanging in schools across America, is easily the most
recognizable symbol within a flood of modern imagery. After all, what person in
the United States today has not held the miniature of this image that is on every
dollar bill? It was, and remains, the consummate image of promise and
achievement for this great country.

[Thomas J. Goebel, *Class of 2008*]

[1] Carrie Rebora Barratt and Ellen G. Miles, *Gilbert Stuart* (New Haven and London: Yale
University Press, 2004), 3.

[2] James Thomas Flexner, *Gilbert Stuart* (New York: Alfred A. Knopf, 1955), 101.

[3] Ellen G. Miles, *George and Martha Washington: Portraits from the Presidential Years*
(Washington, D.C.: National Portrait Gallery, Smithsonian Institution, 1999), 43.

[4] Barratt and Miles, 147.

[5] Ibid., 149.

[6] Samuel Lorenzo Knapp, quoted in Barratt and Miles, 151.

[7] Flexner, 123.

[8] Ibid., 127.

[9] Barratt and Miles, 152.

[10] Dorinda Evans, *The Genius of Gilbert Stuart* (Princeton: Princeton University Press, 1999), 63.

[11] Ibid.

[12] Ibid., 66.

[13] Ibid.

[14] Ibid.

[15] Ibid., 67.

19

Gavin Hamilton (Scottish/British 1723–1798) [C. Goebel and Martin Hopkinson]
Allegorical Figure of Painting, ascribed title, ca. 1768–1785
Pastel
Unsigned
102.4 x 74.1 cm., 40-1/4 x 29-1/4"
Paul A. Anderson Chair in the Arts Purchase, Augustana College Art Collection, 2000.67

The *Allegorical Figure of Painting*, a large pastel created by Scottish artist Gavin Hamilton, appeared at the dawn of the Neoclassical period. Hamilton was a key figure in both founding and defining this important movement in art history and was celebrated as a major European tastemaker of the time. Through his passion for the study and collecting of Classical antiquities, he advanced a revival of the characteristics of ancient art which appropriately helped generate Neoclassicism. Spurred on by the rediscovery of the lost Roman cities of Pompeii and Herculaneum (buried by the volcanic eruption of Mount Vesuvius in 79 C.E.), Neoclassicists rejected the previous *feminine*, decadent Rococo style in favor of a return to ancient Greco-Roman ideals, which they perceived as demonstrating such noble attributes as honor, loyalty and intelligence. These aims were pursued through depictions of ideal beauty and proportion, classical drapery and sources for subjects based in Classical history and mythology. Hamilton used ancient pieces as a basis for his own works, believing "the ancients have surpassed the moderns, both in painting and sculpture."[1]

Although he began as a portrait painter, Hamilton's body of works consists primarily of history paintings. He continually encouraged others to adopt his viewpoint on the superiority of the Classical age to the more recent past or present. His intense enthusiasm towards Neoclassicism was inspiring. Being one of the first artists to seriously work in the Neoclassical style, he had a tremendous impact on a generation of artists through his style and subjects.[2] Hamilton's influence was not restricted to his artwork, as he was also successful as an archaeologist and art dealer, particularly of antiquities. He sought to foster his own vision for collecting and emulating Classical works in his own country.[3] Hamilton's pieces were immensely popular at the time, and he generated a steady income through his many supportive patrons as well as his art dealings. His influence was further spread through multiple prints which were engraved after his paintings.[4] Within his own work, Hamilton's ideals of simplicity and beauty deeply impacted his era.

The artist worked to avoid the embellishments and extravagances found in the previous generation's French Rococo style. His figures demonstrate his goal to attain dignity through simplicity.[5] Many figures in his paintings tend to appear overly smooth because of the high degree of finish he achieved through delicate brushstrokes, a characteristic that became typical of the Neoclassicists.[6]

Hamilton's *Allegorical Figure of Painting*, represents the discipline of painting, symbolized by the painter's palette and brushes that have been cropped off from view. She is looking at a canvas covered with a preliminary sketch of figures which she will presumably finish in oil. This pastel is packed with classical references and represents many ideals of Neoclassical art, such as the use of the ideal figure of a woman with a calm, rather expressionless demeanor. This depiction helps to create a peaceful, serene image to represent the art of painting. Both her demeanor and her clothing are typical of Neoclassicism. The woman's dress, especially at the top, gives the appearance of *wet drapery*, so-called because of its clinging nature, which in true classical form, reveals the beauty of the human figure beneath. The adornments in the woman's hair and her classic Greek profile further reinforce the classical basis for this depiction.

The woman also stands in a typical classical *contrapposto* position with her hip jutting forward and her arm propped against her side. This is a natural stance, based on Classical sculpture, which illustrates an even, natural weight distribution in the figure. The contrapposto pose as well as proper anatomical proportion reflect the artist's clear understanding of the form of the human body, fundamental in classical portrayals of figures. Although the figure is highly idealized, it does not take away from the immediacy of her image. Through Hamilton's use of primary colors and chiaroscuro, the richly toned figure of the woman is effectively illuminated against the shadowed background, reinforcing the easily read simplicity of the Neoclassical style.[7]

Her proportions, the shape of her forearms and the attention to her profile and eyes are similar to other works by Hamilton. The hairstyle and dress of the woman in the painting are also typical of Hamilton's depictions of women.[8] This piece is clearly an important find in Hamilton's work[9] (only previously published in Augustana's *Paul A. Anderson Art History Collection* catalogue). The fresh and original quality of this important piece reflects the style that so effectively enthused a generation, fueled by the Enlightenment, toward revolutions which promised a better world.

[Chris Johnson, *Class of 2007*]

[1] Quoted in Jane Turner, ed., "Hamilton, Gavin," in *Dictionary of Art*, vol. 14 (New York: Grove's Dictionaries Inc., 1996), 108.

[2] Julia Lloyd Williams, *Gavin Hamilton, 1723-1798*, vol. 18 of *Scottish Masters* (Edinburgh: National Galleries of Scotland, 1994), 15-16.

[3] Catherine Carter Goebel, *The Paul A. Anderson Art History Collection*, ed. Catherine Carter Goebel (Rock Island: Augustana College, 2001), 50.

[4] Turner, 108-109.

[5] Goebel, 50.

[6] Turner, 109.

[7] Goebel, 50.

[8] Ibid.

[9] Martin Hopkinson, eminent Hamilton scholar, agrees with this attribution per discussion with Catherine Goebel, Art History Department.

20

Sebastiano
Tempio di Eriteo [Erechtheum Temple], ca. late 18th century
Pen and ink drawing
Signed b.r. below image *"Sebastiano Ittar."* [Sebastiano, Illustrator]
Inscribed b.l. below image *"Monte parneto"* [Mount Parnassus] and b.c.
"Tempio di Eriteo/ Esiste Questo Tempio Nell' Acropoli d'Atene" [This is a
temple on the Acropolis, Athens] (Italian translations kindly provided by
Dr. Thomas Mayer's history seminar class, Augustana College Fall Term
2000)
15.7 x 23.3 cm., 6-1/4 x 9-1/4" image
22.3 x 28.7 cm., 8-7/8 x 11-3/8" sheet
Paul A. Anderson Chair in the Arts Purchase, Augustana College Art
Collection, 2000.36

Today's culture is accustomed to taking photographs of events that occur
throughout our lives that we wish to capture and remember forever. Even more
recently, with the advent of the computer age and digital photography, we have
taken for granted the instantaneous record that we might capture and transmit
to others. This wish to preserve and share an experience is not a newly
developed concept. Sebastiano's *Tempio di Eriteo* (Erechtheum Temple)
demonstrates similar interests, as early as the eighteenth century, in response to
the international Neoclassical movement.

The *Tempio di Eriteo* is a *snapshot*, of sorts, of one of the most revered stops
along the *Grand Tour*. This *Grand Tour*, as it was called, consisted of extensive
travel, primarily in Greece and Italy, often culminating with Rome, the Eternal
City and a center for classical culture. It drew people from all over the United
States and Europe, attracting a variety of devotees seeking intellectual and
cultural enrichment.[1] Many young gentlemen who embarked in their early to
mid-twenties on the *Grand Tour*, considered it a final step in their formal
education before taking on the responsibilities of manhood. The Neoclassical
movement fueled this desire to directly confront the past and to seek
inspiration from the classical cultures of ancient Greece and Rome.

Rome was truly the backbone of the tour and many tourists stayed a year or
more in this city alone. The other highlight along the way was the city of
Athens, where the *Acropolis* (high city) formed the foundation for this Ionic
temple and the famous Doric Parthenon as well. The entire tour could last
several years, since most travelers did not wish to rush the experience[2] and
many had the necessary resources to support it. These gentlemen were in *awe*
of the great architectural accomplishments of the ancient Greeks and Romans.
Artists sought to copy these works of perfection in order to learn from them
and to use them as sources for their own creations. Others desired to take

something tangible back with them, both for its aesthetic value and as a
souvenir of their trip.[3] The return of these travelers, who shared their
collected artifacts and copies with minds full of classical ideals, further
reinforced the Neoclassical movement with their friends and family back home.
Drawings and paintings of famous ruins and monuments, such as the *Tempio di
Eriteo*, proved to be desirable collectibles for travelers. Major sights such as the
Acropolis were commonly sketched and marketed for *Grand Tour* patrons who
coveted images of architectural ruins as well as casts of ancient sculptures.[4]

The *Tempio di Eriteo*, one of many temples on the Acropolis in Athens, is
distinctive for its caryatids (vertical supports carved into female figures)
making up the *Porch of the Maidens* seen on the right side of the drawing.[5]
Sebastiano, the artist, drew a very picturesque atmosphere and applied the
same compositional characteristics to paper that tourists today would capture
in a photograph, and in the same manner, this portable art could be taken
anywhere to be admired by anyone. It is quite simple in format, yet very
detailed in the ruin itself. Sebastiano delineated every column and sculpture in
order to reveal the overall complexity, so that one can better understand the
actual view and wonder at its creation. The man in the lower right corner,
apparently sketching on a large sheet, is either the artist himself or another
individual like him, who sought to capture the intricacies of this classical ruin.
This figure establishes scale and invites the viewer of this drawing to also study
the ruins and develop an even deeper appreciation for its grandeur.

The *Tempio di Eriteo* and other such Grand Tour drawings were not just
memories captured for an eighteenth-century audience. They have also become
modern culture's *snapshots* from the past, and even though they do not reflect
our own personal memories, we can appreciate and enjoy the drawings since
they enable us to experience the ruins within their historic context as if we were
also along on the *Grand Tour* ourselves. This drawing reveals to us in the
twenty-first century, just how people over two centuries ago revered great
monuments erected some twenty-three centuries before their time. In this
manner, such images allow us access both to the ancient as well as the more
recent past and seem to invite us to also visit the Erechtheum in order to
construct our own context for such ancient wonders.

[Jennifer Windmiller, *Class of 2007*]

[1] John Wilton-Ely, "'Classic Ground': Britain, Italy and the Grand Tour," *Eighteenth-Century Life*, vol. 28, no.1 (2004): 149, EBSCOhost (7 July 2005).

[2] David Irwin, *Neoclassicism* (London: Phaidon Press Limited, 1997), 20.

[3] Wilton-Ely, 151-152.

[4] Ibid., 152.

[5] *Caryatids* are columns in the shape of women. Robert Lopez, *The Paul A. Anderson Art History Collection*, ed. Catherine Carter Goebel (Rock Island: Augustana College, 2001), 56.

21

Ernesto Gazzeri (Italian 1866–1965, also active in the United States)
Minerva (formerly titled "Venus"), n.d.
Carved marble sculpture
Signed verso near base "E. Gazzeri/*Roma*"
107.8 x 29.1 x 21.3 cm., 42-3/8 x 11-1/2 x 8-1/2"
Paul A. Anderson Chair in the Arts Purchase, Augustana College Art
Collection, 99.21, pedestal not original to piece SDC99.23

According to ancient mythology, Minerva (the Roman version of the Greek
goddess Athena) was the goddess of wisdom, institutions for the arts and
higher learning and the defender for just causes in war. Believed to have been
born out of Jupiter's head fully grown and in full armor, Minerva had domain
over wisdom and defensive war. She was not considered bloodthirsty like Mars,
the male god of war, and therefore better remembered for her wisdom and
knowledge. In her contest with Neptune, the god of the sea, for the patronage
of Athens, they each offered a gift to the people. Neptune provided the horse
and Minerva, the olive tree. Hers was ruled the more useful gift and she thus
became the patron goddess of Athens.[1]

As the goddess of just war, she is usually depicted in full armor looking
thoughtful and prepared. She was Jupiter's favorite child and therefore
she was given some of his armor, which she often wears in depictions.[2]
Minerva's main attribute is not sensuous beauty like Venus, the Roman
goddess of beauty and love (equivalent to the Greek Aphrodite), although
Gazzeri's version seems to portray her in that idealized role as well, perhaps
inspired by the famous Hellenistic sculpture of *Venus de Milo.* Like this
ancient sculpture, Gazzeri's goddess repeats Venus' exaggerated
contrapposto stance with one foot forward, the loosely slung cloth beneath
her waist which seems about to fall and even the broken points where her
arms are missing.[3] By adding a helmet under her left foot and a crown to
her head, she is transformed from the goddess of beauty to Minerva, the
goddess of war.

Her helmet is the only symbol that clearly identifies her as the goddess of
defensive war. The crown on her head possibly symbolizes her general
status as a goddess. This version does not include an owl, which in other
depictions is often perched near her atop a stack of books, reinforcing her
connection with learning. Minerva was also known for her virginity,[4]
although she did have suitors. Gazzeri likely preferred to focus on her
wisdom and purity rather than her prowess in warfare. Thus he depicted
her as a graceful young idealized maiden instead of a keen warrior ready for
battle. This gentle figure is a representation of Minerva's softer and more
innocent side.

Gazzeri probably became interested in Classical art while at an art academy
where students studied and copied the Old Masters in order to learn from
them.[5] Minerva is based on knowledge of Classical sculpture. This
ideal figure reflects the Greek aim to design mathematical proportional
relationships in order to create beauty. Her contemplative face holds no
emotion. Her hair is arranged in a traditional Roman style and her drapery,
which covers only half of her body, slips diagonally downward across her
lower torso, inviting the viewer to anticipate its fall. The gathering of cloth
resting precariously at her hips has slipped away enough to reveal Gazzeri's
accurate knowledge of anatomy. He used classical *wet drapery* to suggest the
body beneath as well as to demonstrate his artistic ability. He likely studied
human anatomy as evidenced in the contours of the body and muscles.

Gazzeri sculpted Minerva in a more active position than would be typical
for Classical Greek art. Her left foot rests on the helmet, while she shifts her
weight firmly onto her right leg, creating a dramatic shift in the rest of her
body. The contrapposto pose combined with the wet drapery, firmly bent
knee and turned head give the sculpture a sense of liveliness reminiscent of
the later Greek Hellenistic period.[6] Minerva appears as if she is about to
shift or change positions, and although carved in white marble, she catches
the eye of the viewer and almost seems to come to life.

[Jennifer Bock, *Class of 2008*]

[1] Shearer West, ed., "Minerva (Greek: Athena)," *The Bulfinch Guide to Art History: A Comprehensive Survey and Dictionary of Western Art and Architecture* (New York: Bulfinch Press, 1996), 633.

[2] Ibid.

[3] J. J. Pollitt, *Art in the Hellenistic Age* (New York: Cambridge University Press, 1986), 168.

[4] West, 633.

[5] Robert Lopez, *The Paul A. Anderson Art History Collection,* ed. Catherine Carter Goebel (Rock Island: Augustana College, 2001), 58.

[6] Lopez, 58.

22

Drawing by Johann Heinrich Ramberg (German 1763–1840, engraving by Pietro Antonio Martini (Italian 1739–1797)
The Exhibition of the Royal Academy, 1787, 1787
Engraving
Signed in printed text below image at b.l. "H. Ramberg del." and b.c. "Publish'd as the Act Direc.s July 1. 1787 by A.C. De Poggi, No. 7 St. Georges Row, Hyde Park." and b.r. "P.A. Martini *Parms fecit Londini*"
35.5 x 49.5 cm., 14 x 19-1/2" image and sheet
Paul A. Anderson Chair in the Arts Purchase, Augustana College Art Collection, Conservation Funding Assisted by Professor Adrian R. Tió, 2004.9

The Exhibition of the Royal Academy, 1787 is an engraving that was based on the original painting created in the same year by German artist, Johann Heinrich Ramberg. Ramberg, who was born in 1763, pursued most of his career in Germany, but spent some time in England studying from 1781 to 1788 under the great Neoclassical American expatriate and future President of the Royal Academy, Benjamin West.[1] It was during this period in London that he made this piece. Ramberg's ultimate success is demonstrated in the fact that by the turn of the eighteenth century, following his return home, he had already illustrated the writings of almost every major contemporary German author. His popularity decreased over the years, however, as he completed his last major work twenty years before his death in 1840.[2] Pietro Antonio Martini was the engraver who reproduced Ramberg's artwork and translated it into a print. The two artists must have developed a good collaborative relationship since Martini engraved other works by Ramberg.[3]

This print's subject matter does not stem from history or tales of the gods, but instead illustrates real contemporary life in London. There is not much movement or action in the scene, since people are focused on verbal discourse and studying art. The viewers seem naturalistic yet the artist's academic training is revealed in the manner in which many of them stand in a classical contrapposto position. The figures in the print do not have rippling muscles or ideal body shapes as in the typical classical tradition, but are convincing as real people placed within an environment witnessed firsthand by the artist.

The Exhibition convincingly depicts London social life in the eighteenth century. This particular work of art was made to celebrate the Prince of Wales' visit to the Royal Academy's exhibition. The prince's portrait by Sir Joshua Reynolds, the current President of the Royal Academy, hangs in the center of the back wall in the print.[4] The engraving shows many different social classes wandering about the gallery. Some people appear to belong to the middle class while still others are clearly aristocratic, such as the man standing front and center dressed in light clothing. There appears to be a clergyman to his left. Dogs are surprisingly roaming and playing freely in the academy exhibition. The artist establishes people in pairs throughout this work, such as at the far right where a short stocky man parades around the art gallery with a much younger woman and at the left where a couple is exiting the academy.

The Royal Academy was established in 1768 in England as a vehicle for artists to display their works. These exhibits were the first large-scale non-commercial art exhibitions held in England.[5] The Great Room at Somerset House, the headquarters for the Academy then and now, which is depicted in this print, was a massive space that could hold between two and three hundred oil paintings on its walls. Somerset House opened in 1780 and held the Academy's annual summer exhibitions. The institution quickly became a great success, as evidenced in the fact that during the first two months of its opening, over 61,000 viewers made their way through the exhibit.[6]

The manner in which the Royal Academy displayed its art, however, leaves something to be desired to the modern eye. Paintings were stacked from floor to ceiling with frames nearly touching one another. Large paintings, such as history paintings and full-length portraits, tended to hold the enviable positions of being hung *on the line*, an actual line of molding that ran above the doorways in the Great Room. Because of the crowds, paintings placed at this level were the easiest to see as they were closest to eye level.

Since pieces could be hung all the way up to the windows at the ceiling, a common complaint among artists was that their paintings had been *skied* or placed too high for spectators to get a good look at their work.[7] Typically, a large painting would claim the center spot on a wall and smaller pieces would be grouped around it. The committee took into account size, themes, symmetry and general visual harmony when selecting an order, but ultimately the positioning came down to what they thought fit best.[8] This layout shows the care and detail that the academy took in mounting an exhibition as well as the aim to show as much art as possible within a limited amount of wall space.

The most interesting aspect to this work is perhaps this method of exhibiting a massive number of works within a relatively limited space. The paintings are hung so close together that there was little room for explanation or identification. Paintings at the highest level are four or five times higher than the people in the picture. It would be a century later before American expatriate artist, James McNeill Whistler (catalogue 61), would design by most accounts the first major exhibition that *only* placed works on the line, with ample space between them. Whistler also gave attention to the background wall colors so as not to distract from the art at hand. He established the more modern approach utilized almost universally today. For 1787, however, the placement in these exhibits remained cluttered and helped determine the status or acceptance of a certain work of art. The sheer number of paintings in one room, although a status symbol, was confusing and overwhelming. Ramberg captured the essence of eighteenth-century exhibition practice, allowing modern art-goers to appreciate just how far art gallery exhibition techniques have evolved today.

[J.D. Rotzoll, *Class of 2008*]

[1] Jane Turner, ed., "Ramberg, Johann Heinrich," *Dictionary of Art*, vol. 25 (New York: Grove's Dictionaries Inc., 1996), 871.

[2] Ibid., 872.

[3] A similar piece, *Their Majesties and the Royal Family Viewing the Exhibition at the Royal Academy, London, 1788,* was also created by Ramberg and engraved by Martini a year after *The Exhibition.* Jane Turner, ed., "Exhibition: c. 1700—c. 1850," *Dictionary of Art*, vol. 10 (New York: Grove's Dictionaries Inc., 1996), 677-678.

[4] Angela Rosenthal, "Exhibition Review," *Eighteenth-Century Studies*, vol. 35, no. 4 (2002): 602.

[5] Turner, 677.

[6] Ibid., 603.

[7] Ibid., 603-604.

[8] Ibid., 604.

23

John Flaxman II (English/British 1755–1826), engraving by Tommaso Piroli (Italian ca. 1752–1824)
The Choir, 1793, issued in **Compositions from the Hell, Purgatory, and Paradise, of Dante Alighieri, by John Flaxman, Sculptor.**, printed for Longman, Hurst, Rees & Orme, et al., London, 1807
Engraving
Unsigned on this plate
In printed text below image "*Virgilio*," "*Danté*," "*Sentimi presso quasi un muover d'ala/ e'ventarmi nel volto.*" "When a soft breeze as from an heavenly wing,/ sudden upon my visage seem'd to play." and "*Purgatorio Canto. 17*"
15.8 x 20.5 cm., 6-1/4 x 8-3/16" image
23.0 x 32.7 cm., 9-1/16 x 12-7/8" sheet
Gift of Dr. Thomas B. Brumbaugh Art History Collection to Augustana College Art Collection, 2002.18.3

John Flaxman's artistic roots can be traced back a generation to his father who produced plaster casts of ancient sculptures, used to teach classical design and methods to eighteenth-century sculptors. In this manner, artists could study and copy casts of ancient works in their own studios rather than having to travel great distances to see the originals in person. After training and securing a place at the Royal Academy, Flaxman was offered a position as a designer for Josiah Wedgwood, creating classical designs for ceramic decoration. While working for Wedgwood, the young artist perfected his simplified linear approach to art[1] which effectively translated classical sculptural relief to pottery.

Although he had already long been interested in classical art, this opportunity no doubt further fueled his passion for Greek and Roman images. At this time, Flaxman was also busy creating large sculptural monuments and illustrations for books. Outside of his Wedgwood designs, his sculptures are probably the best known aspect of his work, although his name became widespread throughout Europe due to his book illustrations for Classic works by Homer, Aeschylus and Dante.[2]

The Choir is one such illustration, a typical line drawing that was turned into an engraving by Tomasso Piroli from the artist's Neoclassical collection, *Compositions from the Hell, Purgatory, and Paradise of Dante Alighieri.* The composition appears simple and two-dimensional at first glance, but the straightforward approach of the piece is not accidental. Flaxman's *flat* figures in his line drawings are examples of the artist's concern for clean outlines and balanced figural relationships with space. The literary content within the work draws on the viewer's sense of all aspects of art, including the legible, the visual and what appears between the lines.

The seemingly empty space that occupies most of this engraving does not come from a lack of artistic imagination. For Flaxman, the area around the figures was just as important as the figures themselves.[3] Their position in the foreground of the composition provides a dramatic perspective in relation to the angelic creatures that inhabit the background of the piece. Flaxman's compositional technique allows the angels to occupy nearly as much eye-catching space as Dante and Virgil command in the foreground. The simplicity of the draftsmanship makes it easy to decipher spatial relationships between figures. Although Neoclassical in style, Flaxman's balance of figures to their environment, even in a blank space, predicts the viewpoint adapted a century later by Post-Impressionists; that both the figure and the background are equivalent in their importance within a work.[4]

Flaxman typically used ancient Greek mythology and literature as sources for much of his inspiration, particularly in his Wedgwood designs. In this particular image, his source was the medieval poet Dante (1265–1321 C.E.) and his famous opus the *Divine Comedy.* In the first two parts of this epic poem, Latin Poet Virgil (70–19 B.C.E.) leads his companion, Dante, through Hell and Purgatory. Virgil on the left, crowned with a laurel wreath, stares at Dante as he observes the three angels before him in Purgatory. Once again, Flaxman's positioning of the figures within the piece challenges the viewer to decide the nature of interaction: whether or not they are aware of each other's presence, engaged in conversation or oblivious to their separate existence. Dante and Virgil appear as spectators to the angels beyond them, just as we add a third level of observation as we watch both groups within the print. The verse below the engraving reads, "When a soft breeze as from an heavenly wing/ sudden upon my visage seem'd to play." Perhaps the angelic breeze, represented by the horizontal lines flowing to the right of the poets, is a reference to inspiration.

The angels are an example of Christian iconography, symbolizing divine interaction with the everyday.[5] Flaxman's juxtaposition of Christian doctrine and ancient mythology serves as an interesting contradiction within the piece. The angels seem almost tangible within the scene. The idea of angels existing in the presence of real men makes the viewer believe that perhaps they might indeed be present in our own lives. It appears that Flaxman sought to make Roman mythology and Christian faith co-exist within his work. However, the overtone of this series of drawings from *Compositions* is undoubtedly based aesthetically in the Classical Greek tradition.

The cloaked figures in *The Choir*, as well as those in much of Flaxman's art, are timeless representations of the classical tradition, constructed during the height of the Neoclassical era. The artist's outlines speak eloquently to the unforgiving eye. They hide nothing and imply no false pretenses within the work. Flaxman's background as a sculptor provided him with a sophisticated knowledge of space and composition, resulting in such introspective line drawings. *The Choir* calls on the simplest of emotions, yet makes a grand statement as if on the precipice of something great. The potential contained within these simple figures cannot be completely grasped. The drawing is straightforward, yet deeply meaningful. Flaxman found the balance between suggestion and meaning in *The Choir* and communicates to the viewer that what is not shown can be just as important as what is visible.

[Mallory McClintock, *Class of 2008*]

[1] David Irwin, *John Flaxman, 1755-1826: Sculptor, Illustrator, Designer* (New York: Rizzoli International Publications, Inc., 1980), 18.

[2] Ibid., 67.

[3] David Bindman, ed., *John Flaxman* (London: Thames and Hudson, 1979), 17.

[4] Ibid., 17.

[5] Irwin, 104.

SENTIMI PRESSO QUASI UN MUOVER D'ALA.
E VENTARMI NEL VOLTO

Purgatorio Canto. 17.

WHEN A SOFT BREEZE, AS FROM AN HEAV'NLY WING,
SUDDEN UPON MY VISAGE SEEMD TO PLAY.

24

Wedgwood (Josiah Wedgwood, English/British 1730–1795); modeling of figures primarily attributed to Henry Webber (British 1754–1826)
Portland Vase, limited edition released 1791, this vase is more recent
Ceramic
Stamped on bottom edge of rim "Wedgwood"
26.6 x 20.1 x 20.1 cm., 10-1/2 x 8 x 8"
Paul A. Anderson Chair in the Arts Purchase, Augustana College Art Collection, 2000.66

Webster's dictionary defines Neoclassicism as a revival of classic style and form in art, literature, etc., a description which exactly fits the basis for Wedgwood's *Portland Vase*. When Josiah Wedgwood first began to work with the idea of constructing pieces such as the *Portland Vase*, he was definitely inspired by the contemporary revived interest in early Greek and Roman artwork. Wedgwood also knew that most people could not afford to build collections of authentic ancient Classical pieces. He thus determined to create objects that resembled such antiquities, but were affordable and accessible enough that more people could afford to have them in their own homes.

Born in 1730, Josiah Wedgwood was raised in Burslem within a family of English potters. He started his own factory, which he named *Etruria*, in 1769. Throughout his career, Wedgwood developed many revolutionary ceramic materials such as *jasper ware*, white stoneware that could be dyed using metal oxides.[1] His most famous and celebrated piece was known as the *Portland Vase*. The original Roman *Portland Vase*, also called the *Barberini Vase*, was made from deep blue-black glass with an engraved overlay of white glass. It dates from around 25 B.C.E., early in the so-called *Golden Age* of Caesar Augustus. An extremely popular classical piece, especially during the eighteenth-century Neoclassical movement, the vase remains a beautiful and expert example of ancient cut cameo-glass.[2]

It traveled through the hands of many owners including the family of Cardinal Francesco Barberini (hence the title, *Barberini Vase*), Sir William Hamilton (a close friend of Josiah Wedgwood) and eventually the Dowager Duchess of *Portland*, giving it the name by which it is most commonly known today.[3] Wedgwood borrowed the vase for a year from the Third Duke of Portland, the son of the late Duchess, in order to copy the designs and reproduce the vase in his new ceramic invention, *jasper ware*. The process of creating the actual vase took much longer than he anticipated, however, and after multiple experiments and trials, a final perfected

copy was produced three years later, four years after he first obtained the original.[4]

Wedgwood did an amazing job of reviving and advancing the early Greco-Roman style in his own time period. There are many important aspects to examine in this wonderful piece. First of all, the white cameo engravings literally advance before our eyes. Around the base of each of the handles lies a mask of Pan, the Greek god of flock and woods.[5] Every human form on the vase is endowed with Classical idealized features. In one scene, a woman reaches up to grasp the arm of a man leaving a shrine to her left, while to the right an older man watches the couple. Cupid, the Roman god of love, hovers above them, alluding to their affection for one another.[6] On the reverse side, a female reclines between two figures.

Although the exact meaning of the scenes on the vase is still debated by scholars, a popular theory relates them to the myth of Peleus and Thetis, the parents of Achilles, the great Greek hero of the Trojan War, celebrated in Homer's Classical masterpiece, the *Iliad*. It has been determined that the original shape of the vase was an *amphora* (meaning *to carry on both sides*) with a foot that has since been broken and replaced with a circular disc made about a century later. The figure on the bottom disc is probably Paris, the son of King Priam of Troy.[7] The lovers' arms linked together as well as the tree branches, facial expressions and hand gestures, effectively guide the viewers' eyes around the entire piece.

Wedgwood truly desired to make the Neoclassical style available to the masses. This piece reflects the enthusiasm for this style and cultural revival, which can partly be attributed to Wedgwood and his incredible artistic ability to recreate such attractive pieces as the *Portland Vase*. The fact that this artwork is still considered the epitome of what Classical and Neoclassical art should be, a position it has maintained for some two hundred years, secures its place of importance in the rankings of art history.

[Johanna Voorhees, *Class of 2008*]

[1] *Wedgwood Museum*, July 2002, http://www.wedgwoodmuseum.org.uk (7 July 2005).

[2] Milo Keynes, "The Portland Vase: Sir William Hamilton, Josiah Wedgwood and the Darwins," *Notes and Records of the Royal Society of London*, vol. 52, no. 2 (1998): 241, JSTOR (2005).

[3] Ibid., 237.

[4] Ibid., 240

[5] Ibid., 241.

[6] Sherry C. Maurer, *The Paul A. Anderson Art History Collection*, ed. Catherine Carter Goebel (Rock Island: Augustana College, 2001), 53.

[7] Maurer, 53.

25

Attributed to Philibert-Louis Debucourt (French 1755–1832) [Pierre Jonchères]
Femmes en révolte [Women in Revolt], n.d.
Watercolor
Unsigned
23.1 x 37.0 cm., 9-1/16 x 14-9/16" image
27.0 x 39.9 cm., 10-5/8 x 15-11/16" sheet
Gift in Memory of Dr. Thomas William Carter, Augustana College Art Collection, 2004.23

Femmes en révolte portrays a mob of women desperately rioting in the marketplace of a major urban center. The lively colors and loose, flurried lines contribute to a sense of frenzied movement. In the bottom foreground, three women attempt to restrain another from joining the fray amongst scattered produce; in the middle, bodies lie trampled; and in the upper right, women empty what is possibly offal or scalding water onto the crowd beneath them. Above the mayhem rise civilized buildings, the windows blank or filled with mostly faceless spectators. In the background, carriages stand by—filled with gawking onlookers or those able to retreat from an uprising on what should have been an ordinary market day.

The painting was purchased from Parisian art dealer, Pierre Jonchères, who attributed the work to French artist Philibert-Louis Debucourt (1755–1832). The clothing of the women is of a later eighteenth-century, working-class type. If a particular historical event is portrayed, it would be one distinguished by the revolt of women in a market area—a few hastily armed with sticks, furniture and a cup—who lack any clear, armed opponent.

It is likely that this watercolor depicts a subsistence (essential food) riot. During the eighteenth century, in both France and Great Britain, the free market forces of modern capitalism were replacing the purposes and organization of old medieval guilds, resulting in price inflation that out-paced wage increases. In Paris, any inflation in the price of bread and flour justifiably unnerved the lower classes.[1]

On the eve of the Revolution, women's groups of Parisian housewives and the working-class (such as fishwives and laundresses) were accustomed to marching through the city for various ceremonies that gave thanks to church saints.[2] The relatively peaceful 1789 march of women to Versailles demanded that the king take responsibility for *taxation populaire*, setting price maximums for commodities.[3] Violence arose during the 1792 Sugar Crises, when petitions for fixed prices stalled at the Commune and Legislative Assembly.[4] But it is the 1793 riot that clearly attributes violence to female instigation. Unrest was sparked by a cost upturn in soap, tallow candles, coffee and sugar. Police reports documented women protagonists:

> There had been two deputations of women to the Convention on Sunday, 23 February, one of which was composed of laundresses, who complained of the price of soap….But the real outbreak began on the morning of the 25th; it took the form of the mass invasion of grocers' and chandlers' shops and…spread with remarkable speed to every part of the city…. The next day there followed minor incidents in a number of Sections, in which the market women of the centre and laundresses of the rue de Bièvre, in the Faubourg Saint-Marcel, played a conspicuous part.[5]

The subsistence riot of 1793 was most directly linked to female involvement, as well as looting and destruction of property.

While the event might not be specifically identified, this scene is quite uncommon and could prompt more discussion about the intention of the artist. It could depict a specific British event, although the architectural background seems appropriate for Paris. John Bohstedt has demonstrated that historians have exaggerated how many violent food riots were led by women.[6] This watercolor may even be a general rendering of what Bohstedt terms "the myth of the feminine food riot."

Maurice Fenaille's list of titles for Debucourt's paintings and drawings does not include any title that accords with the scene of this watercolor, but it is not a catalog raisonné. If *Femmes en révolte* is by Debucourt, it counts as a Revolutionary memento that reveals a greater depth in his overall work. Debucourt began as a painter but transitioned to color aquatint printmaking, creating amusing genre scenes, especially of jolly village revelers and titillating romantic liaisons. A student of the Academy, his work was first accepted in the French bi-annual Salon in 1781, where he continued to be a regular participant until his death, except during the turbulent years between 1785 and 1810.[7] The *Gazette des Beaux-Arts* compared Debucourt and Jean-Honoré Fragonard.[8] Debucourt retained the rose, blue and gold palette of Rococo-era painters like Fragonard, as seen in *Femmes en révolte*. French writers saw Debucourt as their successor to Flemish genre painters such as Rembrandt Van Rijn, Adriaen van Ostade and Jan Steen. Edmond and Jules de Goncourt called him the little master, "le petit mâitre."[9]

The dealer who attributed this painting to Debucourt referenced the artist's work titled *Almanach national*. That piece is a French Revolution-era allegorical tribute dedicated in 1791 to "the friends of the Constitution."[10] A sharper edge to Debucourt's outlook appears in two prints: the 1787 *Promenade de la Gallerie du Palais-Royal*, and the 1792 *La Promenade publique*. Both images critique a strolling line of dandies, satirized for their costumes, attitudes and wasted affluence. These examples, along with *Almanach national*, suggest that although Debucourt's works were primarily tailored to please the public, he was not unsympathetic to the need for social change. The French Revolution pioneered political reform and a new consciousness about art themes. It is plausible that this watercolor is by an artist active circa 1790 who sensed a new era and responded by painting one of the key events of that challenging time.

[Sherry C. Maurer, *Director of Augustana College Art Museum* and Tiffany Chezum, *Class of 2008*]

---

[1] A worker might spend 50 percent of his income on bread, with another 16 percent spent on other groceries. George Rudé, *The Crowd in the French Revolution* (Oxford: Clarendon Press, 1965 reprint), 20-22.

[2] Darlene Gay Levy and Harriet B. Applewhite, "Women of the Popular Classes in Revolutionary Paris, 1789-1795" in Carol R. Berkin and Clara M. Lovett, eds., *Women, War and Revolution* (New York: Holmes & Meier Publishers, 1980), 13.

[3] Jack Richard Censer and Lynn Hunt, *Liberty, Equality, Fraternity: Exploring the French Revolution* (University Park: Pennsylvania State University, 2001), 75-77, and, Levy and Applewhite, 11.

[4] Levy and Applewhite, 19.

[5] Rudé, 115.

[6] John Bohstedt, "The Myth of the Feminine Food Riot: Women as Proto-Citizens in English Community Politics, 1790-1810," in Harriet B. Applewhite and Darlene Gay Levy, eds., *Women and Politics in the Age of the Democratic Revolution* (Ann Arbor: The University of Michigan Press, 1993 paperback edition), 21 and 32.

[7] Biographical information on Debucourt was found in two sources: a six-page essay by Malcom C. Salaman in *Masters of the Colour Print V.—P.L. Debucourt* (London: "The Studio" Limited, 1929), and the nine-page "Preface" by Maurice Vaucaire in Maurice Fenaille's *L'Oeuvre gravé de P.-L. Debucourt (1755-1832)* (Paris: Librarie Damascène Morgand, 1899).

[8] Ibid, vi.

[9] Ibid, vi-vii.

[10] The image of this print is available on the Web by searching Google "images" with the title of the piece and choosing the site www.histoireimage.org. Composed of two stacked images, the top triumphal arch frames an allegorical representation that originally included a profile of the French King Louis XVI hung at the top center. Paired below are scenes of the French people from various walks of life, united in their approval of the new regime.

26

Artist unknown after Marie-Louise-Elisabeth Vigée-Le Brun (French 1755–1842)
Copy of **Self-portrait**, n.d., after 1790 original painting
Oil on linen
Unsigned
58.8 x 42.8 cm., 23 x 16-7/8"
Paul A. Anderson Chair in the Arts Purchase, Augustana College Art Collection, SDC2004.11

The original self-portrait of Marie-Louise-Elisabeth Vigée-Le Brun (1755–1842) was painted in 1790 for a collection at the Uffizi gallery of artists' self-portraits.[1] The daughter of French pastellist, Jean-Baptiste-Pierre LeBrun, an artist of the Académie de Saint Luc, Elisabeth spent her first five years in the country, raised by a peasant woman. At the age of five she was sent to a convent school, where she demonstrated natural artistic talent. She attended her father's drawing classes until his death, followed by other non-traditional means of training until she was old enough to be admitted into the same academy as her father.[2] Such opportunity and accomplishment for a female artist of the eighteenth century were rare.

In her memoirs, Vigée-Le Brun recalled showing her father a drawing when she was only seven or eight years old. He "…went into transports of joy, exclaiming, 'You will be a painter, child, if ever there was one!'"[3] She also related that she soon came to realize what an "…inborn passion for the art I possessed. Nor has that passion ever diminished; it seems to me that it has gone on growing with time, for to-day I feel under the spell of it as much as ever, and shall, I hope, until the hour of death."[4]

Vigée-Le Brun was greatly influenced by seventeenth-century painter, Pieter Paul Rubens, and her style reflects his rich painterly example. Her flesh tones became more vibrant and less opaque after studying his technique.[5] By 1770, she was considered a professional portrait artist and in 1778, she received her first commission to paint Queen Marie Antoinette from life. By this time, Vigée-Le Brun's fame had grown, and soon after she became the official portrait painter to the queen. She was granted membership to the Académie Royale de Peinture et de Sculpture and became one of the first women in the history of art to be recognized as a serious artist.[6]

Her subjects were dominated by society's elite, making her a frequenter of the most aristocratic Parisian circles. Being a female artist in the eighteenth century gave rise to scandal and criticism, however, and in 1789 she was accused of having been involved in liaisons with three different men. The eruption of the French Revolution and her ruined reputation made it impossible for her to continue to work in France. She fled to Italy, where she found many influential patrons. Her impressive skill and social connections made her an international success as she spent time painting in such countries as Russia, Switzerland and England.[7] Vigée-Le Brun's style is generally considered pre-Revolutionary, with Neoclassical and Romantic elements.

This painting, done with oils on linen, is a nineteenth-century copy of Vigée-Le Brun's original *Self-portrait* created in 1790. Copies of the Old Masters were often painted by students and followers in order to improve techniques and teach subtleties in application. The fact that this piece was copied in the nineteenth century provides evidence that this painter was greatly respected by subsequent generations. This self-portrait reveals Vigée-Lebrun's mature painting style, with its almost invisible brushstrokes and fine academic finish. It seems to capture a moment, as the artist, in the middle of painting Marie-Antoinette's image, turns to pose for her own portrait. The subject of her canvas, the queen of France, reinforces the painter's important status. The almost monochromatic background is interrupted only by the faint outline of a canvas and the face of Marie-Antoinette, but essentially serves as a backdrop for the main subject. Vigée-LeBrun's face appears flawless and her eyes reflect an engaged intellect. It is this perfect, finished expression that led many critics to unfairly call her portraits "vacuous."[8] The artist's use of black and white with a touch of red, as well as the sophisticated play of light and shadow, lends the painting drama and purpose, reflecting her own independent nature and never-ending drive to succeed.

As with many successful portrait painters, Vigée-Le Brun was known to flatter her subjects, even herself, when she painted. In this image, she would have been thirty-five years old, but painted herself looking much younger, possibly in her twenties. Her clothing is simple and unembellished. She did not wear the lavish styles of dress, hair and makeup in vogue at the time, but insisted on simple gowns without lavish makeup or wigs. She also often wore a turban on her head, as seen in this painting. In addition to her not being bound by fashion, she often insisted that her subjects also not wear fashionable makeup and wigs.[9] She likely wanted to get at the heart of the person and not allow props to overshadow the personality. Because of her talent, her sitters were willing to indulge her wishes as she became known as the most fashionable portrait painter in Europe. Her collection of portraits, which encompassed a wide range of nobility, can be seen as a catalogue of many of the most important people in Europe at the time.

[Jennifer Johnson, *Class of 2006*]

[1] Olga S. Opfell, *Special Visions: Profiles of Fifteen Women Artists from the Renaissance to the Present Day* (North Carolina: McFarland & Company, Inc., 1991), 76.

[2] Ibid., 39-40.

[3] Lionel Strachey, transl., *Memoirs of Madame Vigée Lebrun* (New York: George Braziller, Inc., 1989), 3.

[4] Ibid., 4.

[5] Joseph Baillio, *Elisabeth Louise Vigée Le Brun, 1755-1842* (Seattle: University of Washington Press, 1982), 10.

[6] Ibid., 12-13.

[7] Opfell, 46-47.

[8] Ibid., 42.

[9] Ibid., 41.

27

Francisco José de Goya (Spanish 1746–1828)
El sueño de la razon produce monstruos [The Sleep of Reason Produces
Monsters], Plate 43 from ***Los Caprichos*** [The Caprices], etched 1793–1798,
published 1799, posthumous proof (English title translations kindly
provided by Dr. Louis C. Belby and Dr. Michael Finnemann, Augustana
College Spanish Department, 1999)
Intaglio
Signed b.l. in plate "Goya"
21.6 x 15.1 cm., 8-1/2 x 6" image
30.6 x 20.5 cm., 12 x 8-1/8" sheet
Paul A. Anderson Chair in the Arts Purchase, Augustana College Art
Collection, 2000.21

El sueño de la razon produce monstruos (The Sleep of Reason Produces
Monsters)[1] was first published in 1799 in Francisco Jose de Goya's etching
series entitled *Los Caprichos*. This particular illustration reflects Goya's
unique combination of elements that helped to define Romanticism,
including original symbolism, personal references and exquisite art styling.
This image is actually a self-portrait of the artist, surrounded by many
potentially sinister creatures that threaten to engulf him as he sleeps.[2]
These include bats, owls, a cat and a lynx, representing the potential
evils of the world often associated with superstition and witchcraft. The
accompanying text further explains Goya's message: "When abandoned
by Reason, imagination produces impossible monsters; united with her,
she is the mother of the arts and the origin of their wonders."[3] This
scene illustrates what one might encounter while asleep, when reason has
disappeared and the imagination is allowed free reign. As the identifiable
creatures descend upon the sleeping man, those further in the background
lose substance and detail, becoming faceless, unknown forces. The artist
buries his head in his arms, lost in a world of the subconscious.

"*El sueño*" is one of eighty prints in the *Los Caprichos* series, originally
bound together and published by the artist himself. In an advertisement
for the prints, they were described as "themes from the multitude of
follies and wrong-doings which are common to all societies, of prejudices
and lies countenanced by custom, ignorance or self-interest."[4] Goya
depicted a broader moral message addressing the descent of society and the
atrocities people were capable of committing through fear, ignorance and
irrationality.[5]

The print series was separated into two halves by the central image of the
series, "*El sueño*," at number 43. The first half addressed human foolishness
and the second dealt more with supernatural creatures.[6] This etching
was originally designed to be the first in the collection, but was likely
moved to the middle because of its resemblance to subjects discussed by
Jean Jacques Rousseau, considered a controversial philosopher by religious
leaders of the Spanish Inquisition. As Goya took greater interest in the
struggles of the Spanish peasants, it became difficult to maintain a balance
with his privileged position as court painter for King Carlos IV without

compromising his humanistic principles.[7]

Inspired by the ideals of the Enlightenment yet disillusioned by the reality
surrounding him, Goya's works contained the seeds for the Romantic style.
By delving into the unknown and the irrational in his art while appealing
to the emotions, especially fear, Goya went against what the previous
intellectual and almost stoic Neoclassical movement upheld. Such Romantic
elements that would further inspire twentieth-century Surrealists are
apparent in this etching's themes. Romantic preoccupation with dreams
and the imagination are at the core of this piece. The man sprawled across
his desk, tormented by an assortment of beings, can be read as an early
image for the pervasive Romantic theme of the *suffering* artist.

Goya's personality is also revealed in elements of his *Los Caprichos* prints.
In part, the series was inspired in reaction to his growing sense of isolation,
resulting from an illness that caused him to go deaf.[8] As he grew older,
and perhaps in response to his deafness, Goya created works that became
increasingly dark and pessimistic. It can be speculated that perhaps he
perceived that the monsters in his own world were lurking everywhere,
and he was powerless against them since he was incapable of hearing their
approach.

The print is highly detailed compared to earlier prints of the same genre.
Goya used a modern method of engraving, the *aquatint*, which he combined
with the traditional method of etching. The sublime background was
created by adhering a layer of resin across the plate surface, that was etched
to create a tonal texture, in order to produce a mysterious and atmospheric
effect.[9] This work, with its rich iconography and imaginative expression,
summarily rejected the rigidity of the Neoclassical movement in favor of the
free expression of the modern Romantic.

[John H. Deery, *Class of 2008*]

---

[1] In the Spanish language "sueño" can mean either *sleep* or *dream* and has been interpreted
variously as both for this engraving. However, with these two translations come two very
different interpretations of the title and perhaps the meaning of the piece. For a more in-
depth discussion, see Paul Illie, "Goya's Teratology and the Critique of Reason," *Eighteenth-
Century Studies*, vol. 18, no. 1 (1984): 35-56.

[2] In an earlier drawing for the etching, an inscription reads, "The Author Dreaming. His
only intention is to banish harmful superstition and to perpetuate with this work of fancy the
solid testimony of Truth." Alexander Nehamas, "The Sleep of Reason Produces Monsters,"
Representations, no. 74 (2004): *37*, JSTOR (2005).

[3] R. Stanley Johnson, trans. *Francisco Goya (1746-1828): Los Caprichos* (Chicago: R. S.
Johnson Fine Art, 1992), 32, quoted in Lauren Habenicht, *The Paul A. Anderson Art History
Collection*, ed. Catherine Carter Goebel (Rock Island: Augustana College, 2001), 53.

[4] Quoted in Nehamas, 37.

[5] Ibid., 41.

[6] Ibid., 38.

[7] "A Handbook of the Collection: 'The Sleep of Reason Produces Monsters,'" The Herbert F.
Johnson Museum of Art, Cornell University, 2005, http://www.museum.cornell.edu/HFJ/
handbook/hb128.html (16 February 2005).

[8] Sarah Symmons, *Goya* (London: Phaidon Press Limited, 1998), 153.

[9] Ibid., 164.

28

Artist unknown
John Philip Kemble as Hamlet, related to, or version of 1801 original painting by Sir Thomas Lawrence
(English/British 1769–1830)
Oil on canvas
Unsigned
79.0 x 54.1 cm., 31-1/8 x 21-5/16"
Purchase with Gift of Dr. Karin Youngberg, Augustana College Art Collection, SDC2005.24

William Shakespeare's *Hamlet* is a play in the interrogative mood. It begins with the question "Who's there?" whispered on the battlements of the castle of Elsinore. The precipitating event of the play is the appearance of the highly problematic ghost of Hamlet's dead father, demanding revenge on the brother who murdered him. The play's famous soliloquy, "To be or not to be," asks whether a painful life is worth living. The most powerful scene of the play is set in a graveyard where Hamlet asks the gravedigger, "How long will a man lie in the earth ere he rot?" And yet, Hamlet's final words seem to deny the possibility of definitive answers to life's questions, "The rest is silence. . . ."

But the greatest question of the play is the nature of its enigmatic protagonist. Hamlet is soldier, student, courtier, introvert, lover, intellectual, contemplative, and much more. Over the centuries, the character of Hamlet has come to embody the qualities valued at different cultural moments.

The present image is a version of Sir Thomas Lawrence's *Portrait of J. P. Kemble as Hamlet* (1801). The original painting is one of four massive canvases, each focusing on Kemble in one of his famous tragic roles. Through this group, Lawrence hoped to infuse portraiture with a new dignity and importance by merging the portrait with the widely admired genre of historical painting. In the new form of theatrical portraiture, Lawrence wanted to fuse "polarized classes of pictures in an attempt to create a new, but academically acceptable, form of history painting." [1]

Sir Thomas Lawrence (1769–1830) was a prolific English portrait painter whose work was much sought after by fashionable English society. The son of an innkeeper, Lawrence's professional success was crowned by a knighthood, by his selection as Royal Painter after the death of Sir Joshua Reynolds in 1792 and by his election as President of the Royal Academy in 1820.

Lawrence's ambition to elevate the genre of portraiture by combining it with the dignity and power of theatrical performances was furthered by the stature of his model, the English actor John Philip Kemble (1757–1823). Kemble specialized in serious dramatic roles that required a kind of aristocratic grandeur. He played Shakespeare's Roman hero Coriolanus as well as Hamlet. Kemble's acting style exhibited a notable dignity reinforced by his finely chiseled Roman features. These qualities are well captured in the portrait showing him in the role of Hamlet.

The original of *Kemble as Hamlet* is located in the Tate Gallery in London. A pencil sketch of the painting is held by The National Portrait Gallery. The version of Lawrence's painting in the Augustana College Art Collection is likely of the same period as the original and was probably produced in Lawrence's studio, perhaps by Lawrence himself. The painting was frequently reproduced throughout the nineteenth century as a lithograph and mezzotint. Moreover, the Staffordshire Pottery produced a popular porcelain figure from an engraving of the painting executed by G. Adcock.

The Lawrence painting is identified in the Tate catalogue with *Hamlet* (V. i), the famous Graveyard scene in which Hamlet with his friend Horatio engage in a darkly comic conversation with two grave-diggers. At one point Hamlet picks up a skull which the digger's spade has unearthed and contemplates fragile human mortality which this *memento mori* recalls. But when the grave-digger identifies the skull as belonging to Yorick, a court jester and Hamlet's childhood playfellow, Hamlet throws down the skull in horror and disgust. The scene ends in the violence of a confrontation with Laertes who is bringing his dead sister Ophelia to her grave and who blames Hamlet for her death.

The graveyard scenes subsequently painted by artists like Ferdinand-Victor-Eugène Delacroix in the 1830s contain clear visual elements of this dramatic scene. But in Lawrence's image, only the skull, and the faint outline of grass and gravestone in the front left corner suggest the graveyard. Instead Hamlet stands inert and serene against a largely dark background into which he seems to melt. Even his feathered hat and the crimson lining of his fur-lined cloak are nearly swallowed up by the darkness.

Lawrence's painting is perhaps best seen, not as an evocation of a particular scene, but as a kind of *epitome* in the sense of a summary or abridgement of the entire play. His black clothing denotes both his mourning for his father and his melancholic, introverted disposition present throughout the play. Soldier-like, he wears the sword with which he "crossed" the ghost of his father (I. v) and with which he will face Laertes in his final duel (V. ii). He holds the graveyard skull limply in his left hand (V. i). On a blue satin ribbon he wears an oval jewel containing his beloved father's picture which he used to shame his mother for her infidelity (III. iv). But the focus of the painting is Hamlet's luminescent face, framed from below by an open white collar. His features reflect the serene calm of the last soliloquy, "There is a special providence in the fall of a sparrow. . . the readiness is all" (V. ii). His eyes are turned upward, like some medieval saint at the moment of martyrdom. Behind him, the faint lines of dawn appear against the battlements of Elsinore, suggestive of the first rays of morning that drove his father's ghost back to his grave in Act I, scene i. But Hamlet's expressive eyes are turned resolutely toward the darkness.

Although smaller than Lawrence's original, the painting in the Augustana College Art Collection has considerably more backlight, revealed by the skillful restoration work of James Konrad. This light allows us to see more clearly many of the most significant elements of this fascinating work.

[Karin Youngberg, *Professor of English,*
Conrad Bergendoff Professor of Humanities]

[1] Shearer West, "Thomas Lawrence's 'Half-History' Portraits and the Politics of Theatre," *Art History* 14 (1991): 225–49.

103

29

Artist unknown
Burial of Atala, related to, or version of 1808 original painting by Anne-Louis Girodet de Roussy-Trioson (French 1767–1824)
Oil on canvas
Unsigned
48.9 x 66.1 cm., 19-1/4 x 26"
Augustana College Art Collection Purchase with Gift of Adam J. DeSimone and David A. DeSimone, with Framing Assistance from Lisa M. Jacobson, SDC2005.18

Originally a pupil of the Neoclassicist and Revolutionary painter Jacques Louis David, Anne-Louis Girodet de Roucy-Trioson diverged early and dramatically from the work and politics of his mentor.[1] This work is an especially interesting transitional piece. We can still see some striking links to David's Neoclassicism in the anatomically detailed and idealized vision of the human body, the sense of wet drapery in the elegant lines of the figures' "poor" clothing, and the contemplative facial expressions of the dead girl and even of her bereft lover. In other ways this painting appears to go in an entirely new direction.

Artistically innovative but politically conservative, Girodet was attracted by the emotional neo-Catholicism of early Romantic writers like François-René de Chateaubriand. While previous paintings, notably his 1806 *Flood*, suggest links to Chateaubriand by their extravagant "natural" settings and emotionally charged subject matter,[2] this painting is an explicit reference to one of Chateaubriand's most famous works, his novella *Atala*. Set in a still appealingly wild North America and peopled with Christianized Native Americans who become star-crossed lovers, *Atala* had all the elements that would seize the imagination of that first generation of Romantics: an exotic setting and cast of characters, an idealized vision of "primitive" humanity, and a tragic love story laced with religious mysticism.

Girodet's painting is a somewhat free interpretation of one of the closing scenes of the novella: the burial of the heroine, Atala, who has committed suicide rather than give in to her passion for the young hero, and has learned too late from the hermit priest that the vow of chastity she took on her mother's deathbed was not required of her by God. Although Chateaubriand describes other scenes from Atala's final hours in great detail, he tells us of her burial only that he and the hermit "carried the beautiful one to her earthen bed."[3] Girodet's envisioning of the scene, in which the young Chactas is seen desperately clutching Atala's legs rather than actually

assisting in the burial, is certainly true to the spirit of the character, who is portrayed throughout the tale as more passionate than functional. Girodet's palette would also seem to be evocative of the tonality and themes of Chateaubriand's prose: the hermit, who will ultimately articulate the gentle mystical Catholicism that is the "lesson" of the story,[4] is in earth-tones almost indistinguishable from the environment to which he is organically connected, while the two tragically misguided young people are in colors that contrast with their surroundings: the fiercely chaste heroine in a ghostly silvery white (mirroring the color of the spade that has dug her grave), the passionate young hero in a red echoed only by some flowers in the distance. The cross held by the dead heroine, described as "ebony" in Chateaubriand's story,[5] appears here in earth-tones, and is echoed by the cross on the distant hillside as well as by the cross-shaped handle of the spade in the foreground, underlining both the overriding Christian message of the text and the fact that the heroine is (improbably) being accorded a Christian burial, despite her suicide, through the efforts of the sensitive hermit.

 The inscription on the cave wall, "J'ai passé comme LA FLEUR! J'ai séché comme L'HERBE des champs" ("I have passed away like a flower; I am withered as the grass of the fields.")[6] is taken directly from Chateaubriand's novella, although the emphasis (capitalization and punctuation) was added by Girodet. Chateaubriand tells us that this is one of the "verses of an ancient poet named Job"[6] chanted by the old priest as he prepares the body for burial. This verse is not to be found in the book of Job in any form recognizably close to this, but the second of the two examples cited by Chateaubriand is an exact quote: "Wherefore is light given to him that is in misery, and life unto the bitter in soul?"[7] Yet it is the slightly fictionalized Biblical "verse," more impressionistic and personal, that Girodet chose for the inscription to his painting, which again suggests a deep underlying affinity for the kind of highly individualistic and imaginative Christianity offered by Chateaubriand.

[Taddy R. Kalas, *Associate Professor of French*]

[1] Frederick Antal, *Classicism and Romanticism* (New York: Harper & Row, 1973), 19.

[2] Ibid., 22.

[3] François-René de Chateaubriand, *Atala/René*, trans. Irving Putter, (Berkeley: University of California Press, 1980), 74.

[4] "God will forgive you because of your heart's innocence. … men's bodies and hearts hold no mystery for God; He will judge you for your intention, which was pure.…" (Ibid., 64).

[5] Ibid., 72.

[6] Ibid., 73.

[7] Ibid., 73; Job 3:20.

30A

Attributed to John Constable (English/British 1776–1837) [C. Goebel]
Study for **Landscape: Boys Fishing**, related to 1813 painting
Oil on canvas
Unsigned
44.7 x 63.6 cm., 17-5/8 x 25-1/16"
Lent Courtesy of Private Collection

30B

See reproduction, not in exhibition
John Constable (English/British 1776–1837)
Landscape: Boys Fishing, now also titled **A Lock on the Stour**, 1813
Oil on canvas
Approximately 101.6 x 125.8 cm., 40 x 49-1/2"
National Trust, Fairhaven Collection, Anglesey Abbey, UK © National Trust
Picture Library

Note: some scholars have the original title as **Landscape: Boys fishing**.

30C

Engraved by David Lucas (1802–1881) after John Constable (English/British
1776–1837)
A Lock on the Stour, Suffolk, or, **A Lock on the Stour, County of Suffolk**
(**Landscape: Boys Fishing**) from Part IV of **English Landscape Scenery**, 1831
Mezzotint
Signed in printed text below image b.r. "Engraved by David Lucas" and b.l.
"Painted by John Constable R.A."
14.2 x 17.4 cm., 5-9/16 x 6-7/8" image sight
Lent Courtesy of Private Collection

English Romantic painter, John Constable noted that: "The sky is the source
of light in nature, and governs everything: even our common observations
on the weather of every day are altogether suggested by it."[1] He masterfully
combined objective scientific analysis with subjective emotional response
in order to arrive at a highly personal style, at once poetic and realistic. His
approach echoed French novelist François-René de Chateaubriand's 1795
statement that "...landscape should be *drawn* from the *nude* if one wants to
give it resemblance, in order to reveal, so to speak, the muscles, bones and
limbs. Studies made indoors, copies after copies, will never replace work after
nature."[2]

In this exhibition, we have the rare opportunity to view an unsigned oil sketch,
presumably painted directly from nature (catalogue 30A) and attributed to
John Constable. It is most likely a study created sometime before 1813 for
Landscape: Boys Fishing (catalogue 30B), a large oil painting exhibited in that
year at the Royal Academy.[3] In a contemporary review, critic Robert Hunt
described this painting as "silvery, sparkling, and true to the grayish-green
colouring of our English summer landscapes."[4]

The large oil was again exhibited in the following year at the British Institution,
this time with the title, *Landscape; A Lock on the Stour*. Following this
exhibition, its consequent sale "to a stranger," the Bond Street bookseller
John Carpenter for twenty guineas (and "books beyond that sum,") signaled a
promising art career for Constable. The artist's friend, Dr. John Fisher wrote
him of its perceived success: "[I] heard your great picture spoken of here by
no inferior judge as one of the best in the [R.A.] exhibition....I like only one
better & that is...the Frost of [Joseph Mallord] Turner. But you need not repine
at this decision of mine; you are a great man like Bounaparte [sic] & only are
beaten by a frost [referring to Napoleon's retreat from Moscow in the winter of
1812-13]."[5]

The largest surviving work that Constable had painted up to this time, the
scene places the viewer looking upstream toward the reach of the Stour River

between Bridge Cottage and Flatford Lock. The vantage point is from the
south bank, looking toward the footbridge in the distance. In addition to the
visible cumulus clouds, there must be further ones to the left which create the
foreground light and shadow.[6] The upper gates of the lock are detailed at right
and the whole composition is balanced with trees framing both sides. The
focal point is the interaction of the two boys fishing near the center.

Landscape: Boys Fishing (catalogue 30B), is now at Anglesey Abbey, the
Fairhaven Collection (The National Trust, Great Britain). For over twenty
years, however, scholars have debated its identity as the original celebrated
painting. Michael Rosenthal described this version in 1983 as "a bad painting,
where obtrusively detailed work clashes with areas of matt green." Yet he felt
that these discrepancies in quality were based in the painting's poor condition
and subsequent deficient restoration. He concluded, particularly since
Constable was not popular at this time and no one else was painting along
the Stour, that the painting is probably genuine since, if not by this artist, one
would need to make a strong argument for a *pasticheur* (imitator).[7]

The 1991 Tate Gallery catalogue further suggested that the painting's
appearance is currently "distorted by discoloured varnish, [and] by thin,
smeary overpainting" and proposed that careful restoration would likely
"return it to its original and undoubtedly more lively appearance."[8] However,
in 1996, Graham Reynolds questioned its authenticity because the "colouring
and handling" are "totally discordant" in comparison to genuine works by
the artist. He doubted the Tate conservation theory as it would be "extremely
unusual" for one of Constable's paintings to have "technical deficiencies" that
would require such immense conservation, but acknowledged that there may
indeed still be the "original painting concealed underneath the damage and
repaint."[9]

Attribution and ultimate authentication of works of art generally involve a
long, complex and at times, contradictory process. If indeed the oil sketch
(catalogue 30A) is the preliminary study for this painting, it would answer
a number of unresolved art historical questions concerning the Fairhaven
Collection piece (catalogue 30B) as well as the mezzotint reproduction of the
scene, published eighteen years later in 1831 as *A Lock on the Stour, County
of Suffolk* (*Landscape: Boys Fishing*) by David Lucas in Part IV of his *English
Landscape Scenery* (catalogue 30C). It would likely also raise new questions.

The oil study (catalogue 30A) exhibited here for the first time, has not
been previously discussed by Constable scholars. Yet, it has the striking
characteristics of Constable's best *plein-air* sketches. Today, most connoisseurs
prefer his unfinished studies to his more self-conscious exhibition pieces.
Rosenthal perceived that the discrepancies between the large *finished* oil and
the established small open air sketches might be explained by Constable's
difficulty in transferring studies to finished works. He proposed that this oil is
likely Constable's weak translation in expanded scale, because details within it
correspond to preliminary drawings. It would be instructive to discuss these
small sketches in order to surmise the place of this study (catalogue 30A).

Fleming-Williams published two pencil drawings which were likely used
in preparation for the finished work. In comparing these to the study on
exhibition, the same probing approach is demonstrated, and other than the
difference in medium, they appear to belong to the same artistic hand. One
depicts the lock gates at right and the other, the trees at left. The author
concluded that based on the evidence, there seem to be no oil sketches "painted
direct from the motif."[10] However, the possibility exists that the *missing link*
has resurfaced in this study.

Several scholars trace the finished oil of *Landscape: Boys Fishing* to tiny oil
sketches with a similar composition; only the boys are positioned in the
foreground leaning over the lock gates, rather than at the center.[11] This
oil study is thus the only one that connects the finished oil's main figural
relationships with a sketch. It also relates to the smaller sketches in its general
composition and inclusion of two boys fishing. Also, the red shirt on the left
figure in the study more closely resembles the figures in a smaller sketch than
those in the finished painting. The style of constructing the individual figures
is also close between the small sketches and this oil study.

Further insight might be gained through comparing this study (catalogue 30A),
with the finished oil (catalogue 30B) as well as the mezzotint (catalogue 30C).
The mezzotint project was initiated by Constable in 1829 in order to publish a
selection of his paintings and oil sketches as a cohesive group of prints entitled

30A

English Landscape Scenery. He already had established a tendency to rework paintings, and his mezzotints often suffered the same fate. The prints also tended to exhibit richer chiaroscuro and darker, more turbulent skies than the oil paintings on which they were based, perhaps in response to his wife's death the year before in 1828, producing a more dramatic "depressive and melancholic view" than the more "serene, noontime, summer's day" of the originals.[12]

Details, such as the figure in the distant boat, relate between the mezzotint and the study but do not appear in the *finished* oil. Yet the study's two figures crossing the footbridge are not present in either the finished work or the mezzotint, nor are the study's ten birds flying directly over the cottage. The two main characters in the middle ground are very close in size and positioning between the three, however the clothing is slightly altered between study and finished work, and the right figure's hat in the study seems to be missing in both the mezzotint and large oil.

Such subtle changes are typical as artists work through sketches and studies toward a completed painting, and in this case, perhaps even further toward a later reproduction. The more dramatic color and sky of the study might even reflect the finished oil beneath the over-painting (which, due to its fragile nature, has not yet been restored). Perhaps an alternate theory to account for the more robust sky could be the inference that here, as in the instance of a mezzotint after his 1812 oil sketch *Summer Morning*, Constable actually made a later sketch, based on an earlier painting, but far more dramatic in effect. As in this case, the overall composition remains very close, but the mood and details were revised.

Possibly the most persuasive element toward the oil sketch's (catalogue 30A) attribution can be found in the sky, as earlier discussed, the hallmark of Constable's oeuvre. Although the mezzotint and *finished work* have the same basic cloud formations, they lack the immediate vibrancy and emotional depth of *this* sky, clearly studied on the spot. By the time it was reinterpreted into the larger painting and once again, through the mezzotint, the dramatic sweep was all but lost. Or, if this sketch is indeed a later interpretation of his earlier exhibited oil, in preparation for a mezzotint, it perhaps reflects greater sophistication in his depictions of such cloud banks.

The study's clouds are typical of Constable's sketches, as are the red under-painting, brushstrokes to indicate trees and foliage as well as the figural compositions. The conservator who examined the oil sketch's canvas, paint and stretchers has suggested it dates, based on scientific evidence, to the very early nineteenth century.[13] An eminent Constable scholar, upon studying photographs of the piece, indicated that his initial impression was that it does indeed have the right *feel*, and we should proceed further with the investigation. At this point, although much more investigation remains, it seems reasonable to conclude that this study is most likely the *missing link* between the small sketches and the finished work and reproductive mezzotint of *Landscape: Boys Fishing.*

Perhaps one of the most intriguing aspects of this critical inquiry is that like Constable, who did his utmost to blend art and science as well as direct observation with poetic interpretation, scholars use much the same measures for authentication. There is the science of analyzing data, conducting chemical analysis, researching provenance;[14] and yet also relevant are the art historian's trained eye and *feel* for the painting, which invite analytical and at the same time instinctual responses to the piece. Thus far, a consensus is building to support the conclusion that this is indeed an original Constable oil sketch.

Constable believed such works portrayed profound *moral* landscapes, a notion that can be traced to the writings of French philosopher, Jean-Jacques Rousseau. England provided a relaxed religious hierarchy that more easily accepted such manifestations. Within this Romantic philosophy, God was seen as Creator of the Universe, and thus the forms found in nature were examples of His handiwork. Through the use of imagination and the study of nature, artists could better understand the conception of their own duality, providing greater insight into a superior spirituality through communication with the Divine.

Constable's work also mirrors William Wordsworth's peaceful literary reflections that, "Nature never did betray! The heart that loved her."[15] Constable remained throughout his life in England, explaining his narrow geographic scope: "Still I should paint my own places best; painting is with me but another word for feeling, and I associate 'my careless boyhood' with all that

lies on the banks of the Stour [River]; those scenes made me a painter, and I am grateful."[16]

His biographer, C. R. Leslie related how: "I have seen him admire a fine tree with an ecstasy of delight like that with which he would catch up a beautiful child in his arms."[17] Constable even referred to his studies of trees as *portraits* and described his inexhaustible curiosity toward nature thusly: "The world is wide; no two days are alike since the creation of the world; and the genuine productions of art, like those of nature, are all distinct from one another."[18] Such careful and respectful observation reflected his belief in God's order and the splendor of all of His creations.

Clouds particularly captivated him as he went *skying*, reflecting a growing contemporary interest. In fact, meteorologist Luke Howard published the first modern nomenclature for cloud types in 1820 in his *Climate of London*. In his writings, however, Constable never used such scientific terminology, describing them in more poetic fashion, as in the case of an 1822 cloud study under which he recorded poetic verse by Robert Bloomfield: "...Scatter'd immensely wide from east to west, The beauteous semblance of a flock at rest. These to the raptured mind, aloud proclaim, Their mighty shepherd's everlasting name."[19]

Within this oil study (catalogue 30A), we can sense the hand of the artist who stated in his discourses: "...I was born to paint a happier land, my dear old England; and when I cease to love her, may I, as Wordsworth says 'never more hear, Her green leaves rustle, or her torrents roar!'"[20] Despite such dedication to his own country, it was France that truly built upon Constable's theories. Romantic painter Théodore Géricault advised his colleague, Eugène Delacroix, to steep himself in Constable, and such fresh observations ultimately led to Impressionism (catalogue 42). Yet Constable's spiritual side also reached into the future, with artists like Vincent Van Gogh who felt that "true painters are guided by that conscience which is called sentiment, their soul."[21] So many subsequent art schools seem like modern echoes of the duality of his works. Yet perhaps it was only Constable who could astutely blend reality and scientific curiosity with spirituality and poetry in order to create a highly individual, lyrical naturalism.

[Catherine Carter Goebel, *Professor of Art History, Paul A. Anderson Chair in the Arts*]

[1] C. R. Leslie, *Memoirs of the Life of John Constable* (Ithaca: Cornell University Press, 1980), 85.

[2] Hugh Honour, *Romanticism* (New York: Harper & Row, 1979), 63.

[3] Leslie Parris and Ian Fleming-Williams, *Constable* (London: Tate Gallery, 1991), 131.

[4] Ibid., 132.

[5] Graham Reynolds, *The Early Paintings and Drawings of John Constable*, text volume (New Haven and London: Yale University Press, 1996), 179.

[6] John E. Thornes, *John Constable's Skies* (Birmingham: The University of Birmingham Press, 1999), 105.

[7] Michael E. Rosenthal, *Constable: The Painter and his Landscape* (New Haven and London: Yale University Press, 1983), 63.

[8] Parris and Fleming-Williams, 132.

[9] Reynolds, *Early Paintings and Drawings*, 80.

[10] Ian Fleming-Williams, *Constable and His Drawings* (London: Phillip Wilson Publishers Ltd., 1990), 191-2.

[11] Parris and Fleming-Williams, 130-32.

[12] Graham Reynolds, *Constable: The Natural Painter* (New York: Schocken, 1965), 115.

[13] I am indebted to James Konrad, Adjunct Assistant Professor of Art, for his sensitive conservation of this piece and his considered opinion as to its probable authenticity.

[14] Art dealer Ron Povlich has kindly provided provenance that traces this study to an estate near Henry Ford's home in prominent Grosse Point Farms, Michigan, perhaps even belonging to a Ford relative.

[15] Karl Kroeber, *Romantic Landscape Vision: Constable and Wordsworth* (Madison: University of Wisconsin Press, 1975), 41.

[16] Leslie, 86.

[17] Ibid., 282.

[18] Ibid., 273.

[19] Ibid.

[20] Ibid., 101.

[21] Peacock, 50.

30B

A LOCK ON THE STOUR, SUFFOLK.

30C

31

John James Audubon (b. Saint-Dominique, now Haiti, American 1785–1851)
Whippoorwill, 1830
Hand-colored engraving, Havell edition, number 17, plate 82
Signed in printed text b.l. below image "Drawn from Nature and Published by John J. Audubon F.R.S. F.L.S. & c." and b.r. "Engraved. Printed & Colored by R. Havell Jun.1ˢᵗ 1830."
Inscribed b.c. in printed text below image "Whip-poor-will Male 1.F.2.3./ *quercus tinctoria*/ Vulgo Black Oak" and b.r. "*Caprimulgus vociferous.*"
66.4 x 53.0 cm., 26-1/4 x 20-1/8" image
83.5 x 61.7 cm., 32-7/8 x 24-5/16" sheet
Gift of Audubon Elementary School, Rock Island-Milan School District Number 41, Augustana College Art Collection, 96.24

Modern artist Pablo Picasso once stated, "Art is a lie that tells us the truth." In the artwork of John James Audubon (1785-1851), the lie is that these birds look lively and are situated in their natural habitat. In most instances, however, they were actually drawn after they were already dead. Yet, there is a lot of *truth* in Audubon's works, such as the depiction of their natural environment, plumage and eating habits.

Even as a child, Audubon was interested in wildlife, constantly sketching birds. When he was dissatisfied with a drawing, he destroyed it, even if it was admired by friends and family.[1] In 1802, he was sent to study in the studio of the great Neoclassicist, Jacques Louis David, the principal artist during the French Revolutionary period. Audubon did not stay long, however, preferring to draw from nature rather than classical sculptures.[2] He hunted, studied and continued depicting birds throughout his youth and early adulthood. Eventually, he moved to Kentucky to start a trading store. His business failed, likely due to a general financial recession at the time and perhaps because he was distracted from maintaining a store by his greater concern for observing and drawing birds.[3] With few financial options, Audubon ventured out on a journey that would formally begin his artistic career, a trip that would take him across the nation to find and record the birds of America. In 1826, six years after he began, he went to England bringing with him the drawings he had amassed, which represented only about half of the final project. They were almost immediately a complete success.[4]

Audubon was actually a scientist at heart. He took on the enormous project of not only drawing all the birds of North America, but also of understanding and depicting their habitat, making countless notes to supplement his pictures. His artwork further advanced science into the realm of art, utilizing the natural ability of one field to compliment and further inform the other. Audubon was obsessed with making sure the birds he portrayed were exact replicas of their natural forms.

He grew up hunting and transformed this hobby into scientific research toward his sketches, using recently deceased birds as models for his drawings. He refused to use stuffed specimens for representation in his artwork and instead utilized his love for hunting by killing many birds in order to use them as models to correctly capture the details of various species. So as to more scientifically record each type, he used both male and female examples in every drawing. He also made each bird life-size which,

besides the incredible detail within the pages, was a major contributing factor toward the success of *The Birds of America*.[5]

Audubon's artwork can be characterized in at least two different ways. With his obvious interest in science and straightforward portrayals of real creatures, his work can be described as *Realism*. However, his love for nature shines throughout every work—a trait for which the *Romantics* were noted. His interest in a complete collection, toward better analysis and understanding, relates to Enlightenment ideals on knowledge and learning, as in the famous eighteenth-century *Encyclopédie* (catalogue 15A and 15B). Audubon's works have a certain originality to them. They have elements of simplicity and balance which seem to link *Neoclassicism* and *Modernism*, as if foreshadowing the new aesthetic achieved later in the nineteenth century through the influence of Japanese prints.

Whippoorwill was drawn in 1830. It is a hand-colored engraving, much like the works of *Romantic* artist, William Blake. Through this method, Audubon linked mass-production through printing from a copper plate, with individuality by coloring each image by hand in watercolor and colored inks. For this reason, each version printed of *Whippoorwill* is really a one-of-a-kind work of art. Audubon's art was scientifically researched as he strove to make all of the birds he painted look life-like and true to nature.

This particular print showcases three whippoorwills on the hunt, their bodies illustrated from three different angles in order to fully define the species. The birds are not drawn with a sketchy technique, but are depicted using full strokes. The sensitive use of color furthers the feeling of realism throughout the work. Audubon even added a detailed sketch of a whippoorwill's foot, offering further scientific analysis for the viewer. Some of the colorings for the whippoorwills correspond with those within the tree branch on which two of them are perched. This may be a coincidence, but it is more interesting to think that Audubon reinforced the natural camouflage within the birds' feathers. Since Audubon was a scientist at heart, he drew these birds in the midst of their natural vegetation and also illustrated what they ate. *Whippoorwill* is one of 435 prints in his massive collection known as *The Birds of America*, which aimed at presenting an encyclopedic collection of native birds.

Audubon enjoyed observing birds and capturing their beauty while revealing their diversity to the world. He cared deeply about his subject matter and his mission to record the various species and this is evident in this particular work. While he truly enjoyed hunting, he was also passionate about preserving wildlife and the environment. This goal came to fruition in his prints, where he could effectively combine science with reverence for the beauty of nature. *Birds of America* was one of the most influential bodies of art in the nineteenth century and reflects the ardent enthusiasm of a pioneering naturalist.

[Kady Fairfield, *Class of 2008*]

[1] Francis Hobart Herrick, *Audubon the Naturalist: A History of His Life and Time*, 5th ed. (New York: D. Appleton-Century Country, 1938), 173.

[2] John Chancellor, *Audubon* (New York: The Viking Press, 1978), 30.

[3] Ibid., 86.

[4] "John James Audubon, 1785-1851: The American Woodsman: Our Namesake and Inspiration," Audubon, 2001, http://www.audubon.org/nas/jja.html (1 February 2005).

[5] Chancellor, 7-8.

PLATE 82

Whip-poor-will. Male 1.2.3.3.
Female 2.2.3.3.
Quercus tinctoria.
Vulgo-Black Oak.

Caprimulgus vociferus

Drawn from Nature and Published by John J. Audubon. F.R.S. F.L.S. &c.

Engraved, Printed & Coloured by R. Havell Jun.ʳ 1830.

32

Artist unknown
Miniature Portrait of Young Girl, attributed to ca. early 19th century
Watercolor on ivory
Unsigned
8.0 x 6.5 cm., 3-1/8 x 2-1/2"
Paul A. Anderson Chair in the Arts Purchase, Augustana College Art
Collection, 2000.4

The nineteenth-century American *Miniature Portrait of Young Girl* is heir
to a long tradition. Miniatures grew from earlier forms of art, such as
illuminated medieval religious manuscripts. The word "miniature" derives
from *minimum*, the Latin name for the vibrant red lead ink used in such
manuscripts. Illuminated manuscripts often included a small painting
showing the person who had financed the manuscript's reproduction, in
prayer or handing the sacred text to a saint. Such a portrait acknowledged
the patron's generosity as well as offered an image of religious devotion and
perhaps evidence of salvation via a good work.

A second type of early influence—ancient portrait medallions, coins,
and cameos—suggests a more public emphasis. Painted on vellum, early
miniatures portrayed the kings, queens, and nobles in European courts. In
England, for example, Henry VIII was painted in miniature in 1525-27, with
court artists often emphasizing royalty's finery and accoutrements of power.[1]
These miniatures likely reinforced the viewers' sense of elite status and fealty
to the ruler. When alternative means, such as wealth, provided social status,
people other than nobles became appropriate subjects for portraits.

Miniatures came to the American colonies from Britain in the 1700s. At
first those with political prominence were painted, such as the Revolutionary
War heroes and early presidents. Upper and middle-class Americans
became enamored with miniatures, commissioning them for life's signal
moments, including births, engagements, marriages, and deaths.

Small enough to be carried or worn and housed in finely crafted cases,
lockets, or brooches, miniatures served as private reminders of loved ones.
Their elaborate settings emphasized the high regard in which the person
portrayed was held. An 1803 locket housing a miniature of Benjamin
Frederick Augustus Dashiell features a portrait on a thin oval of ivory,
protected by a cover glass set in a gold-over-copper bezel. The locket's back
displays a hair ornament decorated with delicate, gracefully curved gold
wire and small pearls, mounted on opal glass and set off against a spiral
comprised of two nesting magenta-colored foil ovals.[2] The hair ornament
common to miniatures underscores their intimate nature. Often the hair
of the person portrayed was in a locket's back, displayed under glass and
overlaid with the beloved's initials in gold filigree or pearls. Miniatures
memorializing the deceased often included locks of hair, symbolizing the
persistence of affection beyond the grave.

The affection meant to be conveyed by a miniature was echoed in the craft
required to create one. Miniature painting was difficult, requiring sharply
pointed brushes, fine scribing tools, and reducing and magnifying glasses.
What came to be the preferred medium, ivory, created its own challenges.
Thin translucent sections of ivory allowed a painter to achieve subtle tonal
graduations that gave skin a glow of inner light and clothing an elegant
sheen. But ivory is a difficult surface on which to paint. It had to be readied
with abrasives that removed organic oils, and then bleached and smoothed.
Paints too needed special preparation. Gum arabic, alum, and even sugar
candy were added. Errors were difficult to correct, and artists created their
effects by sgrafitto, laying down layers of paint and carefully scratching and
cross-hatching the surface to achieve their effects, and by delicate stippling
to create shadows and a sense of form.

The *Miniature of a Young Girl* was painted by an unknown American artist,
most likely self taught, given the uneven technique. There is evidence of

painterly skill: the girl's tousled hair is handled with finesse, set down in fine
lines creating feathered locks that fall with a naturalness over the forehead.
Refined brushwork creates the delicately blended hues of the girl's face. But
there is awkwardness in the girl's hands, and neither the flowers nor clothing
are represented with equivalent vividness.

The *Portrait* comes to us without documentation to help date it. The overall
tenor of the *Portrait*, close to what we would term *cute*, suggests it was
painted in the first half of the nineteenth century, a period when family and
intimate relations were seen as fit subjects for art and when children were
idealized for an innocence seen as emblematic of divine goodness.[3] The
child's sea-green dress in the classically inspired Empire-style suggests
the portrait is from about 1800-1820.[4] However the style also appears in
later miniatures, such as Clarissa Peters' *Child in a Pink Dress*, painted in
the 1850s, shortly before miniatures fell out of favor with the rise of the
daguerreotype, an early version of photography. Probably the strongest
evidence is the child's short hair style, which was popular for a brief period
in the 1820s.[5]

Does the miniature memorialize a dead child? Nineteenth-century
iconography of death typically shows flowers with closed blooms. The
flowers in the girl's hands are not skillfully rendered, but appear to be sweet
pea blooms, which lack prominent blossoms. In the nineteenth-century
"language of flowers," sweet peas were associated with "departure." But
other pea blossoms were associated with the "everlasting, an appointed
meeting, and lasting pleasure."[6] If the flowers have a language, they offer us
contradictory advice. Whatever the flowers are, they offer equally puzzling
possibilities. Other evidence is ambiguous as well. The powder-blue and
white sky is not naturalistically portrayed, casting a mild sense of unreality,
appropriate for a child's innocence and perhaps intended to evoke the
ethereal realms of heaven. But such backgrounds are common in other
miniatures as well, including those not painted to memorialize the deceased.

Whatever its intent, the portrait conveys strong affection for the child.
The miniature's size and rectangular shape suggest that it was not carried
or worn, but displayed. Perhaps the portrait was more akin to a studio
photograph, meant, of course, to be a likeness, but also to capture something
particular about the child. Today nearly 180 years later, it is hard not to
be intrigued by the image, to wonder who the child was and who loved
her enough to have her painted. Viewing the *Girl*, we experience neither
awe of God or fear for our soul, as the viewer of a medieval manuscript's
portrait might have, nor identification with those with hereditary power,
as Tudor court members likely did. Rather we make a connection with
the past via sympathetic affection. And yet, this sentimental miniature
is not so different from the devotional image of medieval manuscripts.
Both are aware of the passing of time and the presence of death. Behind
the sentimental affection evoked by the *Miniature Portrait of a Young Girl*
resides an awareness of old enemies—time's inevitable passing and a fear of
death—and an old strategy of endurance—the attempt to immortalize what
we love in art.

[Michael Nolan, *Director of Assessment
and Grants Officer*]

[1] Robin Bolton Smith and Dale T. Johnson, "The Miniature in America," *Antiques* vol. 138, (1990): 1043.

[2] Robin Jaffee Frank, *Love and Loss; American Portrait and Mourning Miniatures* (New Haven and London: Yale University Press, 2000), 8-9.

[3] See, for example, Jane Tompkins, *Sensational Designs; The Cultural Work of American Fiction, 1790-1860* (New York: Oxford University Press, 1985), 128-132.

[4] Blanche Payne, *History of Costume, From the Ancient Egyptians to the Twentieth Century* (New York: Harper & Row, Publishers, 1965), 476-483.

[5] Frank, 200.

[6] 1882 "Cyclopedia of Commercial and Social Information and Treasury of Useful and Entertaining Knowledge on Art, Science, Pastimes, Belles-lettres, and Many Other Subjects of Interest in the American Home Circle", http://www.apocalypse.org/pub/u/hilda/flang.html.

33A

Sir David Wilkie (Scottish/British 1785–1841)
Study for the Highlander in **General Sir David Baird Discovering the Body of the Sultaun Tippoo Sahib after having Captured Seringapatam, on the 4th May, 1799**, ca. 1835–1838
Graphite and watercolor
Unsigned
18.0 x 12.5 cm., 7-1/16 x 5" image
25.3 x 19.9 cm., 9-15/16 x 7-13/16" sheet
Lent Courtesy of Dr. Thomas B. Brumbaugh Art History Collection

33B

See reproduction, not in exhibition
Sir David Wilkie (Scottish/British 1785–1841)
General Sir David Baird Discovering the Body of the Sultaun Tippoo Sahib after having Captured Seringapatam, on the 4th May, 1799, 1839
Oil on canvas
348.5 x 267.9 cm.
National Gallery of Scotland, Edinburgh, © National Gallery of Scotland

The great Scottish painter, David Wilkie (1785–1841), first studied under John Graham in Edinburgh and later trained at the Royal Academy, elected a full academician in 1811.[1] Wilkie primarily created genre paintings, which established his reputation, often using his own family members and neighbors as models.[2] *The Chelsea Pensioners* (1822) was his most famous and successful painting of this type. It attracted such enthusiastic crowds when it was exhibited at the Royal Academy that it was necessary, for the first time, to erect barriers to protect the piece from its admirers.[3]

Such genre subjects reflect the British love for storytelling and character sketches that Wilkie effectively bridged from William Hogarth's eighteenth-century morality scenes (catalogue 14) to William Powell Frith's later Victorian pieces (catalogue 50). Wilkie also produced a large number of history paintings. These works, considered by academics to be more elevated in stature than genre, probably better reveal his Romantic temperament. In such works, he employed rich color and drama, often reflecting his strong interest in exotic lands—particularly evident in the subject of one of his last great history paintings, *Sir David Baird Discovering the Body of Sultaun Tippoo Saib* (1839),[4] for which this drawing is a study.[5]

The rising interest in exotic people and places greatly affected Romantic artists like Wilkie. The large painting was commissioned in 1834 by Baird's widow to commemorate her husband's leadership in defeating the "last independent sultan of Mysore…[marking] the final consolidation of British rule in India."[6] In the overall composition, Baird is presented in a dramatic pose as he looks down upon his defeated enemy. He stands upon the roof of the cell in which he had been imprisoned by Tippoo's father and to his right, appears his fellow officer, Colonel Wellesley, the future celebrated hero, the Duke of Wellington.[7]

The painting is characterized by beautiful brushstrokes based on Wilkie's study of the Old Masters in Italy and Spain, as well as the rich chiaroscuro effects of Dutch Baroque master, Rembrandt Van Rijn. The composition recalls the traditional Christian depiction of the *Raising of Lazarus*.[8] Dramatic illumination against the night, the baroque device of *tenebrism*, is achieved through the inclusion of the lantern on the left and the torch on the right, held by the Scottish soldier for which this particular piece is a study. The subtle effects of such lighting were explored in the drawing before Wilkie executed the finished painting.

This exquisite study, made of graphite and watercolor, is a portrait of the face of the Scottish torchbearer. It is mostly sketched in black, but enriched by the subtle hint of red outlining the eyes, nose, mouth and jaw in order to emphasize his facial features. The angle of the man's head adds dimension to the piece in that he looks as if he is coming out at the viewer and at the same time looking down at the defeated enemy.

In a letter to Lady Baird, Wilkie described this character as "the Highlander stooping with the torch."[9] And when the painting was exhibited at the Royal Academy in 1839, the catalogue further defined the importance of this figure in the overall composition: "…in front, on the General's left hand, bending forward with a torch is a Highlander, a McLeod of the old 71st [the Highland Light Infantry] who, with his comrades on leaving the trenches, were reminded by the General of the old scores they had now to settle for the severe imprisonment they had formerly endured as captives at Seringapatam."[10]

The great care that Wilkie took in capturing the personality and physical appearance of his subject is sensitively rendered in this drawing. Examining such sketches reveals the artist's steps and invites the viewer to make connections between the study and the final piece, much like fitting the pieces of a puzzle together. In this manner, drawings help viewers see the breakdown of an artist's thought process as well as the time and planning that went into each work of art. As one critic summarized the general critical reception at the time: "…in this picture, so deficient as a whole, [there] are beautiful parts,"[11] as evidenced in this delicate and perceptive study.

Wilkie went to great pains to effectively portray the painting scene—even constructing a model in order to scientifically capture the appropriate effects of light and shadow. His preparatory sketches for the painting have been evaluated as his most "…Rembrandtesque in their nervous penmanship and somberly washed backgrounds…the most magnificent of all his drawings."[12] Wilkie himself described the painstaking process to Lady Baird in 1834: "The drawings I am proceeding with, trying changes and rearrangements in the details of the group, or, what is more the case, trying to give form and shape to what in the first sketch was vague and confused."[13]

Wilkie, along with landscape painters, John Constable and Joseph Mallord Turner, was estimated in his own time as one of the *three* greatest Romantic British artists of the first half of the nineteenth century. He was a close friend to Constable (catalogue 30) and a more distant acquaintance and competitor of Turner. His own short life likely best exemplifies Romantic myth—dying young on his return from the Middle Eastern journey on which he embarked the year after exhibiting this painting.

His consequent burial at sea was commemorated by Turner in his famous painting, *Peace—Burial at Sea* (1832), a fitting and final tribute to the artist. Turner stated that he aimed to show the scene "…as it must have appeared off the coast,"[14] engulfed in atmosphere, the light falling on the coffin about to be lowered into the sea. When criticized for the deep symbolic black of the ship's sails, Turner aptly responded, in true Romantic fashion, in regard to the great artistic and personal loss that he felt with Wilkie's death, "I only wish I had any colour to make them blacker."[15]

[Lisa Johnson, *Class of 2008* and
Catherine Carter Goebel, *Professor of Art History,
Paul A. Anderson Chair in the Arts*]

[1] William J. Chiego, organized by, *Sir David Wilkie of Scotland, 1785-1841* (Raleigh: North Carolina Museum of Art, 1987), xvii.

[2] Lindsay Errington, *Tribute to Wilkie* (Edinburgh: The National Galleries of Scotland, 1985), 7.

[3] Chiego, xi.

[4] This painting, which was exhibited at the Royal Academy in 1839 as *Sir David Baird discovering the body of Sultaun Tippoo Saib, after having captured Seringapatam, on the 4th of May, 1799*, is currently in the collection of the National Gallery of Scotland.

[5] Dr. Thomas B. Brumbaugh, Professor Emeritus, Vanderbilt University, identified the sketch's figure within this painting.

[6] Chiego, 42.

[7] Ibid.

[8] Ibid., 256.

[9] Ibid., 254.

[10] Chiego, 256.

[11] *Blackwood's Edinburgh Magazine* (1839), 47: 311, quoted in Chiego, 43.

[12] Ibid., 66-67

[13] Ibid.

[14] Graham Reynolds, *Turner* (Oxford: Oxford University Press, 1969), 187.

[15] Ibid.

33B

33A

34

Ferdinand-Victor-Eugène Delacroix (French 1798–1863)
Study of Lion Heads, ascribed title, date range 1832–1861
Graphite drawing
Unsigned, estate stamp b.r. in black ink "E.D."
24.2 x 31.3 cm., 9-1/2 x 12-3/8" sheet
Gift of Mr. and Mrs. Michael Moss, Augustana College Art Collection,
95.26.2

Ferdinand-Victor-Eugène Delacroix was born in 1798 in Charenton-Saint-Maurice, France.[1] His family was of moderate wealth, but after his father's death when Eugène was only seven years old, followed by his mother's death nine years later, the family was left in a dire financial position.[2] The artist started his artistic training and, in 1822, submitted his first painting to the Paris Salon, entitled *The Barque of Dante*. This emotionally charged illustration of Dante and Virgil in Phlegya's barque, based on Dante's fourteenth-century literary masterpiece, the *Divine Comedy*, announced the arrival of Delacroix and the Romantic movement to the art world.[3]

Delacroix pursued this new style throughout his career, and he was even considered its leader in France at the time. After his death in 1863, he was hailed as one of the three great French Romantics, along with the writer Victor Hugo and the musician Hector Berlioz[4] and was greatly esteemed by the next generation of avant-garde painters, the Impressionists. Romanticism was a dramatic departure from the Neoclassical movement that preceded it. While Neoclassicists focused more on intellect, reason and history, the Romantics advocated infusing emotion in art and investigated the more mysterious realms of dreams and nightmares, as well as powers greater than humanity, fascinated by that which could not be proven. This drawing illustrates Romantic fascination not only with nature as observed in landscape, but with exotic and dangerous animals that inhabit such environments. The potential drama offered by such subjects challenged the privileged position of humans as defined in the classical tradition and reinforced by the Neoclassicists of the previous generation.

While Delacroix was universally celebrated for his rich and innovative use of color, his talent is immediately apparent in his sketches as well. The *Study of Lion Heads* was most likely undertaken during a journey to Morocco and Spain, where he saw a variety of such animals.[5] Another influence for the subject would have been seventeenth-century Pieter Paul Rubens' *Lion Hunt* (1617–1618). Delacroix, although admiring the appeal to the imagination that Rubens offered, criticized the confusing composition, describing one of the lions as a "furious beast," and another as having a "hideous grimace."[6] The date for Delacroix's sketch is not known, but his trip to Morocco was in the year 1832, and his lion paintings range in date from 1829 (*Lion of the Atlas*) to 1861 (the last of his various *Lion Hunt* paintings). This likely then places the sketch somewhere between 1832 and 1861.

Within the overall *Study of Lion Heads*, there are seven smaller sketches,

all unfinished, five of lions and two of lionesses. The lions speak to anyone viewing them; the graphite pencil effectively contrasts the harsh, dark lines of the lions' eyes with the lighter, wispier lines of their manes. The lion in the lower right corner has the most riveting eyes, delineated with the darkest shading. He seems to pull viewers toward him, as if to determine when to pounce as they symbolically transform into his prey. He seems to be waiting, anticipating and hungry. Since most of the lions' heads are unfinished, they take on an even more mysterious look, as if they are camouflaged and fading back into the paper itself. They are all sketched in graphite with the power and force of this medium beautifully capturing their essence. Lions, the traditional *kings of the jungle*, have symbolized strength, fearlessness and power in various cultures throughout the centuries. This sketch exemplifies the type of careful preliminary consideration Delacroix took in preparation for his final paintings, demonstrating how the foundation, the armature beneath the color, was just as important to him as the finished canvas.

Some of Delacroix's finished works are very similar to such preparatory sketches. In *Lion of the Atlas*, many of the characteristics of the lions in this sketch are repeated. The same ferocious eyes are visible, and although the angling of the head is different (the ears are pulled further back), the basic head structure is similar. In his painting *The Lion Hunt* (1855-1856), the figure of the female lion, attacking the horse, her teeth and claws sunk deep into the horse's flesh, has many of the same qualities as the finished lioness in the sketch. The position of the lioness's head and her eyes are similar; the head is in a flatter position and the eyes closed or at least squinting. In these paintings, however, the lions are active and ferocious, mouths open and teeth barred, reflecting the Romantic fascination with emotion and the ultimate struggle between *man* and nature.

Delacroix was truly swept up in Romanticism and advanced its cause through his new techniques, subject matter and overall artistic ability. Like most Romantics, he emphasized nature and its intriguing potential for danger. This sketch demonstrates the versatility of Delacroix's artistic talents, far beyond his celebrated use of color, within the more restrictive medium of graphite. With this deceptively simple medium, he has effectively captured the ferocity, power and mystery that lions engender, not only to the Romantic imagination, but to modern sensibilities as well.

[Regina Gorham, *Class of 2006*]

---

[1] Wellington, ed., trans. Lucy Norton, *The Journal of Eugène Delacroix* (Ithaca: Cornell University Press, 1980), xxxiii.

[2] Barthélémy Jobert, *Delacroix* (Princeton: Princeton University Press, 1997), 20-21.

[3] Robert Rosenblum and H.W. Janson, *19th Century Art* (New Jersey: Prentice Hall, Inc., Publishers, 1984), 124.

[4] Ibid.

[5] Later, during a visit to the Natural History Museum in Paris, Delacroix remarked that the giraffes were "obviously stuffed by people who had never seen the creature alive." Quoted in Wellington, 56.

[6] Ibid., 57.

35

James Smillie (Scottish American 1807–1885) after Thomas Cole
(American 1801–1848)
The Voyage of Life—Youth, 1849
Hand-colored engraving
Signed in printed text below image at b.l. "Painted by Thomas Cole" and
b.r. "Engraved by James Smillie" and b.l. "Printed by J. Dalton"
Inscribed at center below image "The Voyage of Life—Youth./ From the
original painting distributed by the American Art-Union./ Published
exclusively for the Members of 1849./ Entered according to Act of Congress
in the year 1850 by the American Art-Union in the Clerk's Office of the
U.S. District Court for the Southern District of New York."
50.8 x 67.4 cm., 20 x 26-1/2" image
60.1 x 78.5 cm., 23-11/16 x 30-7/8" sheet
Purchase Through Gift of the Reynold Emanuel and Johnnie Gause Leak
Holmén Endowment for the Visual Arts, Augustana College Art Collection,
98.12

Immediately following the American Revolution, the art scene in America
was focused primarily on portraits and history paintings of such notable
heroes as George Washington (catalogue 18) and Paul Revere. However,
a new and independent America needed a revised national art identity,
something distinctly *American*. Such an identity was found in the vast
wilderness and rugged landscape that stretched within the boundaries of
this young country. Already in Europe, landscape painting was increasing
in importance in the wake of the Industrial Revolution which led to a
renewed interest in nature, perhaps inspired by the presumed disappearance
of such beauty through modernization. American Romanticism coupled
with national pride inspired artists led by Thomas Cole to depict the beauty
of the American landscape and raise it to a grand scale level.[1]

International Romanticism fostered appreciation for nature that America,
with its untouched and unspoiled wilderness, seemed to fulfill. Whether
the type illustrated was categorized as *sublime* or *picturesque*, Romantics
expressed their views with powerful visual and verbal images of nature.
America's most important landscape painter was truly Thomas Cole, who
combined the modern interest in nature with the traditional didactic notion
that: "the subject [of art] should be pure and lofty…, an impressive lesson
must be taught, an important scene illustrated—a moral, religious or poetic
effect be produced on the mind."[2] He endeavored to bring landscapes to the
level of history paintings by reinforcing nature's association with God.

In 1839, Samuel Ward commissioned Cole to paint a four-part, allegorical
series called *The Voyage of Life: Childhood, Youth, Manhood, and Old
Age*. He wanted these paintings to convey a basic Christian moral dealing
with the journey of life and the passage of time. Cole developed the
paintings specifically to be exhibited side-by-side in order to emphasize
the chronological stages of life of the main character, complimented by the
corresponding changes in the seasons as time passed.[3] He painted with
various colors and richness to create different moods in the landscapes
and added religious and literary aspects as well. The series is laden with
symbolism, from the vegetation and seasons to the presence of the *Hours*
and the metaphoric role of the river itself.

In the first painting, *Childhood*, the baby voyager is joyously floating in a
boat steered by an angel out of a dark cavern, corresponding with childbirth.
On the boat itself, figures of the Hours are carved, representing the passing
of time, further emphasized by the hourglass, measuring the sands of time.
The landscape around the baby blooms with early spring and his innocence

toward what lies ahead is reflected in the shortened scope of the scene.

The second painting, *Youth*, represents confidence and expectation. It is
the most optimistic scene of the series, and was therefore the most popular.
The hand-colored engraved version, pictured here, was part of a print series,
commissioned by a minister in 1849, the year after Cole's death. This patron
recognized the greater didactic potential that multiple affordable images
offered a larger audience, toward further spreading their "pure moral tone
and Christian sentiment."[4] In *Youth*, the infant has become a young man.
Although still inexperienced, he now holds the rudder and steers the small
craft into the waters ahead, as his guardian angel watches from the bank.
The stream is very clear, and the towering trees on the riverbanks and rich,
green foliage of summer represent a youthful life full of promise. Cole
painted a late morning summer scene in order to convey a feeling for the
climax and full fruition of life. The youth is optimistic as he seeks his *castle
in the sky*, a cloudy, ethereal structure that Cole described as "emblematic
of the daydreams of youth, its aspirations after glory and fame."[5] The river
seems to head straight for the castle in a gentle current, but in the distance
a sharp curve can be seen with rapids that the boy will soon encounter as he
enters manhood in the next scene.

In the third painting, *Manhood*, the series veers from the positive to a
more somber mood. The voyager stands helpless in his small boat while
the waters crash turbulently around him and demonic figures hover above.
Within the rough autumn landscape, he grasps his hands in prayer looking
heavenward toward the angel who watches from above. It was in manhood,
Cole believed, that the pains of experience brought with them reality and
ultimately sobered "youthful daydreams."[6]

In the final painting, *Old Age*, the *stream of life* has emptied into a vast
ocean. The old voyager, led by the angel, floats forward as the heavens open
up to receive him. The figure representing the Hours at the front of the
boat has broken away, signifying that the aged character's time on earth has
indeed ended. The didactic story comes to a close: the man has successfully
journeyed through the various stages of life and is now ready to receive his
reward for being faithful.[7]

Thomas Cole's four-piece series effectively portrays the story of humanity.
From unspoiled beauty and innocence, through determination, adversity,
and prayer, the selection molds together the splendor and hardships of
life. Cole's skill for generating these feelings and stressing landscape
colors influenced many other artists such as Asher B. Durand (Cole's
longtime friend and fellow painter of the *Hudson River School*), Frederic E.
Church and Jasper Francis Cropsey.[8] Thomas Cole was truly an American
Romantic who effectively transformed landscape paintings into moral
statements accessible to a broad American audience.

[Julius Gylys, *Class of 2008*]

[1] Earl A. Powell, *Thomas Cole* (New York: Harry N. Abrams, Inc., 1990), 10-11.

[2] Quoted in Matthew Baigell, *Thomas Cole* (New York: Watson-Guptill Publications, 1981), 10.

[3] Powell, 88.

[4] The Reverend Gorham D. Abbott hired James Smillie to complete the engravings. Quoted in Joy S. Kasson, "The Voyage of Life: Thomas Cole and the Romantic Disillusionment," *American Quarterly*, vol. 27, no. 1 (1975): 42-56, JSTOR (18 July 2005).

[5] Powell, 89.

[6] Ibid., 92.

[7] Kasson, 43.

[8] Powell, 10.

36

Charles Meryon (French 1821–1868), printed by Auguste Delâtre (French 1822–1907)
La Galerie Notre Dame [Notre Dame Passageway], 1853
Etching and engraving on chine-collé
Signed t.l. in image with monogram and b.r. in plate "*A Delâtre Imp. R. S. Jacques'_ 266*"
28.3 x 17.5 cm., 11-1/8 x 6-7/8" image
29.8 x 18.0 cm., 11-3/4 x 7-1/8" sheet
Paul A. Anderson Chair in the Arts Purchase, Augustana College Art Collection, 2000.29

Charles Meryon was a highly talented artist who unfortunately led a sad and turbulent life. Despite praise and support from prominent figures of his time, such as writers Charles Baudelaire (catalogue 41) and Victor Hugo, he spent most of his career in poverty, struggling with some form of mental instability, now interpreted as either *melancholia* or manic depression with severe paranoid delusions.[1] Despite such problems, or perhaps even because of them, Meryon was able to create architectural etchings that were as detailed as they were atmospheric, blending aspects of several different art movements into unique and deeply personal works.

Born the illegitimate son of a French ballet dancer and an English physician, Meryon entered the naval academy at the age of sixteen. He later embarked on a tour of duty that took him around the world for seven years, and it was likely during this time that he first began drawing. Meryon left the navy a few years later, in his mid-twenties, in order to pursue an artistic career, initially aspiring to be a painter.[2] He probably sensed that this would be a difficult goal as he was already aware that he had some deficiency in his color vision. Even knowing this, he attempted to make an oil painting based on one of his drawings. It then became obvious that his color blindness was severe enough to prevent him from ever becoming a serious painter. This deficiency, which is now identified as *daltonism*, particularly affected how he perceived the colors of red and green.[3]

Rather than being disheartened by his discovery that painting was not a viable option, Meryon enthusiastically and astutely turned his attention to etching. Despite his color blindness, he clearly possessed a unique sensitivity to subtle variations in shades of certain colors and the delicate gradations of light and dark, making the primarily black-and-white medium of etching a perfect choice.[4] He embraced the technique wholeheartedly, focusing his attention on medieval Gothic architecture.

This choice of subject was inspired at least in part by the current Parisian reconstruction initiated by French ruler Napoleon III, who hoped to improve the poor living conditions of lower class sections of *old* Paris. The streets there were narrow, dark and dirty, as they were arranged like a labyrinth, making travel difficult and ultimately promoting disease through lack of ventilation. Napoleon III discerned that such environments also facilitated rebellion, since the roads were impassable for his troops. These streets, and the landmarks near them, were thus destroyed in order to build wider, cleaner, arrow-straight avenues.[5]

Meryon and some of his contemporaries openly objected to this plan for demolition and to the advancement of progress in general. His primary means of protest was recorded in his series of etchings of sights in old Paris that were slated for destruction. He identified with the spirit of these old Gothic buildings in an intensely personal manner, indicative of a Romantic temperament, beyond what other artists ever achieved.

Meryon created a style that some critics consider a unique, innovative blend of Romanticism and Classicism with perhaps even an early element of Impressionism.[6] His accurate, highly-detailed renderings of architecture and use of careful preliminary drawings, reflect the influence that traditional academic classicism had on his technique. His keen interest in the complex interactions between light and shadow, *chiaroscuro*, predicted the similar aspirations of the Impressionists later in the century.[7] At the same time, he strongly believed in adding his own deeply personal touches to such pieces, creating a dream-like, gloomy, melancholic atmosphere which effectively rendered clear-cut engineering and architecture within the interpretive light of macabre fantasy. This latter tendency, easily felt in all of his works, is what firmly placed Meryon within Romanticism.

Although Meryon was not particularly well-received by the general French public, he was respected and admired by many contemporary intellectuals. Victor Hugo, the renowned author of *The Hunchback of Notre Dame* and a Romantic genius in his own right, recognized Meryon's original talent: "Without color, with nothing save shadow and light, chiaroscuro pure and simple and left to itself: that is the problem of etching. M. Meryon solves it magisterially. What he does is superb. His plates live, radiate, and think."[8] Many scholars today would agree with this assessment and believe Meryon was an integral influence on the *Etching Revival* that would soon take place in nineteenth-century France.[9] His immediate impact might also be noted in James McNeill Whistler's etching of *Black Lion Wharf* (catalogue 40), drawn a few years later in 1859, which depicts London's colorful Thames Embankment, similarly threatened by modernization.

La Galerie Notre Dame is one of six etchings by Meryon of the impressive Parisian Cathedral of Notre Dame, also a source of inspiration for Hugo. Meryon typically coupled his bold chiaroscuro with painstakingly accurate attention to detail that earned him much praise. The shadows are strongly emphasized, almost exaggerated, for effect. He also employed his own brand of iconography in many of his works, such as the crows added here, some flying in the background sky, and others landing within the passageway, which smoothly connect interior and exterior spaces. Since Meryon held a rather high-minded, rigid sense of morality,[10] they may also have represented the degraded moral state of Paris as he saw it, perhaps symbolizing that old Paris, in its current state, had effectively "gone to the birds."[11]

In recent years, Meryon has received more of the attention he so richly deserves. Regardless of a troubled life and mind, he knew precisely how to express himself within his art, through a medium and subject he loved and for which his talents were suited. His unique, innovative style, both sublime and powerful, is no longer obscured by a past that generally seemed incapable of understanding his originality and passion. He was truly one of the great forces for Romanticism and its legacy in defining the importance and integrity of unique individual interpretation.

[Alisha Boley, *Class of 2006*]

[1] Roger Collins, *Charles Meryon: A Life* (Devizes: Robin Garton Ltd., 1999), 187.

[2] M. Therese Southgate, "The Cover," *Journal of the American Medical Association*, vol. 276, no. 9 (1996): 661.

[3] Collins, 104.

[4] Ibid., 105.

[5] Ibid., 119-120.

[6] Ibid., 154-155.

[7] Gabriel P. Weisberg, "The Meticulous Romanticism of Charles Meryon," *Art News*, vol. 74 (1975): 54.

[8] Quoted in William Aspenwall Bradley, *French Etchers of the Second Empire* (New York: Houghton Mifflin Company, 1916), 6.

[9] Collins, 256.

[10] Bradley, 31.

[11] Amy DeLamoreaux, *The Paul A. Anderson Art History Collection*, ed. Catherine Carter Goebel (Rock Island: Augustana College, 2001), 88.

37

Honoré Daumier (French 1808–1879)
Le Monsieur qui ricane (**The Scoffer**), terra cotta original dated ca. 1849–1850
Cast bronze
Cast signature verso on base "Daumier"
25.4 x 7.9 x 7.9 cm., 10 x 3-1/8 x 3-1/8" with base
Lent Courtesy of Private Collection

"Ce Daumier, quel sculpteur!"[1] (That Daumier, what a sculptor!"), remarked Auguste Rodin, the so-called founder of modern sculpture. Most of his contemporaries had no idea that Honoré Daumier was one of the first French artists to experiment with modern Realist sculpture. Famous as a lithographic illustrator for the popular press (catalogue 44), his sculptures were a means by which he could study character and form, in three dimensions, which he would then translate onto the lithographic stone. It is interesting that in the nineteenth century, when sculpture as a medium was largely dominated by academic Neoclassicists, the most innovative sculptors leading up to Rodin were painters and draftsmen. Daumier and Edgar Degas found the tactile quality of clay useful in furthering their designs in drawing and painting and through their experiments, attempted to advance its pace with other media.

At the end of his career, Daumier's friends organized an exhibit of his works at Durand-Ruel's gallery. His audience, who expected only the usual black and white illustrations, must have been stunned to view the beautiful Realist oil paintings and "heads in colored clay" as well as two "studies in plaster" from his private studio.[2] These small sculptures were not cast in bronze until after the artist's death. They were rough and energetic and one must assume, primarily produced as a means for study by the artist, much like a preliminary sketch. Each work had its own uniqueness and individuality by virtue of the artist's penchant for caricature, often exaggerating the subject's most prominent characteristics and features. Daumier's art as a whole does not have an elevated idealistic vision, unless this was defined as truth to nature in depicting the dignity of the common person, like many Realists of his time. His works appealed to the general eye—one did not need to have a background in the Classics, history, theology or literature to appreciate them. In an age dominated by the bourgeoisie, these elements appealed to an audience that preferred recognizable and easily comprehensible imagery.

Le Monsieur qui Rican(The Scoffer), was named by Maurice Gobin in his catalogue raisonné[3] of Daumier sculpture. The movement of the coattails and hair are similar to the portrayal of the photographer in Daumier's lithograph of Nadar (catalogue 44). The artist used a rough-modeled realism to detail the character of his subject. With the elderly man's receding hairline and his modeled flesh, a finer sense of variation is revealed which gives him a distinctly caricatured face. Dressed in outmoded frock coat and trousers streaming over his protruding belly, the subject projects a mix of self-confidence within a smug posture. The sweeping diagonals revitalize the figure. His gaze looks off into the distance, balanced by his shoulders and chest which propel him forward as he arches his back in a dramatic curve, thrusting his hands solidly into his pockets.

This model clearly shows Daumier's skill in sculpting, demonstrating the figure's dramatic expression which has been described as *Goyaesque*.[4] Although it may not be his most famous piece, *Le Monsieur* demonstrates Daumier's masterful ability to take a seemingly immobile model and make him tell a thousand words. Since he was not known for his sculpting, the dating and the order of the numerous casts of his sculptures are difficult to establish, and remain controversial to this day. This particular piece has been described as "uncharacteristic," largely due to the fact that it is signed *Daumier*, rather than the usual H.D. of his other sculptures.[5]

Similar to all of his sculpted works, it still bears the *fingerprint* of the artist, appearing unfinished and fresh, like his wonderful lithographs delineated through his animated, wiry line. Daumier's simplicity of workmanship distinguished him from many other artists. His direct grasp of character was perhaps his best tool, for he gave his viewers a sense of perception of various personalities to which everyone can relate. In its naturalistic portrayal of a portrait, with the immediacy of a quickly captured photograph, he successfully created a sculptural parallel to the new experiments and innovations of the Realist and Impressionist painters— clearly an original way of seeing and working. Rodin, more than anyone, saw in such sculpted studies by the *scribbler*, the pedestal foundation on which to build a school of modern sculpture.

[Aron Lees, *Class of 2008* and
Catherine Carter Goebel, *Professor of Art History,
Paul A. Anderson Chair in the Arts*]

---

[1] Jeanne L. Wasserman, *Daumier Sculpture: A Critical and Comparative Study* (Boston: Harvard University, 1969), 5.

[2] Ibid.

[3] Maurice Gobin, *Daumier Sculpteur, 1808-1879* (Geneive: Pierre Cailler Editeur, 1952), 47.

[4] Wasserman, 231.

[5] Ibid.

38

Attributed to Jean-Baptiste Camille Corot (French 1796–1875) or Paul Désiré Trouillebert (1829–1900) [C. Goebel]
Boatman in the Forest, ascribed title, attributed to ca.1839
Oil on canvas
Unsigned
31.0 x 25.7 cm., 12-1/4 x 10-1/8"
Lent Courtesy of Private Collection

Boatman in the Forest is a landscape scene, attributed to Jean-Baptiste Camille Corot, recognized as one of the greatest landscape painters of the nineteenth century. He was a member of the French Barbizon school and a part of the Romantic-Realist movement. The painting consists of a solitary boatman surrounded by a forest of trees. The brushstrokes are short and firm, yet display the feathery quality of the artist's mature 1860s style.

Other than the red highlight on the figure's hat, as well as a few strokes of red throughout the figure, there is only an understated and subtle modulation of color. This red highlight is a hallmark of the artist. The details are few, yet it would be a mistake to say that Corot did not give them proper consideration. "I never hurry to the details of a picture," Corot once said.[1] He would first ensure that the masses and general character were well established. As he stated: "An artist can't control whether he is born a genius with a natural ability to paint, but anyone without disabilities can become aware of the relationship of forms and of colors."[2] Although this painting depicts a realistic view of nature, it also includes a sense of imagination that is indicative of a Romantic temperament. Since Corot served as a bridge between Romanticism and Realism, he was appropriately termed a *Romantic Realist*.

Corot was influenced by Italianate Neoclassicism as well as the Romanticism of English artist, John Constable (catalogue 30). His teacher, Achille-Etna Michallon encouraged him. Corot recalled: "I made my first landscape from nature…under the eye of this painter [Michallon], whose only advice was to render with the greatest scrupulousness everything I saw before me. The lesson worked; since then I have always treasured precision."[3] He made sure to keep his vision clear and simple, yet sensitive to classical balance within the work.

He worked in Italy for three years, continuing his formal training in pictorial depictions of scenes as well as careful analysis of technical qualities inherent to painting light, texture, atmosphere and water. This study widened his outlook, but did not sway him from the principles passed down from Michallon. He was more interested in the landscape of Italy than the art that he found there. He did not let any of the Renaissance masters seduce him from painting nature through his own eyes.

When he returned to France, he was thus prepared to embark on the career of a landscape artist. In 1840, he traveled to Paris, where he spent his summer months in the small village of Barbizon. There, he worked in the forests of Fontainbleau, becoming friends with artists of the Barbizon school, especially Théodore Rousseau. He also painted at other locations throughout the country, such as Ville-d'Avry, where his parents had owned a country home since 1817.[4] This painting was likely done in this area, known for its many lakes and beautiful atmosphere. A critic at the time described the genius that he saw in such works, noting that Corot: "…has such a feeling for the poetry and intelligence of art that he manages to obtain astonishing results. Seen from up close, his canvas…is a jumble of gray and chalky tones; seen from a few steps back, it is a painting filled with truth."[5]

Due to the small scale of this piece and its direct and subtle rendering of the figure and atmosphere, one might conclude that it was a *plein-air* study, perhaps for a larger painting. By this time, Corot was producing many works in order to meet the considerable demand for his paintings. As recent art historians have noted: "The red-hatted boatman is probably the most ubiquitous staffage figure in Corot's late oeuvre. One scholar has counted over forty works in which he appears, his hat always providing a strong note of color to complement the verdant foreground of the landscape."[6]

True to his training, like other Barbizon artists, Corot illustrated peasants and their environments in a straightforward and sympathetic manner. The boatman engages in some sort of activity in the foreground, perhaps pulling in a boat or fishing line or net, if the foreground brushstrokes are read as wetlands fed from the distant water. If this area is ground, he also could be gathering firewood. His position is reminiscent of Corot's earlier painting, *Landscape with Lake and Boatman* (1839), but painted in his mature, more silvery, loose style of brushstrokes. The trees are rendered in beautiful detail, yet with soft painterly brushstrokes. The sky, although mostly grey, has subtle warmth with pink and yellow infusing the atmosphere, hinting at twilight and the end of a workday.

Although Corot's new style still included looking upon the world in simple Realist terms, it added a sense of imagination typical of Romanticism. The scenes before him were not recorded as a collection of facts, but more as a reflection as to how they stirred his emotions, similar to the sensitive perceptions of English Romantic painter, John Constable (catalogue 30). Contemporary critic, Théodore Duret noted this quality, in remarking that Corot recorded not only the landscape elements of a scene, but also "the exact sensation that he has experienced."[7] As the critic Maxime du Camp further suggested in 1864, Corot: "never copies nature, he dreams it and reproduces it as he sees it in his reveries: gracious reveries that belong to the land of fairies…Is his color correct? Is his drawing exact and pure? It doesn't even occur to me to think about it, so powerfully does this poetry move and captivate me."[8]

Boatman in the Forest is likely a *plein-air* study by Corot. It has also been suggested that the artist might be Corot's contemporary imitator and former student, Paul-Désiré Trouillebert (1829-1900)[9]. The painting has all of the elements typical of Corot's mature style and seems to display the true touch of the master. There were so many imitators and even direct forgers of Corot's work, even during his lifetime, that attributions are difficult to assert. What *can* be definitively stated, however, is that this painting was most likely painted by the artist, whom Théodore de Banville described as "not a landscape painter…[but actually a] poet of landscape."[10]

[Marissa Saunders, *Class of 2007* and
Catherine Carter Goebel, *Professor of Art History,
Paul A. Anderson Chair in the Arts*]

[1] Sidney Allnutt, *Corot* (New York: Frederick A. Stokes Company, 1910), 31.

[2] Gary Tinterow, Michael Pantazzit and Vincent Pomarède, *Corot* (New York: Metropolitan Museum of Art, 1996), 8.

[3] Ibid., 14.

[4] Ibid., 35.

[5] Ibid., 217.

[6] Ibid., 293.

[7] Ibid., 261.

[8] Ibid.

[9] Zeljko Lah, art dealer for this piece, has suggested to Catherine Goebel, the identity of Trouillebert as a possible attribution, if not Corot. The conservation data reinforces that the piece is from Corot's time and the frame is identical to those framing many of Corot's works in the Louvre Museum.

[10] Tinterow, 262.

39

Attributed to Barbizon School (follower of Corot)
Woman Sewing Amongst Cows, ascribed title, attributed to mid-19th century France
Oil on linen
Unsigned
39.3 x 53.5 cm., 15-1/2 x 21-1/8"
Purchase with Gift of Mr. Dan Churchill, Augustana College Art Collection, SDC2004.12

Woman Sewing Amongst Cows is a beautiful nineteenth-century landscape scene with all the necessary elements. From the babbling brook to the background filled with an open field, the artist clearly knew how to construct a pleasing piece. This painting originated from the French Barbizon school, which bridged the Romantic Movement with Realism. These artists were influenced by Dutch landscapists of the seventeenth century, and in particular, by English Romantic painter, John Constable (catalogue 30A).[1]

The Barbizon was the first major organized group of nineteenth-century landscape painters, centered in the village of Barbizon, located within the verdant Forest of Fountainebleau. The woods around Barbizon were kept in their pristine condition for the pleasure of the king, since they surrounded the Palace of Fountainebleau, the hunting palace for the French royalty. This area thus provided artists with unspoiled natural scenery to inspire them with subjects for their artwork.

At first glance, viewers might note the deep shade that the trees cast over the foreground, enveloping the woman and the cows. She sits peacefully as she quietly works, presumably sewing, while tending the cows. Barbizon artists were often called *Romantic Realists,* to acknowledge that although like Realists, they focused on everyday observed reality, they often included a slight interpretive sense of Romantic grace. Such works clearly transitioned the two movements.

Although placed within a bucolic setting, this woman does not seem to be completely comfortable. While she sits in the shadows, presumably a relaxing way to spend the day, she appears intent on her work at hand. Unlike the Romantics, who might be captivated by the beauty surrounding them and surrender to its power by communing with nature, she simply focuses on her work. Barbizon painter, Jean François Millet, probably best reflected this philosophy as he described one of his own works, similar in spirit to this: "I have avoided (as I always do with horror) anything that might verge on the sentimental. I wanted her to do her work good-naturedly and simply—as if it were a part of her daily labor, the habit of her life...I want the people I represent to look as if they belonged to their station, and as if their imaginations could not conceive of their ever being anything else."[2]

The advent of Realism developed in response to the tastes of the growing

bourgeoisie who demanded art with which they could personally relate. As the leader of the Realist movement, Gustave Courbet wrote: "...painting is an essentially *concrete* art, and can consist only of the representation of things both *real* and *existing*...To be able to translate the customs, ideas, and appearance of my time as I see them—in a word, to create a living art—this has been my aim."[3] And as his colleague Corot, one of the leaders of the Barbizon movement stated: "No man should become an artist who is not passionate about nature."[4]

As in many of Corot's paintings, the cows are given more attention than the woman. This is not a work of history or mythology, but instead, represents the present in a prosaic manner. There is no great action or moral, simply a normal day in everyday modern life. In the distance, the light rakes across the field, revealing more cattle as well as buildings. The style of brushwork in this painting is lively, yet gentle. This is consistent with nineteenth-century Barbizon landscapes by Corot, who generally did not reveal every detail, yet managed to communicate the story of his figures within their environment. The cows here appear to be comfortable with the woman's proximity as they graze, and one cow meanders to the creek. The artist might be painting something with which he was familiar and had directly observed from life, undoubtedly in the Barbizon environs.

The illuminated background contrasts against the dark foreground. Amongst the shadows is the woman dressed in white with a blue jacket, echoing the colors of the sky and clouds above. White spots across the canvas reflect the subtle nuances of light filtering through the foliage. The grass is a dark green with lighter shades scattered throughout. The leaves of the trees are green in some places but almost black in others, lending the scene a convincing appearance of the transient qualities of natural light and shadow.

This painting is likely by Corot (catalogue 38) or another member of the Barbizon school. The subject matter, as well as the style of painting, reflects this artist's work. Also as in most of Corot's paintings, the red highlight in the woman's brown hair is a typical accent that this artist generally added to accentuate his main figures within an otherwise subdued palette. These artists, although trained by Neoclassicists, developed their own subject and style, which was more intuitive and original in response to their direct confrontation with nature. In this manner, they related to their audience, the inspiring presence of nature, as *Woman Sewing Amongst Cows* continues to do today.

[Brian Allured, *Class of 2005* and
Catherine Carter Goebel *Professor of Art History,
Paul A. Anderson Chair in the Arts*]

[1] Herbert Read, ed., *The Thames and Hudson Dictionary of Art and Artists* (London: Thames and Hudson, 1984), 29.

[2] Robert Goldwater and Marco Treves, *Artists on Art: from the XIV to the XX Century* (New York: Pantheon Books, 1972), 292.

[3] Ibid., 295-96.

[4] Gary Tinterow, Michael Pantazzi and Vincent Pomarède, *Corot* (New York: Metropolitan Museum of Art, 1996), 5.

40

James Abbott McNeill Whistler (American 1834–1903)
Black Lion Wharf, 1859, from **A Series of Sixteen Etchings of Scenes on the Thames and Other Subjects** or **"The Thames Set"**
Etching and drypoint, state III/III
Signed b.r. in plate as part of image "Whistler 1859"
15.2 x 22.4 cm., 6 x 8-3/4" image
18.5 x 22.8 cm., 7-5/16 x 9-3/4" sheet
Paul A. Anderson Chair in the Arts Purchase, Augustana College Art Collection, 2002.16

James McNeill Whistler was one of the most controversial artists of his time. Born in Lowell, Massachusetts, he spent his early childhood in Russia where his father served as a railway engineer for the czar. He became fluent in French, the international language of the time, later returning to the United States to attend his father's alma mater at West Point Academy. Although he excelled in drawing, he was eventually expelled due to his accumulation of demerits and general neglect of his other courses.[1]

Whistler's family next enlisted him in the U. S. Coast and Geodetic Survey, hoping that he could utilize his artistic skills toward a practical application in making maps. He unfortunately found this work tedious and due to his lack of effort, was soon dismissed. This employment, however, was important in teaching him the various steps involved in making etchings.[2]

Whistler next determined to go to Paris to become a fine artist. He spent the rest of his career, working and exhibiting, primarily in London and Paris. Although he later refused to be identified with a particular art movement, during these formative years when he created *Black Lion Wharf* (1859), he considered himself part of the modern French Realist school.[3] The general public regarded Whistler as a painter, yet his etchings were more universally appreciated by the critics.

In the 1850s, however, etching was considered secondary to painting. Most artists who etched were amateurs or illustrators. Whistler, on the other hand, was an exceptional etcher who aimed to elevate the medium. He sent his etchings from the *Thames Set*, including *Black Lion Wharf*, to the Royal Academy exhibition in London in 1862, where they were highly acclaimed. Due to the successful reception of these beautiful etchings, Whistler was instrumental in the British etching revival, hailed by many as the greatest etcher since Baroque master, Rembrandt Van Rijn (catalogue 12).[4]

While most of Whistler's contemporaries viewed the lower Thames River area of London as part of the "grimy urban residue of the industrial revolution," as a Realist, he found the area fascinating and suitable for his etchings.[5] Whistler was perhaps the first of his time to appreciate the beauty of the lower class haunts around the Thames docks as he also realized that the area was quickly changing due to industrialization.[6] Following Charles Meryon's example in Paris (catalogue 36), Whistler sought to record these colorful areas before they were lost to modernization.

Whistler urged his British audience to look beyond the story and to view works for their aesthetics rather than their content. He therefore strove to make all of his works pleasing to the eye. His effort was apparent in his most famous etching, *Black Lion Wharf*. Whistler wanted people to concentrate on the blocks of black and grey and the "ramshackle background of docks and decaying buildings," a view with which many could easily identify.[7] In *Black Lion Wharf*, he etched every detail along the Thames. All the buildings were shown with their varying textures of brick. He developed

a "theory of foregrounds" based on the scientific knowledge of the function of the lens of the human eye. In this etching, for example, the background appears "in focus" while the foreground (except for the figure in the front) is "out of focus."[8]

The people in the foreground of such etchings were generally depicted as disproportionately large. Whistler did this to show that the dockhands were not insignificant, but rather an important element in the scene. His figures appear disheveled, but offer no apology for their appearance or lower social status.[9] They seem to be drawn in a naïve style suitable for working class subjects and typical of similar characters depicted in works by French Realists, Gustave Courbet and Jean François Millet.[10]

In previous etchings, Whistler used a picturesque line which he adapted from Rembrandt. Now, he employed a clean line similar to Wenzel Hollar, William Hogarth and Charles Meryon.[11] The composition appears to recede due to a *repoussoir* (spatial illusion) device, yet at the same time has an interesting two-dimensional pattern across the surface. *Black Lion Wharf* follows a formula that Whistler used in many of his etchings, especially within the *Thames Set*, whereby the foreground is dominated by a large figure in a boat or on the wharf and the middle ground is left blank and is perceived as water. Whistler also commonly created a diagonal line which helped link the three different planes of the piece.

In *Black Lion Wharf*, Whistler put the horizon line containing the buildings about two-thirds of the way up the etching and alternated between undeveloped and patterned areas. The three planes are all shallow and the foreground figures are the *repoussoir* elements. The buildings in the back of the piece hang like a backdrop. Multiple etched lines surround the boat to the right of the large figure, indicating that it is in motion.[12] The whole reads as a unique and beautiful composition.

James McNeill Whistler certainly enlivened the art world with his unconventional subjects and masterful etchings. He frequently experimented with different techniques and styles. *Black Lion Wharf* was not only one of his most popular works, but also was one of his own personal favorites. Whistler decided to hang this etching on the background wall in his famous painting, *Arrangement in Grey and Black: Portrait of the Artist's Mother* (1871), commonly known today as *Whistler's Mother*. Whistler was famous for challenging convention both in his personal and professional life, but more importantly, he is considered today to have been one of the most talented and innovative artists of the nineteenth century.

[Stephanie Schneider, *Class of 2006*]

[1] Stanley Weintraub, *Whistler—A Biography* (New York: Weybright and Talley, 1974), 17-24.

[2] Joseph and Elizabeth Pennell, *The Life of Whistler* (New York: The Modern Library, Inc., 1928), 115-16.

[3] Katherine Lochnan, *The Etchings of James McNeill Whistler* (New Haven: Yale University Press, 1984), 74.

[4] Catherine Carter Goebel, ed. *Tracing Line Through Time: A Whistler Centenary Exhibition* (Rock Island: Augustana College, 2002), 13.

[5] Weintraub, 61.

[6] Lochnan, 82-3.

[7] Weintraub, 61.

[8] Lochnan, 95.

[9] Ibid., 82.

[10] Ibid., 85.

[11] Ibid., 83.

[12] Ibid., 87-96.

41

Edouard Manet (French 1832–1883)
Charles Baudelaire, Full Face III, dated 1865 but prepared 1868 for 1869
publication
Etching and aquatint, state IV/IV
Signed b.r. in image in plate "Manet" and in printed text b.l. below image
in plate "*Peint et Gravé par Manet 1865*" and b.r. below image in plate
"*Imp. A. Salmon*"
9.5 x 8.2 cm., 3-13/16 x 3-1/4" image
24.9 x 23.4 cm., 9-7/8 x 9-1/4" sheet
Paul A. Anderson Chair in the Arts Purchase, Augustana College Art
Collection, 2002.5

Few pieces of artwork are as inherently emotionally charged as those created
as memorials for deceased friends. Such is the case with Manet's insightful
portrait of Baudelaire. Charles Baudelaire, the important French poet and
critic, and Edouard Manet, the so-called leader for French modernism, were
good friends from their first meeting in the mid-1850s until Baudelaire's
death in 1867. They loved Parisian life, and this shared sympathy led
them to support new and original approaches to the contemporary world,
celebrating modern life through art.

During the course of their friendship, Baudelaire and Manet were pioneers
for artistic modernity, in part in reaction against the belief that art should
be timeless and classical. Such traditional conservative views discouraged
artists from creating contemporary subjects in their paintings which might
specifically date them, presumably rendering them meaningless to future
generations. In 1863, Baudelaire published his influential essay, *The Painter
of Modern Life*, which argued that artists should most definitely depict
modern life. He challenged painters to capture the world around him, since
a true modern is: "…endowed with an active imagination, always roaming
the great desert of men, [and] has a nobler aim than that of the pure idler,
a more general aim, other than the fleeting pleasure of circumstance.
He is looking for that indefinable something we may be allowed to call
'modernity,' for want of a better term to express the idea in question. The
aim for him is to extract from fashion the poetry that resides in its historical
envelope, to distill the eternal from the transitory."[1]

This essay appeared at the same time as two of Manet's most controversial
works: *Le Dejeuner sur L'Herbe* (Luncheon on the Grass) which featured a
nude woman, interpreted as a prostitute, picnicking with college students
in a contemporary setting, and *Olympia*, which defined the modern
nude goddess as a prostitute.[2] Surely such choices of subject matter
were inspired through his conversations with Baudelaire, who urged *fine
artists* such as Manet, to emulate the example of illustrators like Honoré
Daumier (catalogue 44) and Constantin Guys. "What Baudelaire saw in
them [Daumier and Guys] was the connection between sure knowledge—
caricature's biting essence of truth—and fugitive expression—its
breathtaking shorthand. In his essay on caricature, Baudelaire wrote: 'the
word modern refers to manner and not to date.'"[3] Although Baudelaire
died four years after publishing *The Painter of Modern Life*, its influence
echoed for many decades through the advent of Impressionism and Post-
Impressionism.

This etched portrait of Baudelaire by Manet is the fourth state of four,
entitled *Charles Baudelaire, Full Face III*. Etching is a technique whereby the
artist covers a copper plate with a waxy resist, draws an image into the resist,
exposing the copper. The plate is then submerged into acid, causing the
image to be bitten into the copper. The plate is then inked and transferred
to paper through pressure from a press, resulting in a limited number of
prints.[4]

In the spring of 1864, Baudelaire traveled to Brussels, where he remained
until a debilitating stroke forced him to return to Paris and enter a nursing
home in 1866. During his convalescence, Manet and his wife frequently
visited Baudelaire's bedside. Manet also joined the group of friends that
would regularly come to amuse him. Baudelaire once noticed Manet's
absence and called for him, an episode Nadar, the popular photographer
(catalogue 44) and a mutual friend, later recounted to the artist to remind
him of Baudelaire's deep affection for him.[5]

Manet began this etching in 1865, while Baudelaire was still in Brussels, and
he completed the fourth state in 1868, after his death. The first state of the
etching is unadorned, and Baudelaire's face is clearly lit and visible. Manet
completed the second two states during Baudelaire's mental decline. They
predict the impending sense of loss, evident in the inclusion of memorial
scrolls, inscribed with Baudelaire's name and embellished with flowers.
Manet also added dramatic *chiaroscuro* (contrast of light and shadow) to
the image which caused Baudelaire's eyes to appear shrunken, emphasizing
his skull-like forehead. In this fourth and final state, published after
Baudelaire's death, viewers sense the *memento mori* (reminder of death)
tribute through which Manet commemorated his close friend.[6] The fourth
state etching was exhibited at the Salon of 1869 and published in the same
year in a biography on the poet.[7]

The final version of Manet's portrait of Baudelaire effectively communicates
the deep-thinking theorist whose life ended far too soon. He wears the
topcoat and cravat of the *bourgeoisie*. His influence was immense as
his criticism fueled the Realist and Impressionist movements and his
controversial book of poems, *Les Fleurs du mal* (1857), helped inspire late
nineteenth-century Symbolism. Baudelaire was a pivotal voice for art and
literature, expressing his important outlook as early as 1846, in his salon
review, where he aptly informed his readers that: "Parisian life is rich in
poetic and wonderful subjects. The marvelous envelopes and saturates us
like atmosphere; but we fail to see it."[8] Through his articulate statements,
Baudelaire did indeed make contemporaries (then and now) see the
"marvelous" in their depictions of *modern life*, as evidenced in Manet's
exquisite artistry, which enables viewers to access Charles Baudelaire, the
man, as well.

[Nikki Kromphardt, *Class of 2005* and
Catherine Carter Goebel, *Professor of Art History,
Paul A. Anderson Chair in the Arts*]

[1] Charles Baudelaire, "The Painter of Modern Life," *in Selected Writings on Art and Literature*,
trans. P.E. Charvet (Hammondsworth: Penguin, 1972) 395-22.

[2] This information was obtained from classroom lectures in Catherine Goebel's A.H. 366
class, Winter 2004-05, Augustana College.

[3] James H. Rubin, *Impressionism* (London: Phaidon Press, Inc., 1999), 32.

[4] Descriptions of etching provided in Catherine Goebel's A.H. 366 class, Winter 2004-05,
Augustana College.

[5] Lois Boe Hyslop, *Baudelaire: Man of his Time* (New Haven: Yale University Press, 1980),
51-52

[6] The four states are illustrated in Jean C. Harris, *Edouard Manet: The Graphic Work* (San
Francisco: Alan Wofsy Fine Arts, 1990), 187-190.

[7] Ibid., 190.

[8] Baudelaire, 104-107.

Peint et Gravé par Manet 1865   Imp. A. Salmon.

42

Attributed to Louis-Eugène Boudin (French 1824–1898) [C. Goebel]
The Beach at Trouville, ca. 1864
Oil on canvas
Unsigned
24.1 x 35.3 cm., 9-1/2 x 13-7/8"
Lent Courtesy of Private Collection

Impressionism and nature paintings became fashionable by the late nineteenth century. The Barbizon school, and in particular Camille Corot (catalogue 38) established the importance of landscape subjects in France by mid-century. The group's focus was reinforced by critic, Charles Baudelaire (catalogue 41) who encouraged artists to depict modern life. Claude Monet, perhaps the most famous landscapist of all time, defined Impressionism with his colorful, light-filled compositions. Although *Monet* is currently a household word, few today could cite the artist whom he credited as his greatest source of inspiration: Eugène Boudin (1824–98). A landscape painter, Boudin instructed this famous Impressionist, at a time during his youth when he had no clear direction and supported himself through caricature drawing.

In an interview in 1900, Monet described Boudin's pivotal role in his career:
  ...Boudin came to me, complimented me in his gentle voice and said: "I always look at your sketches with much pleasure; they are amusing, clever, bright. You are gifted; one can see that at a glance. But I hope you are not going to stop there. It is very well for a beginning, but soon you will have enough of caricaturing. Study, learn to see and to paint, draw, make landscapes. The sea and the sky are so beautiful—the animals, the people, and the trees, just as nature has made them, with their characters, their real way of being, in the light, in the air, just as they are."

  But the exhortations of Boudin did not take. The man himself was pleasing to me. He was earnest, sincere; I felt it but I could not digest his painting, and when he offered to take me with him to sketch in the fields, I always found a polite pretext to decline. Summer came—my time was my own—I could make no valid excuse. Weary of resisting, I gave in at last, and Boudin, with untiring kindness, undertook my education. My eyes were finally opened, and I really understood nature. I learned at the same time to love it...I was governed by the advice of Boudin...[1]

The Beach at Trouville (1864) is attributed to Boudin and is likely a smaller version of the published oil on panel of the same scene.[2] It demonstrates the robust impression of nature gained through *plein-air* painting (directly before the subject in open air), to which Boudin introduced Monet six years earlier. The location at Trouville, a popular beach resort with the bourgeoisie, as well as Empress Eugénie and Napoleon III, provided a constant source of inspiration for the artist. Of the eleven works that Boudin exhibited at the Paris Salon between 1864 and 1869, seven were beach scenes from Trouville.[3] As the critic Castagnary historicized in his review of the 1868 Salon: "Boudin had invented a genre. He was the first to think of showing formally dressed Parisians, surrounded by air and sun on stretches of beach where the wind is blowing; this was successful and deserved to be."[4] Boudin also clearly believed that this body of work would ultimately be his legacy, as he wrote in his notebook: "People are starting to ask me for lots of seascapes. I shall do other things but I will always be the painter of beaches."[5]

By 1864, Boudin had already painted such views for at least two years and had derived a basic formula whereby the sky consumes nearly two-thirds of the composition and the beach and sea together make up the other third. Also typical is the horizontal orientation with bands of sky punctuated with clouds, sea with boats and bathers, and the beach as stage-set for various diverse figures on holiday, seemingly unaware of the artist's presence.

In this beach scene, the viewer's eye is inevitably caught by the pair of women on the right, whose fashionable hoop skirts billow in the breeze. The Second Empire period, like the eighteenth-century French Rococo, "was an era of adoration of the female of the species...[particularly by the] creators of fashion."[6] A quizzical dog seems to interact with these self-absorbed women, his tail ably suggested by the thinnest brushstroke.

A *bathing machine*, off center to the left, provides a changing place to take refuge from the elements, its geometry at odds with the organic flow of the various figures that enliven the beach. Two women seem to brace themselves against the wind to its right, while a couple interacts at left. A group of three women further left appear to gossip as they react to the shore breeze, as does a gentleman to the far left, who gazes toward the far right at the two approaching women, effectively holding the composition together. There are very few facial details, yet personalities and expressions are convincingly suggested.

The distant spaces are beautifully and subtly rendered while the atmospheric perspective cools the colors as they retreat. The facility of the brushstroke, quickly noted, effectively indicates the figures in the distance: the boaters at left, the bathers just off center and the seated figures within the concave bay at right. In closely examining such consummate *plein-air* painting, viewers can appreciate the enthusiasm with which Monet embraced Boudin's philosophy.

When this painting was conserved, it was determined that the canvas and the paint are indeed from Boudin's era. The small scale is typical for these particular works, especially if this was a *plein-air* study for the larger painting. It is unsigned and does not appear to be a copy by a later nineteenth-century painter. This smaller version appears fresher than the larger one, evidence of its immediate interaction with the source. Furthermore, there are some intriguing differences between the two versions which contradict a theory of its being a copy. For example, there are many more bathers in the water in this version and the far left man, here, turns toward the women at right. In the larger version, he looks out toward the sea. The scene at the distant right includes many more seated figures and extends further than the published version. And the two women to the right of the changing booth are conceived differently and are in different costumes. Finally, the overall effect here is much more spontaneous and true-to-life. The figures have greater character and weight, painted in an overall fluid brushstroke, suggesting that this could have been Boudin's own small oil sketch, or *pochade,*[7] for a larger salon piece.

Boudin was certainly one of, if not *the* first, of the Impressionists, exhibiting with the group in 1874. Like Baudelaire, he firmly believed in *modernity,* as defined by Baudelaire, to "extract from fashion the poetry that resides in its historical envelope, to distill the eternal from the transitory."[8] Boudin's interpretation was not framed along Baudelaire's urban Parisian boulevards, but within the open expanse of the sea and its environs. Boudin explained his choice in 1868, marveling that he was celebrated "...for daring to include the things and people of our time in my pictures, for having found a way of making acceptable men in overcoats and women in waterproofs...these bourgeois, who stroll on the jetty towards the sunset, have the right to be fixed on canvas, *to be brought to the light.*[9] Through Boudin's masterful touch, they remain in this light today.

> [Dana Ziganto, *Class of 2007* and
> Catherine Carter Goebel, *Professor of Art History,*
> *Paul A. Anderson Chair in the Arts*]

[1] Linda Nochlin, *Impressionism and Post-Impressionism, 1874-1904* (Englewood Cliffs: Prentice-Hall, 1966), 37-38.

[2] The larger oil on panel version has been published as *Scène de plage à Trouville,* 1864 in G. Jean-Aubry and Robert Schmit, *Eugène Boudin* (Neuchâtel: Editions Ides et Calenders, 1987), 41, and as *The Beach at Trouville,* 1864 in Vivien Hamilton, *Boudin at Trouville* (London: John Murray, 1992), 74.

[3] Hamilton, 63.

[4] Ibid.

[5] Ibid.

[6] Ibid., 74.

[7] Ibid., 63.

[8] Charles Baudelaire, *Baudelaire: Selected Writings on Art and Literature,* Translated by P. E. Charvet (New York: Viking, 1972), 395-422.

[9] Ibid., 20.

43

Charles Camille François Pécrus (French 1826–1907)
Pont des Arts, attributed to ca.1860–1870
Oil on canvas
Signed b.r. "C. Pécrus"
33.0 x 46.4 cm., 13 x 18-1/4"
Lent Courtesy of Private Collection

French Impressionist Charles Pécrus was seemingly lost for many years to history books covering the movement's famous practitioners. Impressionism matured in the second half of the nineteenth century with such notables as Edouard Manet (catalogue 41), Claude Monet and Edgar Degas (catalogue 56 and 58). Breaking with the traditions of the conservative French art academy, Impressionists used a "seemingly haphazard technique . . . [that created] an unfinished look . . . [of] an instantaneous impression of a scene in nature."[1]

Recently rediscovered as an accomplished painter within the Impressionist movement, Charles Pécrus's place is currently being reevaluated by art historians. Pécrus was born in 1826 in Limoges, France and began studying at the prestigious École des Beaux-Arts (School of Fine Arts) in 1850. By 1855, he was painting professionally and his career showed great promise, as evidenced by the fact that within two years, he had exhibited four works in the highly competitive French Salon. By 1858, like many avant-garde painters of his generation, he had moved to Montmartre, the artists' quarter in Paris.[2]

His two main subjects in painting were generally quite distinct: tiny, genre scenes depicted in a precise manner and beautiful landscapes. In this pursuit, he was encouraged by friends such as Louis-Eugène Boudin (catalogue 42), the pivotal landscape painter from Trouville, who greatly influenced Monet. Pécrus was described as a "modest man who remained in the wake of two masters, E. Boudin and [Johan Barthold] Jongkind, who had opened the way to him."[3]

Pécrus believed that the bourgeoisie vision of the world with its "force of stability [anchored] in the past" was artificial. He felt, drawing upon Boudin's technique, that "seizing the fleeting variations of the water, the sky, and the air" in his painting would give his era a greater and more realistic vision.[4] Following this approach, Pécrus "wanted to make his painting come alive, . . . [and] he painted his characters in interiors, in particular, young women in simple scenes and attitudes of everyday life . . . [where] the scenery, however, had to harmonize itself with those that it was bringing to light."[5] Although Pécrus often worked alongside Boudin, their styles differed. Boudin often painted with a "touch [that] was more nervous and sometimes even jerky," and Pécrus "painted more gently while giving a light impression of blurriness, especially nearing the end of his life."[6]

Pécrus' oil on canvas of the *Pont des Arts* in Paris is an example of his eventual desire to combine his interests in genre and landscape. *The Pont des Arts* (Bridge of the Arts) possesses great historical significance as many important Parisian figures crossed this centrally located bridge. The bridge's wood and steel construction (the first of its kind in Paris) began in 1802 and finished two years later. Connecting the Louvre on the right bank to the Institut de France on the left, the pedestrian and toll bridge has been repeatedly damaged by boat traffic and bombings, and its most recent reconstruction in 1985 left it with seven arches, two fewer than the original nine-arch bridge illustrated here.

The building and reconstruction of this bridge hailed the innovative modernization of Paris initiated by Napolaeon III. The redesign or *Haussmannization* of Paris, was undertaken by Baron Haussmann during the mid-nineteenth century. Many Parisians felt that "Balzac's Paris [catalogue 36]—crumbling with age, slum-ridden, unsanitary, prone to cholera epidemics, over-crowded—was to be brought up to date."[7] Following this modernization, Parisians once again felt that their city was worthy of its reputation for bustling contemporary life. With renewed national pride, the updated and renovated scenery along the Seine River was now enjoyed by strollers who felt that they could engage in everyday activities within the heart of the city, in a tranquil and sanitary environment.

This urban landscape was likely painted by Pécrus during the later period of Paris' nineteenth-century modernization. Artists captured the renewed intimacy that Parisians now felt toward their capital city. Furthermore, the depiction of such architectural achievements, as rendered in this Impressionist painting, reflected Pécrus' wish to pay homage to the newly renovated bridge. Just as Pécrus' friend Monet demonstrated an "apparent desire to place Impressionism within the great traditions of French art" with his painting series of the Gothic Cathedral at Rouen, Pécrus likely had the same motivation when he chose to portray this magnificent example of French engineering within its urban environment.[8]

In this painting, Pécrus created a modern urban landscape, which includes genre scenes at the city's center. Parisians are portrayed in a variety of poses and locations along the Seine. Some are in the foreground engaging in daily activities accompanied by their dogs, others are strolling along the river and a few in the distance are crossing the Pont des Arts. Portraying these figures together in this scene demonstrated that Paris enjoyed much active life and leisurely flow.

Upon analyzing the technical aspects of Pécrus' brushstrokes, one can note that the lack of sharpness around the edges of the figures and the seeming blurriness of atmospheric perspective combine to give the painting that unfinished look for which the Impressionists are famous. Pécrus' interesting mix of colors is evident in his shades of black in the dog and owner in the foreground and in the famous bridge behind them. This specific technique was probably learned from Boudin who mixed shades of black in a similar fashion in his figures.

In terms of stylistic composition, it is interesting to note that although this is an *urban* landscape, nearly two-thirds of the painting depicts the vast sky, river and trees lining the walkway. In fact the balance of nature and figures is quite similar to that achieved by Pécrus' colleague Boudin in his resort depictions of the beaches at Trouville (catalogue 42). With his Impressionist love for landscape, this painting also clearly reflects Pécrus' growing tendency to dedicate his work solely to nature. Perhaps he wanted to portray the harmony that existed in Paris between its active commercial life and the interspersed glimpses of nature within its superstructure. Paris was thus at the same time natural, traditional and modern, in the sense that there were large sections in the crowded city where one could still find open, expanding, sunlit stretches, such as along the river and in its beautiful parks (catalogue 66A and B).

Although Charles Pécrus is not yet well-known, he should not be underestimated because "he had been a modest artist, looking for neither showy fame nor even honors . . . [but his talent] is now obvious to whoever can have a comprehensive view of his work."[9] Special exhibitions of his paintings will soon cross the Atlantic to the United States, enabling his work to ultimately reach a larger audience. Pécrus is thus now receiving the recognition that he so richly deserves as one of the original French Impressionists.

[Colleen Jaycox, *Class of 2006*]

[1] Marilyn Stokstad, *Art History*, Second Edition, Volume Two (New York: Harry N. Abrams, Inc., 2002), 1019.

[2] Jean Pécrus and Serge Pécrus, *Charles Pécrus*, 1826-1907 (Painting exposition, Honfleur - Lisieux, France, 1979.), 2. Translation provided by Colleen Jaycox.

[3] Ibid.

[4] Ibid.

[5] Ibid., 1-2.

[6] Ibid., 4.

[7] Colin Jones, *The Cambridge Illustrated History of France* (New York: Cambridge University Press, 2001), 214.

[8] Stokstad, 1029.

[9] Pécrus, 6.

44

Honoré Daumier (French 1808–1879)
Nadar élevant la photographie à la hauteur de l'art [Nadar Raising
Photography to the Height of Art], published in ***Le Boulevard***, 1862
(English title translation kindly provided by Dr. Roger Crossley, Augustana
College French Department, 1999)
Lithograph
Signed b.l. in image "H. D." and in printed text b.c. below image "*Imp.
Bertauts, Paris*"
28.8 x 22.1 cm., 11-3/8 x 8-11/16" image
42.2 x 29.4 cm., 16-5/8 x 11-9/16" sheet
Paul A. Anderson Chair in the Arts Purchase, Augustana College Art
Collection, 2000.28

Honoré Victorin Daumier was a French artist who delighted a mostly
bourgeois audience with his illustrations. His alliance with this middle class
was credited to the growing power of the press and newspapers.[1] Daumier
turned his drawings into prints by producing them as lithographs. He
enjoyed using this medium because it effectively captured the immediacy
of his sketches, at the same time that it could produce multiple copies.
Daumier preferred lithography because he believed it enabled him to
suppress all signs of labor and alterations from his final proofs. His work
appealed to artists of the Realist and Impressionist movements since it so
beautifully recorded the transient qualities of nature as well as the nuances
of human character. Charles Baudelaire (catalogue 41), an important
French writer and theorist for nineteenth-century modernity, suggested
that Daumier became an artist because "he needed to draw" and that for his
time, working in newspaper illustration was thus "inevitable."[2]

This ease of depiction does not mean that his final images were accomplished
without a struggle, and without numerous corrections on stone. Daumier's
chosen technique enabled him to reach a larger audience through multiple
prints—a democratic approach to patronage. During his lifetime he
created nearly six thousand lithographs, mastering the medium and his
own style through continuous practice. His early works were characterized
by a revolutionary spirit with biting illustrations for *La Caricature* and *Le
Charivari*, popular journals of the day. Although well-received by the public,
criticism of King Louis-Philippe landed him in prison. Interestingly, as he
wrote a friend from his cell in 1832, "…prison will leave no painful memory:
on the contrary—if at this moment I had a little more ink, for my inkwell
is empty which much cramps my style, and forces me to dip my pen every
second and annoys me; except for that, I say, I believe I lack for nothing."[3]
Although released due to public outcry, the political environment and
subsequent censorship laws led to his shift in subject matter from Realist
rebellion to bourgeois everyday life, parallel to the contemporary stylistic
movement in France from Realism to Impressionism.

Nadar Elevating Photography to the Level of Art is a piece that really
defines Daumier's mature style. It portrays a single subject, as most of his
illustrations do, and the drawing is enlivened through Daumier's signature
lively and energetic lines. As with most of his lithographic production,
this piece is done in black and white. It illustrates a gentler side than his
earlier political cartoons. Here, he explores the world of modern life, with
its innovations and foibles. This lithograph, like most of his illustrations,
was published in the press, in this case in *Le Boulevard* (1862). This piece is
especially interesting because of the story behind it.

An innovative photographer, Nadar was struggling to have his photographs
seen as real works of art. He believed that art could be expressed in
many ways, including photography. Nadar would take *bird's-eye view*
photographs from his hot air balloon in order to achieve the vantage points

he desired, in this case, of the city of Paris. He was a pioneer in the field,
who really brought photography to new heights. His innovations influenced
Impressionist painters. Nadar also used photography as a military aid,
taking pictures of German troop movements towards France during the
Franco-Prussian War of 1870. His efforts resulted in his being awarded the
prestigious medal of the Legion of Honor.[4] Nadar was thus recognized not
only as one of the premier photographers of his day, but as a military hero
as well.

Daumier here illustrates Nadar in his familiar hot air balloon which he
dubbed the *Giant*. He appears as an awkward bourgeois entrepreneur,
with hat flying and topcoat disheveled. The windblown effect illustrates
the excitement of the aerial feat depicted. Nadar's hot air balloon not
only serves as his vehicle upward, but also advertises his profession. He
completely focuses his attention through the camera lens on the view below
where the city of Paris declares the importance of photography through
the many advertisements on buildings. The double meaning of this lively
cartoon is evident—Nadar is raising photography to the height of art—both
physically through his bird's-eye view as well as symbolically with his
advocacy for photography's being considered a major art medium, like
painting and sculpture.

Daumier must have recognized in Nadar the spirit of innovation and
dexterity that certainly characterized his own persona. Theodore de
Banville recalled the impression that Daumier made on him: "…I admired
his features, they seemed to be bursting with strength and goodness. His
eyes were small but piercing, his nose was turned up as though to sniff the
breezes of the unknown. His mouth was well-cut, gracious and of large
capacity. He had in fact a fine artist's head, very like that of some of the
bourgeois he painted but burning with the bright flame of the spirit."[5]
Due to his liberal politics, Daumier quietly refused to accept the medal of
the Legion of Honor. Fellow Realist, Gustave Courbet, rebuked him for
not refusing with great flourish and attention, as he had done, in order
to embarrass the government. Daumier, on the other hand, admonished
Courbet for exploiting such a moment, to which Courbet responded:
"There's nothing to be done with Daumier, he's a regular visionary."[6]

Honoré Daumier was a man of versatility. Like his fellow Realists and
Impressionists, he embraced modern techniques, viewpoints and subjects
in order to reach a largely middle-class audience.[7] He perfected the art
of lithography through rigorous practice. His animated style is both
immediately appealing and unmistakable. He was particularly conscious of
the subtleties of his surroundings. His work can be compared to modern
day comic cartoonists in local and national newspapers. Daumier's direct
view of situations invites the audience to look further into his drawings. His
democratic approach to caricatures of both famous and everyday people,
and his brilliant mastery of drawing inspired his own era as well as ours, and
likely many generations to come.

[Matt Brownley, *Class of 2005* and
Catherine Carter Goebel, *Professor of Art History,
Paul A. Anderson Chair in the Arts*]

[1] Catherine Carter Goebel, *Tracing Line Through Time: A Whistler Centenary Exhibition* (Rock
Island: Augustana College, 2002), 92.

[2] Ibid.

[3] Robert Rey, *Honoré Daumier* (New York: Harry Abrams, Inc., 1966), 15.

[4] Goebel, 92.

[5] Jacques Lassaigne, *Daumier* (Paris: The Hyperion Press, 1938), 10.

[6] Ibid., 15.

[7] Goebel, 92.

NADAR élevant la Photographie à la hauteur de l'Art

45

Artist unknown
Child Posing with Saint Bernard Dog, ascribed title, attributed to mid-19th century
Tintype photograph
Unsigned
9.0 x 6.5 cm., 3-1/8 x 2-1/8"
Purchase with Gift of Mr. Daryl Empen ('91) and Dr. Cynthia Empen ('92), Augustana College Art Collection, 2002.21

The history of photography, as compared to other types of art, is relatively short, since the medium was only discovered in the nineteenth century. The year 1839 marked photography's first public appearance, although some earlier experiments had already been conducted.[1] Debate still remains as to who invented the first photograph—between the Englishman, William Henry Fox Talbot or the Frenchman, Louis-Jacques-Mande Daguerre.[2] With this new medium, many more people could now carry portraits of their loved ones, a luxury formerly reserved for the wealthy who commissioned fine miniature paintings, hand painted on ivory. With photography, the middle class could afford portraits, and the process caught on quickly as it was faster and cheaper than constructing a small painting.

Although photographs were made with remarkable speed and ease, they still demanded a period of waiting time for the actual picture to be shot. The first cameras required a subject to sit still for up to five minutes, perhaps longer, making it difficult to create images with fresh smiling faces, rambunctious young children and the family pets. The camera picked up any movement, as the impression was burned, with light, onto the glass or silver plate, and much later, onto film. The process may have been more efficient than miniature paintings, but it generally did not produce a happy, relaxed image of the sitter. This was the unfortunate case until the introduction of *tintype*, more appropriately known as ferrotype photography.[3]

With the invention of tintype photography in 1854, the process of making photographs became quicker and cheaper.[4] With tintypes, pictures could be taken in a second or less and subjects no longer had to hold a pose for extended periods, making the resulting impressions more naturalistic and true to life. The tintype was a simplified and easier method of daguerreotype photography. The daguerreotype technique created beautifully detailed photographs and was very popular within upper class societies, initially, the only people who could afford them.[5] These photographs cost around fifty dollars, which was a great deal of money at the time. They also were extremely fragile because they were produced on thin plates of glass.[6]

The tintype photo became popular largely due to the Civil War, since it allowed soldiers to send pictures of themselves home to their loved ones owing to the metal's resilience.[7] Tintypes also required fewer steps in the photographic process. With the tintype process, photographers did not have to let the base of the photo dry, and no negative was needed; the photo itself was the negative, pictures were therefore created in reverse of the original image.[8] Simply put, tintypes were made by covering thin sheets of iron with a layer of black paint. An iodized collodian coating and silver nitrate solution allowed a picture to be burnt on the black japanned surface when exposed to light. Because the tintype was so easy and low in cost, it became a common medium for money-making vendors on the street, largely replacing painting and drawing.[9] Many amateur photographers worked extensively with tintypes as the market expanded to the lower class.[10] The tintype was so inexpensive, in fact, that the photographs were not even produced on actual tin, but onto metallic sheets, or cheap iron.[11] Some sources suggest that the process was named *tintype* because tin shears were used to part the image from its plate. The tintype remained popular longer than any other photographic material, other than film, lasting from around the mid-1850s until the 1930s.[12] The invention of roll film a few years later, ended the market for tintype photography, yet tintypes are considered desirable art collectibles today and occupy a very important place in the history of photography. This photo was created with the tintype photography technique.

This piece, *Child Posing with Saint Bernard Dog*, is a perfect example of the more spontaneous photograph possible through tintype. The portrait of the child appears to be caught more in the moment, and not staged like past portraits. The face has more life to it and her pose is more naturalistic. The large dog's inclusion in this picture is very engaging, giving the photo further personality and the child more identity. If this portrait had been taken before tintypes were invented, it would have been difficult, and likely ruined by the dog or small child, since they would have had to remain immobile for some time, which would have been virtually impossible. This portrait has an unknown artist, possibly because it was taken by an amateur photographer or even a family member, considering that the process was fairly simple. The setting represents an elegant interior of the day, which might also be a photography studio.

When considering art of today, the idea of the artist has great importance as it did in the nineteenth century and the distant past. Photographers like Nadar (catalogue 44) hoped to elevate photography's position, so that it would be considered a major art medium like painting and sculpture. Yet, these tintype photographs were not considered so much an art form as a simple snapshot, similar to the way people view photographs today. Tintype photography will forever have its important place in history, however, because it was perhaps the most crucial step in the history of photography. The tintype brought photography out of the realms of science and artistic luxury, within the grasp of real people in the modern world.

[Randi Higel, *Class of 2008*]

[1] Graham Clarke, *The Photograph* (New York: Oxford University Press, 1997), 11-25.

[2] Ibid., 16.

[3] "Tintype," *Popular History of Photography*, City Gallery, 2000. http://www.city-gallery.com/learning/types/tintype/index.php, 1. (17 Feb. 2005).

[4] Ibid.

[5] Beaumont Newhall, *The History of Photography: From 1839 to the Present Day* (New York: The Museum of Modern Art, 1964), 47.

[6] John Deason, Art Department, Personal Interview, 8 February 2005.

[7] Tintype 2.

[8] Robert Deaso Leggat, "The Tintype Process," *A History of Photography*, http://www.rleggat.com/photohistory/tintype.htmln, 1. (3 February 2005).

[9] Leggat, 1.

[10] Deason.

[11] Leggat, 1.

[12] "Tintype," 1.

46

Artist unknown
Children Blowing Bubbles, ascribed title, attributed to mid-19th century
Italy
Oil on linen
Unsigned
81.1 x 65.3 cm., 31-15/16 x 25-5/8"
Paul A. Anderson Chair in the Arts Purchase, Augustana College Art
Collection, SDC2004.13

This charming oil painting on linen is likely from nineteenth-century Italy. The artist and title are unknown, but the loose brushstrokes and subject matter relate to nineteenth-century Impressionism. This image of *Children Blowing Bubbles* is a *genre* scene, meaning that it captures a slice of everyday life. Such scenes were popular with the growing bourgeoisie who valued straightforward representations of the real world. Following the Enlightenment, and with the advent of Romanticism, the state of childhood was elevated. As a result, fairytales were collected and beautiful illustrated children's books were published to reinforce the wonder of childhood, reinforcing that children should be allowed to be children, and enjoy themselves with leisure activities. Specific colors of this piece stand out, for example the bright red color on the young girl's bandana and the rosy pink in their cheeks. The bubbles are painted in *trompe l'oeil* (trick the eye) manner, with amazing translucence, making viewers believe they are real and possibly coming out of the artwork itself. The manner in which the bubbles and children seem to extend from the frame reinforces this illusion.

Displayed are a young boy, perhaps four or five years old, and most likely his older sister who appears to be around ten years of age. The girl seems to be taller and more developed in her facial characteristics. In an "older sister fashion," she is holding the cup of bubbles close to the boy, so he can easily share them with her. It seems reasonable to conclude that they are siblings, because of their similar facial features. Also, their close proximity reflects a comfortable familial relationship, similar to those depicted by Mary Cassatt between mothers and their children (catalogue 55). The dark background prevents the audience from being distracted from the subject at hand.

Following the Industrial Revolution, communities changed as labor shifted from rural farms toward urban factories. The western world was now timed, not by nature but by the clock.[1] Social status, based on income and class, was a prominent factor in the eyes of most people. Another interesting trend that came into play during the nineteenth century was the decreasing number of children as family sizes diminished. This meant that parents in middle class households could now devote more attention to each child, yet in the lower classes, many children were still denied play and forced to work, often in unsavory factories.

Before the nineteenth century, children were generally expected to behave as small adults. "Traditionally a child's task was to become an adult, and any activities considered suitable for adults were equally accepted for children."[2] With society's embracing the wonder of childhood, clothing began to reflect a more relaxed attitude. For instance: "little boys had always been dressed in frocks for their first few years and worn trousers but now were wearing colorful knee length frocks and white trousers."[3] Girls could now wear pants to play. Hairstyles ranged from very short and serviceable to long curls down the shoulders. "Children appeared to be sweet and innocent... descended directly from heaven to their earthly homes."[4]

Not only did the outward appearances of children begin to change but their environments did as well. These characteristics were the physical

confirmation that children were allowed more freedom and offered the ability to play. No longer were they limited to walking around like perfect little sanitized dolls that should behave as adults. Although slow to change, efforts also developed to limit and ultimately abandon child labor, acknowledging the importance of childhood development.

Parents began to provide a separate space within the house in which their children could play, called the *nursery, indoor play area* or *day nursery*.[5] By giving their children educational toys, they clearly encouraged their development.[6] Popular toys at the time included dolls, alphabet blocks, children's books, card games, tea sets, sports equipment, farm animals, locomotives and steamboats.

The number of leisure activities in general also increased, not only for children, but for the family as a whole. Family time was important and not taken for granted, as a contemporary source advised: "in the best and happiest homes games and pastimes have their place. There can be no doubt that men and women are helped to happier and better lives by home amusements. The children who are permitted and encouraged to enjoy healthful and innocent games at home cling closer to their homes. They are not tempted to go elsewhere for the amusement for which Nature has given them to desire."[7] Capturing such subtle nuances of children's everyday activities and games was natural for nineteenth-century Impressionists, aided by photographers who constructed portraits (catalogue 45) and genre scenes of children.

Although this particular painter remains unknown, it is possible that the artist was inspired by eighteenth-century genre master, Jean Simeon Chardin. Chardin painted *Soap Bubbles* in 1734, a similar composition showing children blowing bubbles. The position of the children is comparable to this painting in that we see only a portion of the boys' faces because they are looking towards the ground and not towards the audience. In one version, Chardin painted a little boy, presumably the younger brother of the boy blowing bubbles, standing tall as he peers up at his brother and watches him with great interest. The siblings' subject also connects these two pieces. In a majority of Chardin's artworks depicting children, their cheeks were similarly rosy. Also, like this artist, Chardin made a point of inserting a red highlight, as we have here.

Nineteenth-century artists often copied works by the Old Masters as part of their formal training. Works of art from the past also influenced them to interpret similar subjects within their own context. In this manner, painters were inspired to recreate as they made their own relevant masterpieces. Chardin's example was perhaps reinterpreted here in a more animated and spontaneous fashion and technique in order to reflect nineteenth-century sensibilities. It is thus not merely a genre scene, but a document that reflects the changing role of childhood in the nineteenth century. Children who were formerly unable to have the opportunity to play were now able to do so. This artist has effectively captured a quick, lively moment in history, perhaps as fragile and transient as the very bubbles depicted.

[Jessica Whetzal, *Class of 2007*]

[1] Joesph E. Illick, *American Childhood* (Philadelphia: Pennsylvania University Press, 2002), 57.

[2] Karin Calvert, *Children in the House* (Boston: Northeastern University Press, 1992), 48.

[3] Jessica H. Foy and Thomas J. Schlereth, eds., *American Home Life, 1880-1930: A Social History of Spaces and Services* (Knoxville: University of Tennessee Press, 1992), 77.

[4] Ibid.

[5] Ibid., 81.

[6] Ibid,. 84.

[7] Ibid., 146.

47

Artist unknown, American folk artist
Where Do Fairies Hide Their Heads?, ascribed title, attributed to mid-to-late 19th century
Oil on canvas
Unsigned
68.8 x 55.9 cm., 27-1/8 x 22"
Paul A. Anderson Chair in the Arts Purchase, Augustana College Art Collection, 2002.7

It is interesting to look at this portrait in comparison to other nineteenth-century pieces. The tradition of American portraiture had been affected by the Enlightenment thinkers John Locke and Jean-Jacques Rousseau. Their ideas about childhood emphasized children's natural gifts—the capacity to learn and the innocence that precedes experience of social relations outside the family.[1] This departure from a Puritan ideology that viewed children as flawed by original sin led to changes in the portraiture tradition of stiffly positioned, properly dressed figures featured early in the 1800s. The girl in this portrait, apparently starting adolescence, seems to exhibit a more innocent and free nature than children from earlier eras in American painting. Although she is seated upright, the girl tilts her head comfortably as she looks out. Her expression seems comfortable and her long hair flows nearly to her waist.

The paper or magazine in the girl's hands is quite possibly the most interesting part of the portrait. Children in earlier portraits usually held a toy, a flower or an unidentifiable book. These objects signaled family status and values, often revealing American ingenuity in the homemade toys, or preference for pets like squirrels and games or dolls involving motion. Sometimes a child wore beads that showed the wealth of her family. The papers in this portrait bear the heading "Oh where do fairies hide their heads?" The girl is thus linked to a world beyond the United States; she is a reader—or perhaps a musician—who participates, like many other anglo-Americans, in the popular culture of England and Ireland. Although no author and date is given in the portrait, a poem with this very title was written by Thomas Haynes Bayly in 1797. Bayly was a British songwriter and

dramatist who, inspired by a visit to Dublin, wrote many ballads still sung today. The ballad about the fairies hiding their heads was circulated as both a song and a poem; one printing of the poem appeared in 1895 in A *Victorian Anthology*,[2] and it also appeared in earlier collections designed for girls.[3] So it is safe to place this portrait in the mid-to-late nineteenth century. By the end of the century, childhood had become a valued stage that should, if possible, be prolonged. Thus the image of a teenager holding a text about fairies suggests how well-off Americans romanticized their young[4] even in the face of social concern about the condition of child laborers in the factories and mills.

Bayly's poem suggests that the "little spirits" of the fairies appear in our world only when "green leaves come again." In times of frost and snow, the fairies may hide in coral caves of the sea, or even set up winter parties in "red Vesuvius." Once they return in the spring, nothing can stop their music and mischief, and "The maids, to keep the elves aloof/ Will bar the doors in vain; /No key hole will be fairy-proof/ When green leaves come again." This assertion that fairies can't be kept away in spring is a hint that girls will share their mischief and freedom. While the question of where fairies hide their heads in winter is an early version of Holden Caulfield's preoccupation with how fish survive New York cold as well as how children can be saved from adulthood, the poem and portrait do not share this later American literary lament about inevitable loss of innocence. The young girl we see in the painting seems steadfastly and cheerfully situated in her late childhood. Sentimental subject matter in art was a preference of many limners and buyers. It is possible that the young girl's family knew and chose the artist in line with this desire to celebrate their daughter's talent and beauty without fear of its loss.

[Nancy L. Huse, *Professor of English*
and Anne Motto, *Class of 2008*]

[1] Sandra Brant and Elissa Cunningham, *Small Folk: A Celebration of Childhood in America* (New York: E.P. Dutton in association with Museum of American Folk Art, 1980), 4.

[2] Edmund Stedman, ed., *A Victorian Anthology*, 1837-1895, http://www.bartleby.com/246/ .

[3] www.english.ucsb.edu/faculty/rraley/research/anthologies/girls.html l.

[4] Anne Scott MacLeod, *American Childhood: Essays on Children's Literature of the Nineteenth and Twentieth Centuries* (Athens and London: The University of Georgia Press, 1994), *passim*.

48

John Dabour (b. Turkey, American 1837–1905)
Child on Second Empire Balcony, ascribed title, 1872
Pastel
Signed b.r. "Dabour/1872"
76.4 x 63.5 cm., 30-1/8 x 24-15/16"
Paul A. Anderson Chair in the Arts Purchase, Augustana College Art
Collection, 2004.14

Child on a Second Empire Balcony is a beautiful pastel created by John Dabour in 1872. The date indicates that this work was completed at the dawn of the Impressionist movement in Paris (the first Impressionist exhibition occurred two years later in 1874). The image depicts a charming young child posing along the edge of a balcony while she stands directly in front of a room framed by curtains. The composition thus combines elements of genre and portrait paintings—in that she is an actual person depicted within an everyday setting enjoying a common activity.

John Dabour studied in Paris at the prestigious *École des Beaux-Arts* (School of Fine Arts). Shortly after the Civil War, he settled in the Baltimore, Maryland area and is thus generally considered an American artist. His oeuvre consisted mainly of portraits and landscape scenes executed in oil and pastel. His success is evidenced by the fact that he was commissioned to paint a series of portraits for the prominent Latrobe family, members of aristocratic Baltimore society. These portraits reflect Dabour's skill in modeling as well as his unique settings in paintings.[1] It is uncertain if this image was part of that series or even a portrait of one of the artist's own children.

Although the date, in French terms, indicates the early beginnings of Impressionism, it was created when Dabour was working in the United States, developmentally far behind contemporary European movements. American Impressionism began long after the Civil War. Notable American artists such as Thomas Eakins and Winslow Homer pursued Realism during this time and as a result, Impressionism really did not take root until the turn of the century. Dabour's inspiration, thus, was most likely based on his study in Paris where artists like Claude Monet were already experimenting with looser brushwork and scenes of everyday bourgeois life.

Dabour's image reflects the Impressionist immediacy of capturing a specific moment in time as well as the sweet innocence of childhood that Mary Cassatt would establish as her hallmark (catalogue 55). Like Cassatt, an American working in Paris, Dabour presented this child in a believable and sympathetic manner at eye level. One cannot help but be intrigued by her expression, and wonder, exactly what is the focus of her gaze? She seemingly looks out toward the audience, yet beyond us as well.

This image reflects elements of both modernism and tradition. We are presented with seemingly contradictory characteristics, such as an industrial wrought iron railing behind which a beautiful child in classical-revival dress stands. The metal factory-made floral patterns contrast with the natural delicate flower she holds. We are confronted with the immediacy of a sort of photographic zoom-lens view of a balcony in a modern apartment building yet softened by the traditional beauty of the pastel medium, traceable to such artists as Neoclassicist, Gavin Hamilton (catalogue 19).

Most likely, this child spies an inviting distant garden and longs to go there.

Along with portraits, Dabour's portfolio also included many landscape scenes of local urban parks. Such gardens were popular on the American east coast as well as in Paris during this time (catalogue 66A and 66B). Frederick Olmsted, renowned landscape architect, had recently argued for the importance of open space within communities. He promised that it would add a pleasing aesthetic value to the landscape, stating that designers were: "...entitled to restrict...a large tract of land set apart by the public for the enjoyment of rural landscape, as distinguished from a public square, a public garden, or a promenade, fit only for more urbanized pleasures.[2] Dabour captured such landscapes in many of his works, and here, through their implied presence beyond the picture frame, he suggests that this figure is indeed observing nature.

Child on a Second Empire Balcony thus presents a view toward a modern edifice, either constructed in Paris or in America in the French fashion. *Second Empire* refers to the architectural style patronized by Emperor Napoleon III, nephew of Napoleon Bonaparte, during his reign in the *Second Empire*. Such apartments were filled with the *nouveau riche*, newly moneyed families who gained their wealth through non-traditional methods of mercantilism and industry, establishing an aristocratic form of the middle class. Evidence of such social status is reinforced through the expensive and elaborate regal blue velvet drapes highlighted by white lace sheers. These curtains frame the child as the main point of interest for the work, essentially creating a stage-set for the scene.[3]

The pink flower she holds is a trumpet petunia, a native flower of France. This bloom seems to have been plucked from the vine or ivy entangled around the wrought iron railing of the balcony. A repeated pattern of this vegetation is seen throughout the image. Floral patterns are apparent in the lace sheers, the flowers on the vines and on the bottom section of the railing as well. This repeated three petal design might represent the insignia of France, the *fleur-de-lis*, or lily flower, symbol for the king. By the time Dabour created this image, the emblem was adopted and incorporated into most French architecture as was the use of wrought iron.[4]

Stylistic characteristics common to modernist images are evident in this artwork. The gaze of the child invokes a hidden meaning underlying the image. Her stoic expression and strong eye contact toward the viewer establishes psychological interaction with her audience and invites an emotional reaction, reminiscent of Romantic interests in mood and interpretation. Landscaped gardens effectively pulled people from inside of their homes out into nature. By elevating their perceptions, the views became grander. Such aerial perspectives, inspired by modern photography (catalogue 44) and architecture, would become a defining characteristic of modernism.

[Michael Skelton, *Class of 2005*]

[1] E. Bénézit, *Dictionaire des Peinters, Sculpteurs. Dessinateurs et Graveurs* Vol. 4 (Paris, France: Gründ Editions, 1999), 170. "Dabour, John. Né en 1837 à Smyrne (Turquie). XIX siècle. Américain. Peintre de portraits. Élève à Paris de l'Ecole Nationale des Beaux-Arts et de Jeanson. Il résida, outré des PORTRAITS (crayon et sanguine) au Salon des Artistes Francais en 1922." Translated by Kim Vivian, German Department.

[2] Frederick Law Olmsted, *Forty Years of Landscape Architecture: Central Park* (London, England: The MIT Press, 1973), 3-4. "When Mr. Olmsted used the term in his address 'The Justifying Value of a Public Park' in 1870, he considered that he was entitled to restrict the meaning to a large tract of land set apart by the public for the enjoyment of rural landscape, as distinguished from a public square, a public garden, or a promenade, fit only for more urbanized pleasures."

[3] Catherine Goebel, Art History Department, *Notes of Lecture Dated 4-28-03*. Typical characteristics found in works of Modernist period.

[4] Ibid.

49

William Henry Jackson (American 1843–1942)
Panoramic View of the Valley of the Yellowstone—No. 2, 1873
Albumen print photograph
Signed with printed text gold stamp in margins, at b.l. "W.H. Jackson,
Photo" and t.r. "Dept. of the Interior. U.S. Geological Survey of the
Territories. Prof F.V. Hayden, in Charge." and b.r. "Washington, D.C."
26.0 x 33.6. cm., 10-1/4 x 13-1/4" image
40.3 x 49.5 cm., 15-7/8 x 19- 9/16" sheet
Gift of Mr. and Mrs. Victor H. and Isabel Bartolome, Augustana College
Art Collection, 90.1.3

Born and raised in New England, William Henry Jackson began his
photographic career at the age of 15, working for a portrait studio in upstate
New York. He was a young, self-taught artist, who learned much about
photography from his employment at the art studio. Between 1870 and 1878,
Jackson was sent on an expedition to the Yellowstone Valley. He served as
the official photographer for the Geological and Geographical Survey of
the Western territories.[1] Jackson's photographs of the Western frontier
helped consolidate the expansion of America across the West. Images of
the uncivilized barren lands inspired pioneers to explore and settle this
uncharted region.[2]

Jackson was known for combining classical and picturesque elements in
order to create landscape photographs. The dramatic lighting effect is much
like the clear definition used in works by the Neoclassicists and added to
the picturesque quality of the piece. The artistic elements he employed,
combined with the inspiration he created in his audience to explore the
western territory, provided Jackson with a flourishing career. He became
known for his beautiful images that appeared on postcards, advertisements
and other forms of media publications.[3] He was, however, most widely
acclaimed for his exploration of the Western territories, namely the
Yellowstone Valley (known today as Yellowstone National Park).

In photographing the wondrous Yellowstone Valley, Jackson contemplated
both the aesthetic and promotional values that could be captured within his
images. Camera technology in the nineteenth century was far less advanced
than it is today. Equipment was fragile and very large, making travel a
challenge. Despite the difficulty of portabilty to various locations, Jackson
managed to perfect his technique.

In many of his photographs, he angled the camera to make the scene seem
enormous, perhaps suggesting that human beings are negligible compared
to the size of the Western territory. Jackson's son wrote a book about the
life and work of his father and confirmed Jackson's innovation when he
wrote: "In his pictures the pioneer age would have immortality…Where
else could the future generations see the wild majesty of the Western land;

the grim faces of its aboriginals, free and proud in their own country; the
thrust outward of restless white men by road and rail from the Mississippi
to the Pacific? High and far, from the canyon rim and mountain top,
his camera looked out on the West."[4] The land was indeed the subject of
each photograph and the chiaroscuro (light and dark contrast) provided a
monumental and sublime effect.[5]

Panoramic View of the Valley of the Yellowstone—No. 2 was a photograph
taken in 1873. By this time, photography was becoming influential as an art
form. This work is a panoramic landscape photograph, and thereby provides
the audience with an aerial perspective. The medium of the piece is known
as an albumen print, made by coating a thin sheet of paper with egg white
and salt and then floating the paper in a silver nitrate solution to make it
light sensitive. The image is created by exposing the albumen paper under a
wet-plate glass negative in sunlight.[6]

The photograph of the Yellowstone Valley consists primarily of sky. The
texture of the piece creates a mystical haze, accomplished by fading the
color upward. The trees are the only parallel element of the piece, providing
a geometrical linear composition. The horizontal water of the ravines
contrasts the vertically positioned trees, providing a structured sense
of order to nature, similar to a grid pattern. Mountains appear in the
background which reinforce the effect of depth and convey the vastness of
the Yellowstone Valley.

Panoramic View of the Valley of the Yellowstone—No. 2 was one of many of
Jackson's renditions of the valley. It is most comprehensible if read within
its contemporary context of the nation's goal to expand its territory. The
elements Jackson employed in his pieces became popular because of the
uniqueness within the images. He was one of the first photographers
to capture these unknown lands and successfully inspire a historical
movement. Jackson, even today, is considered a pioneer in both America's
historic westward expansion as well as the overall evolution of field
photography.[7]

[Alisha Kumar, *Class of 2006*]

[1] "How the West was Won-Photographically," *The British Journal of Photography*, 150 (March 26, 2003):12.

[2] "How the West was Won: Reinventing the Myth of William Henry Jackson." *Visual Studies Workshop (1989)*, 16.

[3] Ellen Handy, "Postcard Sublime: William Henry Jackson's Western Landscapes," *Visual Resources, 17* (2001): 417-432.

[4] Ibid., 421.

[5] *William Henry Jackson: Pioneer Photographer of Yellowstone*, Buffalo Bill Historical Center Web site, http://www.bbhc.org/wgwa/WHJ.cfm (January 28, 2005).

[6] *"A Gallery for Fine Photography,"* http://www.agallery.com/Pages/photographers/jackson.html. (January 28, 2005)

[7] Vicki Goldberg, "The Mythic West: William Henry Jackson Photographed a Land of the Dreamiest Dreams," *American Photographer*, 23 (1989): 68.

50

Francis Holl (British 1815–1884) after William Powell Frith (English/British 1819–1909)
The Railway Station, 1866, published by Henry Graves & Co.
Engraving
Signed b.l. below image in graphite "W.P. Frith" and b.r. below image in graphite "Francis Holl" and marked b.r. in plate with publisher's monogram; and t.c. in printed text "London; Published October 1st, 1866, by Henry Graves and Co., The Proprietors, Publishers to the Queen and The Prince and Princess of Wales __@ Pall Mall Copyright Registered" 51.9 x 111.4 cm., 20-7/16 x 43-7/8" image
Paul A. Anderson Chair in the Arts Purchase, Augustana College Art Collection, 2000.12

The Railway Station (1862) was originally painted in oil by British artist William Powell Frith and engraved in 1866. The image is impressive with its large dramatic setting, filled with a staggering variety of characters and stories, assembled along the platform of Paddington train station in London. Within the figural group, there is a great range of emotion, including sadness, joy, fear and surprise. The participants are beautifully delineated in a composition that exemplifies the English love for narrative, earlier explored by eighteenth-century artist, William Hogarth in *Marriage-a-la-Mode* (catalogue 14). Unlike Hogarth, however, Frith did not moralize but instead, exploited the Victorian fascination with intrigue as well as the hustle and bustle of modern life.

Frith appropriately constructed an accurate description of Victorian life in England, with a full representation of social classes, ranging from thieves to major leaders of industry. Because it tells so many different stories, it is difficult to discern a singular focus. One of the most interesting aspects of Victoriana relates to Paddington Station itself. This engraving "...presents a view into a world revolutionized with the accelerated transportation of the train, which brought greater speed and efficiency to modern life, making the international regularization of time essential. The train station also represents modernity in that it was the most cutting-edge type of urban architecture, constructed with steel and glass, which would ultimately evolve into the skyscraper."[1] The effect of the structure is magnificent with its arches making it appear as architecturally significant as an ancient Roman amphitheater. The train, a powerful symbol of the modern industrial age, is another key element, completed with the aid of contemporary photographs.

French critic, Charles Baudelaire (catalogue 41), in his French Salon reviews from the 1840s, called for artists to depict the *heroism of modern life* with the "thousand existences" that comprised the "floating life of a great city."[2] Artists like Frith, although conservative in terms in style, narrative and technique, depicted subjects that reinforced these modernist viewpoints and anticipated Impressionist scenes of the 1860s and 1870s (catalogue 42 and 43). Until this time, they were reluctant to paint portraits in contemporary costume. Even Frith was anxious as he anticipated the potential critical response to his illustrating "hats and trousers...[part of] the drawbacks of unpicturesque dress."[3] As Pre-Raphaelite painter, Sir John Everett Millais complained: "Artists have to wrestle today with the horrible antagonism of modern dress...Just imagine Vandyck's Charles I in a pair of checker trousers."[4]

Frith challenged conservative tradition by illustrating modern subjects and finishing them on the scale of history paintings. One critic scoffed at his effrontery in a similar work, describing it as: "a piece of vulgar Cockney business unworthy of being represented even in an illustrated newspaper."[5] This writer clearly referred to such vignettes as George Du Maurier's *Metropolitan Railway Types* (catalogue 51), published in the popular Victorian journal, *Punch, or the London Charivari*. Like Frith, du Maurier focused on the everyday activities of Londoners, generally deemed

appropriate for magazines, but not for academic paintings. Frith also challenged tradition by exhibiting this painting privately, rather than at the esteemed Royal Academy. According to an article in the *Illustrated London News*, *The Railway Station* attracted 83,000 visitors which resulted in a large subscription list for the engraving.[6]

Frith included a portrait of his own family, just left of center,[7] as well as many other contemporaries in the composition. The scene of the mother kissing her child *goodbye* captures the viewer's attention. There are tears in both the eyes of the mother and the children as one is about to board the train. It invites a sentimental reaction, typical of Victorian art in general. One of the unique aspects of this painting is the inclusion of the steam engine train, evidence of the new urban technology, as part of the background rather than the center of attention. Frith thus pleased his growing bourgeois audience by depicting recognizable subjects in a realistic style. He ultimately developed into a well-respected painter, elected a full member of the Royal Academy in 1852. His first large genre painting, *Ramsgate Sands* (1851), was even purchased by Queen Victoria. He continued this type with *Derby Day* (1858) and *The Railway Station* (1862). These three paintings of contemporary Victorian life established Frith as one of the major British artists of his time.

The Railway Station truly captured its historical era. Frith, however, came to be regarded by more avant-garde artists of the day as overly popular and anecdotal in his views. In the famous Whistler V. Ruskin libel trial, American expatriate James McNeill Whistler (catalogue 40, 60 and 61) took powerful Victorian art critic, John Ruskin to court. Whistler charged Ruskin with libel for his press review, which not only attacked Whistler's art, but his character as well. Frith was called as a witness for Ruskin against Whistler. Ruskin and Frith preferred recognizable images that were straightforward and reflected good Victorian traits of hard work and industry. Whistler, on the other hand, felt that fine art was based on the artist's "knowledge of a lifetime"[8] and not the amount of time expended. And if, indeed, artists were simply meant to replicate nature, Whistler further argued, then "the king of artists would be the photographer."[9]

Related to this debate, French illustrator, Honoré Daumier, in the same year as the *Railway Station*, illustrated photographer Nadar in a hot air balloon, with the clever caption: "Nadar Raising Photography to the Height of Art," (catalogue 44). This cartoon referred to photographers like Nadar who advocated public acceptance of their medium at the same esteemed level as traditional fine art. In representing mainstream Victorian viewpoints, Frith's images resemble a quick photographic view from everyday life and were indeed based on photographs. Whistler's colleague in the *Art for Art's Sake Movement*, Oscar Wilde, ironically and conversely summarized that through such straightforward, non-elitist viewpoints, Frith effectively "elevated [or reduced] art to the level of photography."[10]

> [Preston Taylor, *Class of 2007* and
> Catherine Carter Goebel, *Professor of Art History,*
> *Paul A. Anderson Chair in the Arts*]

[1] Paul Arnell and Catherine Carter Goebel, *Paul A. Anderson Art History Collection*, ed. Catherine Carter Goebel (Rock Island: Augustana College, 2001), 94.

[2] Julian Treuherz, *Victorian Painting* (London: Thames and Hudson, 1993), 106.

[3] Ibid., 107.

[4] Ibid., 108.

[5] Ibid.

[6] Aubrey Noakes, *William Frith: Extraordinary Victorian Painter* (London: Jupiter, 1978), 74.

[7] Ibid., 72.

[8] James McNeill Whistler, *The Gentle Art of Making Enemies* (London: William Heinemann, 1892), 5.

[9] Ibid., 128.

[10] Noakes, 14.

51

George du Maurier (French 1834–1896)
Metropolitan Railway Types, published in **Punch, or the London Charivari,** January 10, 1891, page 18
Sepia ink drawing
Signed b.r. "du Maurier"
Inscribed: "Metropolitan Railway Types / The party that never says 'Thank You!'—The party that always says 'Thank You!'/ When you open the door, or shut the window, or give up your seat for her."
14.6 x 18.4 cm., 5-1/4 x 7-1/4" image
Lent Courtesy of Private Collection

George du Maurier played a crucial role in the Victorian public art world during the second half of the nineteenth century. He was unafraid to lock horns, through his art, with some of the most common issues of Victorian English society.[1] *Metropolitan Railway Types* (1891) is a wonderful example of just that. The fine strokes of sepia ink clearly outline the message being sent. This print attacks the issues of modern fashion, transportation and the new social medium of railway trains.[2]

Du Maurier however, did not always aspire to be an artist. His dream was to be an opera singer. Although that never came to fruition, he made a successful career as an active illustrator and published novelist, reflective of the emerging media boom which was building to full force. With it came the explosion of more accessible art and literature. These appeared in the form of magazines, newspapers and the cartoons that they contained. Du Maurier began illustrating for the journal, *Once a Week*, and then after a few years was asked to work for *Punch*, a popular magazine and one of the first to include satire, where he focused most of the rest of his career. He counted among his peers artists Charles Keene (catalogue 52) and Phil May (catalogue 53), as *Punch* enlisted many of the finest illustrators of the time.

The image seen in *Metropolitan Railway Types* is soft and beautifully delineated. The earthy hues of the sepia ink present a subtle contrast to the harsh humor being presented. Du Maurier was often extolled for his criticism of those who tried to unsuccessfully emulate the latest fashions.[3] He often attacked the *nouveau riche* (newly rich) and the devotees of the *Aesthetic Movement*. His subtle humor and good use of iconography evidence a new elevated level in the field of satire. As for symbolism, it is effectively displayed in the humor that the artist communicates. There is a great deal of insight revealed in the images of these two women, through contrasting their appearances and manner of dress, as well as investigating the location where the scene takes place: within a modern railway station.

The setting provides the context for this drawing's commentary. The social norms and taboos of Victorian times were very stringent to say the least. How one behaved in a public place was sure to resonate across the entire social structure. The caption pays tribute to this idea. The concept of good manners and appropriate behavior comes crashing into the media scene with every stroke from du Maurier's hand.

The late-nineteenth century hailed a return to female idealism, which is easily shown with the shapely figure on the right. With this return to idealism also came the concept of image value in advertising, which was also the basis for this parody. The caption reads: "The Party That *Always* Says 'Thank You'…." Du Maurier based his ideal woman on the ancient Greek sculpture, the *Venus de Milo*. He kept a miniature version of this famous statue on his mantle for inspiration. He described this famous piece: "How well I know her! Almost thoroughly by this time—for she has been the silent companion for thirty years."[4] Henry James recognized du Maurier's traditional base when he described the artist's ideal woman as having "an inestimable look of repose, a kind of Greek serenity."[5]

Being socially conservative, du Maurier had little sympathy for the liberated modern woman. This is clearly evident in the sharply discernable difference between the two figures: the ideal, classical lady of manners on the right versus the abrasive and non-ideal independent woman on the left. The woman on the left, of course, lacks the manners to say "thank you." The use of mass media was now in full swing, and the primary combatant was the satirist. Throughout Europe and America, the public was rapidly embracing the modern fact that if you did not look like the advertisements, you were somehow inferior.[6] Du Maurier illuminated this message quite sharply. His eye for the subtleties that society presented was exquisite, and his ability to capture the emotions felt, through his writing and imagery, absolutely accurate.

We are presented with the idea of locomotives as a social setting. They were new, and fast, but few people had thought about their context in society. Now it became one more place to be chivalrous, or to display the latest fashions. Whether aboard a new train, or waiting in a station, people were forced to interact in new ways. The media was there to print it and du Maurier, to witness and draw it. Like William Powell Frith's *Railway Station* (catalogue 50), du Maurier's work revealed the new challenges and pace that modern life offered. As in Frith's depiction, the station becomes a stage-set for modern drama—we are presented with two distinct female types in this image, as well as their audience of gentlemen in the background, who react in quite different manners between them. Du Maurier captured the subtleties of a vastly changing world and its characters within a foundation of classical formal education. As he described his enthusiasm for modernity: "mere life is such a beauty in itself that no stone ideal can ever hope to match it."[7]

[John Bianchin, *Class of 2008*]

[1] On Du Maurier, see "George Du Maurier, Illustrator and Novelist (1834 - 1896): An overview," The Victorian Web, 2004, http://www.victorian web.org/art/illustration/dumaurier/ (september 18, 2004.).

[2] Daphne DuMaurier, *The Young George Du Maurier* (New York: Doubleday, 1952), 43.

[3] Derek Pepys Whitley, *George Du Maurier* (New York: Pellegrini & Cudahy, 1948), 12.

[4] Richard Kelly, *The Art of George du Maurier* (Aldershot: Scolar Press, 1996), 28.

[5] Ibid.

[6] www.victorian web.org

[7] Kelly, 28.

Metropolitan Railway Types.

The party that _never_ says "Thank you!" | The party that _always_ says "Thank you!"

When you open the door, or shut the windows, or give up your seat for her.

52

Charles Keene (British 1823–1891)
Chronic!, published in **Punch, or the London Charivari**, November 1, 1884, page 214
Ink drawing
Signed b.r. with monogram "C.K."
Inscribed: **CHRONIC!** /*Customer (coughing)*. "Have you anything you can recommend for Bronchitis?"/ *Polite Chemist*. "Certainly, Sir. The very Thing! Finest Remedy in the World,/ Sir—send it all over the Country! Ge'tleman in Wales, Sir—never without a/ Bottle—Eight Bottles a Month, Sir, he'll take sometimes!" [*Exit Customer, hastily*.]
20.2 x 13.9 cm., 8 x 5-3/8" image
Lent Courtesy of Private Collection

Charles Samuel Keene (1823–91) was a talented English artist whose works, including this drawing, were frequently published in *Punch*, a popular Victorian journal of the day. Respected as one of the finest draftsmen of his era, Keene illustrated members of society and their surroundings just as he observed them. As he once described: "If you can draw anything, you can draw everything."[1] Keene was apprenticed to the Whymper Brothers, who ran an important wood-engraving studio, where he learned the skills and discipline necessary toward sketching and engraving. After his apprenticeship, Keene lived the life of a bachelor, completely devoted to his work.

Nothing Keene drew was out of the ordinary, and that is precisely why so many people accepted and enthusiastically respected him. His beautiful drawings were originally glued to wood blocks to be engraved for multiple printings for *Punch*, and thus destroyed in the carving process. From 1872 on, however, a new photographic transfer method was discovered, that allowed drawings, such as this one, to be spared.[2] Keene could then keep the original drawings, which were reproduced for publication, often giving them as gifts to grateful friends and colleagues. His work related Victorian storytelling in true form. *Chronic!* exhibits Keene's style of illustrating the subtle humor discerned in viewing people going about their normal business. Most were born into their respective social classes and generally stayed within those structures. Keene carefully observed and immortalized all types of Victorians. As his colleague, H. Stacy Marks related: "Keene was accustomed at that time to draw straight from any object in pen and ink, without preparatory penciling, as a means of obtaining certainty and sureness of hand…[always ready to draw at a given moment, he] wore an ink bottle suspended from…[his] waistcoat buttons."[3]

Observations such as how people dressed and what they did for a living could define the class to which they belonged. Keene's work demonstrates assimilated learning based on direct and careful observation as well as his upbringing in the lower middle class in England. His immediacy was appreciated by fellow artists, such as Edgar Degas and Vincent Van Gogh, who enthusiastically collected his work. While Keene entertained the middle class of England, he thus impressed serious artists as well. At the Academy Banquet of 1891, the year of his death, Lord Leighton, President of the Royal Academy, praised Keene: "Never have the humours of the life of certain classes of Englishmen been seized with such enerring grasp as in his works; never have they been arrested with a more masterly, artistic skill. Among the documents for the study of future days of middle-class and of humble English life, none will be more weighty than the vivid sketches of this great humorist."[4]

In this drawing for *Chronic!*, we have a man making a selection at a drugstore counter. Across from him stands the druggist, who appears aged and experienced. The dignified gentleman placing his order is perhaps knowledgeable in the ways of modern medicine and has the means of purchasing the latest drugs and remedies. Coughing, he asks, "Have you anything you can recommend for Bronchitis?"

His attire displays his wealth. He wears a long coat and a top hat, a symbol of affluence. His rotund figure also demonstrates that he is well-fed. The man shows his authority by leaning over the counter towards the druggist, demanding his attention. While he places his order, the polite druggist listens carefully. He responds, "Certainly, Sir. The very Thing! Finest Remedy in the World, Sir—send it all over the Country! Ge'tleman in Wales, Sir—never without a Bottle—Eight Bottles a Month, Sir, he'll take sometimes!"[5] Certainly the viewer becomes curious as to what the ingredients might truly be in such a popular elixir!

The customer and the chemist share a regular conversation about a common illness. It was these types of interactions that appealed to Keene's audience. People felt they could relate to the characters in his drawings because they were so realistic since they were generally observed and sketched directly from life. Unfortunately, due to their publication via wood engravings translated by other artists, his general audience did not get to see the sparkling superior beauty of his original drawings. Here, beyond the story, we see the brilliant draftsmanship which many artists revered, such as James McNeill Whistler (catalogue 40, 60 and 61) and Joseph Pennell who believed: "He was just C. K., the greatest English artist since [William] Hogarth [catalogue 14]."[6]

Within the drawing, there are eye-catching components, such as the partially revealed sign in the corner, an advertisement for DROPS of some kind. Keene's use of cropping reflects the influence of photography. A quick snapshot could produce the same scene as the one drawn here. Cropping was very popular at this time with other artists, particularly the Impressionists. Further notable aspects of the drawing include the large containers on the shelves behind the druggist, which could have been used to hold a wide variety of substances ranging from herbal remedies to colorful dyes. What popular medicines were used to treat certain illnesses during this time period would be interesting to discern. Keene's objective sketch explains enough for an average person to understand the scene's main idea, but leaves enough information out to invite the observer (then and now) to apply it to his or her own life and experiences.

His major biographer, George Somes Layard, probably best summarized Keene's contribution to his time: "Keene's humour was the humour of observation rather than the humour of invention. An acute observer of Nature, an eager spectator of the passing expressions and moods of his fellow-creatures, an impressionist of the finest quality, given a subject which he could fully appreciate, and he would picture it with an unerring certainty, an uncompromising realism."[7]

[Katie Arnold, *Class of 2008*]

[1] Joseph Pennell, *The Work of Charles Keene* (New York: R. H. Russell, 1897), 34.

[2] Catherine Carter Goebel, *Tracing Line Through Time: A Whistler Centenary Exhibition* (Rock Island: Augustana College, 2002), 84.

[3] Simon Houfe, *The Work of Charles Samuel Keene* (Aldershot: Scolar Press, 1995), 24.

[4] George Somes Layard, *The Life and Letters of Charles Keene* (London: Sampson Lowe, 1892), 440.

[5] Charles Samuel Keene, "Chronic!," *Punch, Or The London Charivari*, Vol. 87 (1 November 1884): 214.

[6] Joseph Pennell, 36.

[7] Layard, 204.

53

Philip (also Philipp) William May, called Philmay (British 1864–1903)
Man Reading Newspaper in Crowd, 1896
Ink with graphite under drawing
Signed b.r. "Phil May 96"
26.7 x 15.5 cm., 10-7/16 x 6-1/8" sheet
Lent Courtesy of Private Collection

Philip William May *(Philmay)* was an English caricaturist and pen-and-ink illustrator who played a crucial role in the late nineteenth-century movement toward artistic depictions of city life. His work was greatly influenced by the escalating production of newspapers and magazines and the introduction of line-block photomechanical reproduction. James McNeill Whistler once declared, "modern black and white art could be summed up in two words—Phil May."[1]

May was born in Leeds to a downwardly mobile family. He quit school at age thirteen, and worked odd jobs until he settled into a career as a self-taught illustrator. "Draw firm and live jolly"[2] was his work-life attitude. Even after he married, May remained quite fond of bohemian life, whiskey drinking and rowdy parties in London.

Throughout his career, he created few book illustrations, preferring instead to work on magazine commissions and commercial advertisements. At the time of this illustration, he was primarily doing cartoons for the comic periodical, *Punch*, in the tradition of Charles Keene (catalogue 52) and George du Maurier (catalogue 51). When asked his opinion of Keene, he declared him to be: "The daddy of the lot of us!"[3] Like Keene, May's illustrations generally portray single situations, forcefully and economically conveyed without moral overtones. Situations are taken from the stage, sporting events and London street life. Common subjects include street urchins, immigrants and the upper class, often displaying a wry sense of humor and observation. As May himself described human character: "Everyone's a good fellow till you know him."[4]

May's illustrations are more complex than the apparent simple, seemingly spontaneous appearance that they suggest. He made and revised many pencil sketches related to a situation prior to "taking down the scaffolding,"[5] as he called it. He paid little attention to background details. He would strip any elements that were unessential to the humor of the sketch before tracing what remained with ink. For strong outlines and figures in the foreground, he used a camel pen. He used a finer tip for the facial features, settings and more distant figures. The resulting illustration is a striking composition of bold black lines and stark white open spaces.

Man Reading Newspaper in Crowd is one of Phil May's distinctive pen-and-ink illustrations. Like a photograph, it crops the edges and accurately captures the various elements and characters present on a typical London street of the day. In the foreground, we observe a heavily outlined figure of an apparently intelligent, upper-class, worldly man intent on reading the newspaper before him. He seems completely uninterested in the bustling street scene around him. Also important is the plump, upper-class, young boy with rosy cheeks in the foreground who seems to be immersed in his own curious thoughts and equally disinterested in the hustle and bustle. We can infer his status from the heavy ink outline and detailed attention to his facial expression.

A woman in the middle ground, gazes curiously toward the man and the boy, as she advances along the walkway. She appears somewhat interested, yet she is also clearly intent on her own daily agenda. Directly behind her is a concert sign, advertising a cultural event and suggestive of refined London city life, a common subject in Phil May's illustrations. Less immediate to the illustration are the faint suggestions of a man and his horse on the right and the grayish figure far off in the background. May used the tree line, along with atmospheric perspective through fading ink color, to gently draw the viewer to the distant white background. The faint graphite outlines left behind suggest that this illustration is likely unfinished, since the artist generally erased such lines after completing the inked drawing.

Phil May suffered with fragile health throughout his life, further compromised by his bohemian lifestyle and alcoholism, tragically leading to consumption and his death before age forty. As Elizabeth Robins Pennell reflected: "...nothing of Phil May's [talk] remains save the familiar refrain 'Have a cigar!' 'Have a whisky and soda!' 'Have a drawing!'"[6] M. H. Spielmann wrote in May's obituary for *Magazine of Art:* "...had he lived he would have done work more powerful still—more broadly and comprehensively human, and...like more great humorists he would have proved his capacity to handle tragedy as well as comedy and farce."[7] His illustrations were widely accepted by both artists and the general public during his brief career. His brilliant, striking pen-and-ink illustrations established his reputation as one of the most talented illustrators of nineteenth-century city life, deriving his style from Keene's beautiful hatching and detail (catalogue 52) and filtering it into a more reductive and modernist aesthetic.

[Kim Weidner, *Class of 2006* and
Catherine Carter Goebel, *Professor of Art History,
Paul A. Anderson Chair in the Arts*]

[1] Leo John Freitas, "Phil(ip William) May," in *The Dictionary of Art*, ed. Jane Turner, Dictionary of Art, vol. 20 (London: Macmillan Publishers Limited, 1996).

[2] C. Fox, review of *"Phil May, His Life and Work,"1863-1903*, by Simon Houfe, *Print Quarterly* 20 (2003): 166.

[3] Simon Houfe, *Phil May: His Life and Work* (Aldershot: Ashgate, 2002) 134.

[4] David Cuppleditch, *Phil May: The Artist & His Wit* (London: Fortune Press, 1981) 74.

[5] Fox, 166.

[6] Houfe, xii.

[7] Ibid., 153.

54

Artist unknown
Two Women Painting from Plaster Models, ascribed title, ca. 1890–1900
Oil on canvas
Unsigned
44.2 x 55.7 cm., 17-3/8 x 21-7/8"
Paul A. Anderson Chair in the Arts Purchase, Augustana College Art
Collection, SDC2005.3

*Two Women Painting from Plaster Model*s is an oil painting on canvas. It is
unsigned, making it difficult to pin down specific information for research.
This challenge, however, encourages us to look deeper into the painting
itself, in order to discern clues in its subject and style which can reveal a
great deal about its context.

The first immediate clue lies in the subject. Since there are two women
painting in an academic environment, it seems reasonable to conclude that
this painting was completed in the second half of the nineteenth century. By
the 1870s in Paris, there were separate alternative classes where women could
work from the model. Even the conservative academic *École des Beaux-Arts*
(School of Fine Arts) finally admitted women by 1896.[1]

In America, artistic opportunities opened sooner for women. Throughout
the nineteenth century, girls were increasingly better educated through
public schooling and in terms of artistic training, women such as the
two pictured here, could study from plaster casts as early as 1844 at the
Pennsylvania Academy of Fine Arts. Anatomy classes opened to women in
1860, and by 1868, women could participate in separate life drawing classes.[2]
In 1861, the well-known American Impressionist, Mary Cassatt (catalogue
55 and 56), began four years of study at this academy, one of the first in
the world to accept women.[3] Like her fellow American expatriate, James
McNeill Whistler (catalogue 40, 60 and 61), however, she decided to pursue
further training as well as her professional career in Paris.

A similar painting by Alice Barber Stephens, entitled *The Female Life
Class* (1879),[4] most likely depicts the Pennsylvania Academy of Fine Arts.
Although women were allowed to study casts, anatomy and life drawing
at this point, it was considered improper for their models to include male
nudes. Thomas Eakins, the innovative American Realist painter and
photographer, taught and directed at this institution until he was forced to
resign in 1886, due to his allowing the female life drawing class to draw from
a nude male model.

The painting's style provides the second clue for analysis. The artist's
brushstrokes are loose and the application fairly broad which suggests
Impressionism or Post-Impressionism, likely dating it somewhere between
the mid 1870s to the early 1900s. It seems that this painting is more

Impressionist than post-Impressionist, because the broken brushstrokes
capture the immediacy of the moment as well as the subtleties of color and
light. The walls appear dramatically cropped, as in a photograph, typical
of Impressionist viewpoints. The painting still follows Renaissance linear
perspective principles, which the more academic Impressionists like Edgar
Degas (catalogue 56 and 58) and Mary Cassatt, who straddled between the
avant-garde and the Old Masters, were also reluctant to abandon.

Along with style and subject, a comparison of the contemporary fashion
and furnishings can help date the painting. The women's dresses are typical
turn-of-the-century design. The hairstyle of the woman on the right also
represents a popular look for this period. If the woman at left has hair
combs to hold her hair back, this also confirms the dating.[5] To further the
argument, the chair in which the woman on the left is seated is the popular
type known as *Bentwood*. This reinforces the theory of dating this painting
to the turn-of-the-century, since *Art Nouveau* was internationally in vogue
(catalogue 69-75) between 1890 and 1900. The bentwood chair was invented
in the late nineteenth century, and its back, consisting of curved (bent)
wood, repeats the curvilinear line that is a hallmark of the Art Nouveau
style. Based on the back and the stabilizing ring around the legs, the chair
in this painting seems to be the 1876 model,[6] similar to the chairs seen in
Henri de Toulouse-Lautrec's (catalogue 69 and 70) famous nightclub scene,
At the Moulin Rouge (1893).

It seems logical to conclude that this painting was made around 1900.
The artist accurately depicted women within the modern art world, where
female painters could now get the formal education they needed to become
professional artists. Considering all of the evidence, it also seems likely
that it was painted by an American artist, since Impressionism was passé
in Paris at this time, but was just beginning to blossom in America. It was
probably painted either by a fellow art student or an instructor, standing
and observing them, as we continue to do today. Within the context of
modernity, this painting records and celebrates the fact that women now
could be involved in the arts, not only as models, but as accomplished
professional artists as well.

[Kate Felde, *Class of 2006* and
Catherine Carter Goebel, *Professor of Art History,
Paul A. Anderson Chair in the Arts*]

[1] Wendy Slatkin, *Women Artists in History: From Antiquity to the Twentieth Century*
(Englewood Cliffs: Prentice Hall, 1990), 110.

[2] Ibid., 96.

[3] Ibid., 118.

[4] Whitney Chadwick, *Women, Art, and Society* (London: Thames and Hudson, 1990), 213.

[5] Patty Koenigsaecker, Augustana College Theatre Department, provided information on
dating via costume and accesories.

[6] Derek E. Ostergard, *Bent Wood and Metal Furniture: 1850-1946* (New York: American
Federation of Arts, 1897), 49.

55

Mary Cassatt (American 1844–1926)
The Manicure, ca. 1908
Drypoint
Unsigned
20.8 x 14.7 cm., 8-1/8 x 5-3/4" image
28.2 x 21.3 cm., 11-1/16 x 8-3/8" sheet
Purchase Through Gift of the Reynold Emanuel and Johnnie Gause Leak
Holmén Endowment for the Visual Arts, Augustana College Art Collection,
2001.27

The Manicure (1908) is a typical mother and child portrayal by Mary
Cassatt. The purpose of such subjects, for which she was famous, is open to
interpretation. In 1902, the Symbolist Camille Mauclair termed Cassatt a
"painter of childhood," adding that "To paint an adult is to record a state of
mind; to paint a child is to record the foreshadowing of a soul...Cassatt may
be the only painter today to have given us an interpretation of childhood
that is contained within the child itself."[1] Art critic André Mellerio wrote
about her depictions of children, two years after this drypoint was printed:
"She has captured the instinctual gestures of a life at its lisping beginning,
opening its naïve, astonished pupils to the light. Glimmers of intelligence,
harbingers of the future, appear in those brilliantly shining eyes...."[2]

Intaglio techniques, dating back to Old Masters like Rembrandt van Rijn
(catalogue 12) and revived by nineteenth-century advocates such as Cassatt's
fellow American expatriate, James McNeill Whistler (catalogue 40) were an
appropriate medium for the new bourgeoisie. Since multiple images could
be printed from the copper plate, such art was affordable to the expansive
middle class. There are twenty known impressions of this particular
drypoint.[3]

The subject of *The Manicure* is enthralling. The mother and child
interaction reflects the warmth of their relationship. Although Cassatt
never married or had children of her own, she instinctively perceived the
psychological *bonding* between mother and child. At a time when British
Victorian subject matter was laden with saccharine sentimentality, Cassatt
delved beneath the surface to create remarkable images that have truly stood
the test of time. In keeping with Impressionist goals toward modernity, she
produced works of uncompromising power. Working in the traditionally
male-dominated world of academic art, her talent and drive enabled her
to effectively compete professionally. Cassatt's lifelong friend and patron,
Louisine Havemeyer, described her as "the most intelligent woman I
had ever met."[4] And even her often difficult colleague, Edgar Degas,
complimented her with "No woman has the right to draw like that."[5]

The challenge to talented women Impressionists like Cassatt and Berthe
Morisot might be noted in an 1889 review of a female exhibition: "Woman is
the ideal which dominates art, the eternal source of inspiration, but just as
the artist could not aspire to attain this ideal—that is, supreme perfection
in his reproduction—woman herself is not able to descend into the arena of
the fight. She inspires, she encourages; she dominates, that is her role—but
she cannot execute.[6] Such chauvinistic assumptions made it difficult for
Cassatt and Morisot to be taken seriously as artists.

Cassatt sensitively captured her models' outward appearance, as well as
inner feelings, through subtle drypoint lines scratched on the copper plate.
It is remarkable how the shading around the mother and child frame them,
adding focus and tenderness to the composition. The manner in which the
mother continues to work as the child's hand touches hers, reflects the subtle
and tender feelings of blissful motherhood.

An interesting feature of this drypoint is the models' anonymity. Cassatt
often used her own family and friends in such scenes. When she hired
models, she preferred peasant women who were comfortable with handling
their own children. The theme of mothers and children became more
pervasive at this time. Traditionally, Degas has been given credit for first
suggesting this subject to Cassatt, since he was truly her greatest artistic
mentor. She later wrote: "The first sight of Degas' pictures was the turning
point in my artistic life."[7] It is difficult to completely discern Degas'
influence and relationship with Cassatt, however, since their correspondence
no longer exists.

Degas would have realized that traditional religious depictions of the
Madonna and Christ child were out of fashion with the bourgeoisie.
Although Renaissance imagery was popular, such themes needed
secularization in order to appeal to their modern audience. Also, following
the Enlightenment, childhood became further revered. At this time, British
publishers produced many books aimed at children that were beautifully
illustrated by such notables as Walter Crane and Kate Greenaway.[8] The
influx of Japanese prints into Europe further inspired printmaking in
general, as well as genre scenes with mothers and children. Cassatt's
Japonisme was not missed by fellow Impressionist, Camille Pissarro, who
admired her "rare and exquisite works...subtle, delicate...The result is
admirable, as beautiful as Japanese work, and it's done with printer's ink."[9]

Secular imagery of children thus had appeal and since Cassatt was a woman,
Degas probably presumed, like critic Joris Karl Huysmans, that such
"impeccable pearls" would be natural for her. Huysman wrote: "...a woman
is equipped to paint childhood. There is a special feeling one would be
unable to render unless they are particularly sensitive and nervous. Their
fingers are too big not to leave some rough and awkward mark."[10]

There are many possible theories as to Cassatt's focus on the theme of
mothers and children. Perhaps as a woman, she was more at home in the
traditional domestic sphere and possibly, because she did not have children
of her own, she longed for the emotional attachment that is shared only
by a mother and her child. She was deeply rooted in her larger family and
enjoyed painting her nieces and nephews. Whatever the reasons, Cassatt
created many works of art with similar subjects and found success with
her beautiful work which has survived the test of time. Impressionism was
the "first avant-garde movement in the history of art in which women were
significant members,"[11] since artists like Degas recognized that Cassatt
possessed "infinite talent."[12]

[Gayln Landem, *Class of 2007* and
Catherine Carter Goebel, *Professor of Art History,
Paul A. Anderson Chair in the Arts*]

---

[1] Griselda Pollock, *Mary Cassatt: Painter of Modern Life* (London: Thames and Hudson,
1998), 185-86.

[2] Ibid., 186.

[3] "The Manicure," www.williamweston.cp.uk/pages/catalogues/single/186/5/1.html, (2005).

[4] Judith A. Barter, *Mary Cassatt: Modern Woman* (Chicago: The Art Institute of Chicago,
1998), 15.

[5] Ibid.

[6] James H. Rubin, *Impressionism* (London: Phaidon, 2001), 252.

[7] Barter, 109.

[8] Ibid., 71.

[9] Ibid., 133.

[10] Ibid., 68.

[11] Slatkin, 111.

[12] Ibid., 109.

56

Edgar Degas (French 1834–1917)
Au Louvre, la peinture, Mary Cassatt or **Mary Cassatt at the Louvre**, ca.
1879–80, 21ˢᵗ state after cancellation
Etching and aquatint published by Vollard, Paris
Unsigned
30.1 x 12.5 cm., 11-7/8 x 5" image
Lent Courtesy of Private Collection

Edgar Degas was one of the few French Impressionists who found it difficult
to abandon old academic traditions. He embraced the quick snapshot
moments of this group, but seemingly could not resist delving deeper into
the personalities of people as he depicted them in complex *slices* of modern
life. *Mary Cassatt at the Louvre* was based on a series of sketches that Degas
undertook between 1879-80, depicting his good friend and colleague, Mary
Cassatt, with her sister, Lydia.

Cassatt stands poised and confident, leaning on her umbrella, as she gazes
at the artworks in the Grand Galleries of the Louvre. Lydia sits behind
her, presumably reading a guidebook. Cassatt was one of the few active
women in the Impressionist movement. Although American by birth, she
decided that greater opportunities awaited her in Paris. As fellow American
expatriate, Henry James summarized: "When we look for 'American art' we
find it mainly in Paris. When we find it out of Paris, we at least find a great
deal of Paris in it."[1] Cassatt (catalogue 55) and James McNeill Whistler
(catalogue 40, 60 and 61) both found European ambience more conducive to
their artistic temperaments.

When Cassatt exhibited at the Salon of 1874, the year of the first
Independent Impressionist exhibition, she signed her full name to her work
for the first time. When Degas saw her painting on exhibition, he exclaimed,
"Voilà, quelqu'un qui sent comme moi," ("Here is someone who feels as
I do").[2] Although this story may be apocryphal, it reflects the genuine
kinship between the two. Cassatt later reminisced about the pivotal role
Degas played in her career:

> In 1877, I submitted again [to the Salon]. They rejected
> it. That was when Degas made me promise never to
> submit anything to the Salon again, and to exhibit
> with his friends in the group of the Impressionists.
> I agreed gladly. At last I could work absolutely
> independently, without worrying about the possible
> opinion of a jury! I had already acknowledged who
> my true masters were. I admired Manet, Courbet, and
> Degas. I hated conventional art. I was beginning to live.[3]

Yet being a female artist, even within the Independents, was a challenge.
Conservative attitudes were apparent among artists and critics. For
example, Pierre Auguste Renoir, who also straddled the salon and
independent exhibitions, summarily remarked: "The woman artist is merely
ridiculous."[4] And critic Roger Marx referred to Cassatt as "that masculine
American woman."[5] Although Degas purportedly described this aquatint's
purpose as demonstrating "a woman's crushed respect and absence of all
feeling in the presence of art,"[6] there is clearly much more to this work.

In this particular print, Degas shows Mary turned away from the viewer
while Lydia, with head tilted downward, looks up at the art on display as if
she has just consulted her booklet. Degas' innovative view of Cassatt from
the back was encouraged by critic Edmond Duranty, who had described
Impressionism as the *new painting* and encouraged artists to depict
subjects from the back as well as various other angles. In this manner,

he argued, they could subtly demonstrate their "age, temperament, and
social position."[7] Male admiration for such shapely female figures, viewed
from the back, was already the subject of many popular press cartoons.
Yet Cassatt seems oblivious to her observers. Although prominent and
fashionable, she is primarily concerned here with studying the art of the
past, an important source even for modernists. Lydia is physically placed
between Degas and Cassatt, as her "presence neutralizes any prurient
reading to focus on the intellectual activity with which Degas intended to
endow his artist friend."[8]

The artwork on the wall is unidentifiable and fades into contrasting shapes
and shadows against an abstracted flat background. The scene is framed
by the door jamb, and the floor dramatically angles upward, presenting a
dramatic *bird's-eye view*. The *chiaroscuro* (contrast of light and shadow)
is sensitively accomplished through the printing technique. Traditional
aquatint etchings were created by covering a metal plate with resin powder
and then heating the plate to melt the particles onto the plate in a general
texture. When the plate was exposed to acid, the spaces around the resin
were deepened, giving depressions to hold a tonal surface and ink, then
printed by pressure of the press transferring the image to paper.

The tall, cropped composition of this print was no doubt influenced by
the recent flood of Japanese artwork and prints into France, due to the
reopening of Japan to Europe. Degas had collected several Japanese
woodblock prints and like many of his contemporaries, practiced *Japonisme*,
adapting characteristics of Japanese style. By rejecting the one-point
perspective of High Renaissance tradition, he experimented with abstracted
shapes inspired by Japanese influence. This particular narrow, vertical
format echoes the traditional format for Japanese pillar prints (catalogue
57). Photography also offered new perspectives and as a result, figures
were generally no longer centered within a piece, but often cropped at the edges,
in order to attain the Impressionist goal of creating convincingly candid
viewpoints of modern life.

Degas was probably the finest draftsman of his generation. His talent here
is illustrated by his ability to capture figures so elegantly with merely a few
lines and shapes. Not only did he demonstrate great technique, but through
his sketching these figures from life, he also effectively captured their body
language and expression. Mary holds her umbrella as a fashionable walking
stick as Lydia slumps down on the bench, her head lifted toward the artwork.
It appears convincing and realistic. These are not idealized characters
from the classical era, nor historical greats from the recent past. In this
print, Degas satisfied the Impressionist goal of depicting seemingly simple
figures interacting within a scene of everyday modern life. He also, however,
accomplished much more in this image, by announcing the position of the
new woman in modern art.

[Megan Crandall, *Class of 2005* and
Catherine Carter Goebel, *Professor of Art History,*
Paul A. Anderson Chair in the Arts]

[1] Griselda Pollock, *Mary Cassatt: Painter of Modern Women* (London: Thames & Hudson, 1998), 76.

[2] Ibid., 91.

[3] Ibid., 114.

[4] James H. Rubin, *Impressionism* (London: Phaidon Press Inc., 2001), 250.

[5] Ibid.

[6] Phoebe Pool, *Impressionism* (New York: Praeger, 1974), 148.

[7] Pollock, 23 and 119.

[8] Rubin, 252.

57

Keisai Eisen (Japanese 1790–1848)
Courtesan with Umbrella, ca. 1822
Color woodcut
Signed b.l. in image with calligraphy "Made by Keisai Eisen" (trans.); chop stamp b.l. in circle *Tanaka* [censor, collector or publisher?] and in rectangle "*Cho (or Naga)*/ Aritaya/Shibashin" [publisher's house/store and location or part of store name] (English translations kindly provided by Augustana College faculty Michiru K. Sherarer and Dr. Jen-Mei Ma)
68.0 x 23.2 cm., 26-3/4 x 9-1/8" image and sheet
Lent Courtesy of Dr. Thomas B. Brumbaugh Art History Collection

When Commodore Mathew C. Perry entered Japan in the mid-1850s, in order to re-open trade with the West, the Japanese people had been virtually isolated from the rest of the world. To outsiders, Japan was new and exciting with intriguing customs that had remained constant for many years. The recent trade agreements brought great change to a country that was traditional within its own sphere and richly exotic to the West. Japan did not have modern technologies and was thus considered primitive by American and European standards. It was also deemed a potential resource for the United States, as Perry wrote: "When we look at the possessions on the east of our great maritime rival, England, and of the constant and rapid increase of their fortified ports, we should be admonished of the necessity of prompt measures on our part…No time should be lost in adopting active measures to secure a sufficient number of ports of refuge."[1]

Japan's role in the development of nineteenth-century decorative style can be compared to China's influence upon eighteenth-century Rococo[2] (catalogue 13). *Japonisme*, the integration of Japanese characteristics into western art, resulted from the importation of Japanese porcelain and woodcut prints following Perry's negotiations. As nineteenth-century British artist, Walter Crane related, this fresh Japanese approach offered: "…a living art, an art of the people, in which traditions and craftsmanship were unbroken, and the results full of attractive variety, quickness, and naturalistic force. What wonder that it took western artists by storm, and that its effect has become so patent."[3]

Elitist Japanese society banned materialism, but times were changing and prints revealed the latest fashions of the townspeople in Edo, the capital city of the Shogun during the Edo period (1603-1868). The growing wealth of the merchant class helped fuel the growth of these types of images. By the nineteenth century, *ukiyo-e* (pictures of the floating world) focused on "the world of fleshly pleasure centering in the theater and the brothel"[4] and revealed a new "mature femininity, full of worldly wisdom."[5] Such woodcuts created a modernist revolution in the second half of the nineteenth century, freeing Impressionists, Post-Impressionists and others from traditional illusionism established during the Renaissance. James McNeill Whistler (catalogue 40, 60 and 61) was one of the first to discover this new approach. He was soon followed by Mary Cassatt (catalogue 55), Edgar Degas (catalogue 56 and 58), Henri de Toulouse-Lautrec (catalogue 69 and 70) and Paul Gauguin (catalogue 78).

Keisai Eisen's *Courtesan with Umbrella* represents one of the "decadent,

coquettish women"[6] typically depicted by this artist. Originally influenced by Katsushika Hokusai, Eisen ultimately developed a personal style based on new innovative color printing techniques.[7] He was a court painter who is thought to have fallen from grace, and perhaps found his female models by running a brothel outside of Edo.[8] This particular woman is a well dressed prostitute in lavishly patterned clothing consisting of four different colors, necessitating multiple blocks for printing. She is likely holding an umbrella, not to protect herself from the rain, but more as a fashion statement. Her pose is complex, as she turns backward to view something behind her. The bold, flattened imagery and dramatic cropping inspired modernist western primitivism.

The vertical format developed from the traditional Japanese hanging scroll or *kakemono-e*.[9] Unlike Renaissance one-point perspective, which draws the viewer's eye into the piece, the Japanese version leads the eye upward, as it was translated to the woodblock as a *pillar* print. The effect was bold and unsettling to the establishment, but revealed new viewpoints to the avant-garde. One might detect a direct link between this pillar print by Eisen and Degas' *Mary Cassatt at the Louvre* (catalogue 56), ca. 1879-80. Both compositions exhibit cropping and flattened perspective, leading toward a dominating female form. Degas effectively transitioned Eisen's abstract vertical qualities to this composition and also borrowed the prostitute motif in works like *The Bath* (catalogue 58) from 1889. Post-Impressionist Vincent Van Gogh even copied and interpreted works by Eisen.

Although this print was created in 1822, it could not be released to the rest of the world until Perry's arrival. With the consequent exportation of Japanese goods, such inexpensive prints were used for packing oriental porcelains for shipment, in the manner of newsprint today. The nature of multiple prints from the woodblocks made this art form more accessible and affordable to its western and Asian audiences. Eisen sadly recounted in his autobiography: "It is indeed lamentable that with all my efforts I was not able to realize my aspirations."[10] He unfortunately died before Japan was re-opened and thus could not witness how his prints directly impacted artists like Whistler, Degas and Van Gogh and indirectly, the course of modern art.

> [Joe Marusarz, *Class of 2005* and
> Catherine Carter Goebel, *Professor of Art History,
> Paul A. Anderson Chair in the Arts*]

[1] Bradley Smith, *Japan: A History in Art* (Tokyo: Gemini Inc., 1964), 230.

[2] Colta Feller Ives, *The Great Wave: The Influence of Japanese Woodcuts on French Prints* (New York: The Metropolitan Museum of Art, 1974), 14.

[3] Siegfried Wichmann, *Japonisme* (New York: Park Lane, 1985), 8.

[4] Seiichiro Takahashi, *Traditional Woodblock Prints of Japan* (New York: Weatherhill, 1972), 9.

[5] Roni Neuer and Susugu Yoshida, *Ukiyo-e: 260 Years of Japanese Art* (New York: Gallery Books, 1979), 329.

[6] Ibid., 330.

[7] Takahashi, 145.

[8] Catherine Carter Goebel, *Tracing Line Through Time: A Whistler Centenary Exhibition* (Rock Island: Augustana College, 2002), 56.

[9] Wichmann, 170-177.

[10] Takahashi, 145.

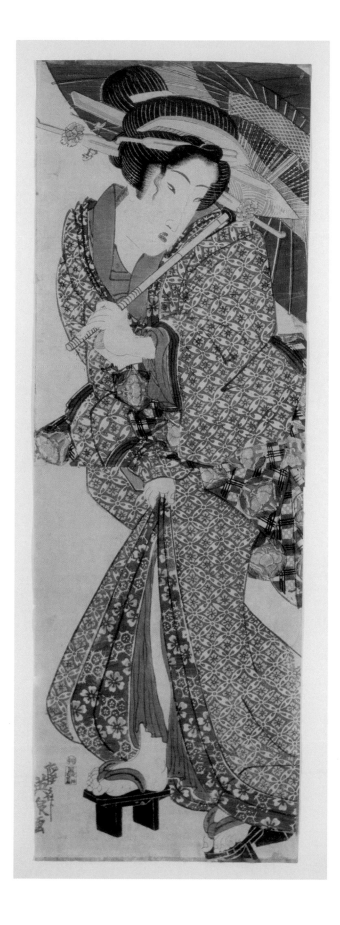

58

Edgar Degas (French 1834–1917) and Georges William Thornley (French 1857–1935)
Le Bain [The Bath] from ***Quinze lithographies*** published by Boussod Valadon, Paris, issued in 1889
Lithograph in brownish bistre ink on chine-appliqué
Signed below image in same litho ink at b.r. "G.W. Thornley" and b.l. "*Chez Mrs. Boussod & Valadon/ 19 B.d Montmartre*" and c.c. "*Imp. Becquet à Paris*"
20.3 x 20.0 cm., 8 x 8" image
39.3 x 57.2 cm., 15-1/2 x 22-1/2" sheet
Paul A. Anderson Chair in the Arts Purchase, Augustana College Art Collection, 2001.17

Le Bain (The Bath), or *Woman Bathing in a Shallow Tub*, was originally completed in 1886 by Edgar Degas. The image was later made into a lithograph through collaboration with Georges William Thornley in 1888. This bather was part of a collection of two hundred images of bathing woman completed by Degas in the 1880s. Most of the bathers began as multiple views in charcoal sketches, ending as pastels on heavily woven paper. The monochromatic tone of this print duplicates the feel of an original drawing. Degas, a French painter, lithographer, sculptor and draftsman, was a leader of the Impressionist movement. Throughout his career, he focused on female figures of ballet dancers and bathers. In both of these themes, he conceived new ways of depicting modern women within their own context.

Le Bain was part of a series of seven genre scenes of the same woman bathing in a boudoir. These seven *portraits* fit in a sequence of images as though a photographer rotated around her, shooting consecutive snapshots from various angles. This action can be traced to the influence of photography, dramatically affecting artists of the time. The photographer Edward Muybridge, in particular, was instrumental with his sequential images of animals in motion. Degas later confided to a biographer: "Perhaps I looked on women too much as animals"[1] in following Muybridge's example. This print also shows photographic influence through cropping and a bird's-eye viewpoint. The presumed standing observer becomes an invading presence, confronted with the immediacy of a close-up photograph.

Other theories suggest additional influence stemming from Japanese woodblock prints that were already inspiring bold new visions from other Impressionists. Degas was fascinated by these prints, both aesthetically as well as topically, and spent much time recreating such imagery. Japanese subjects included women dressing, combing their hair and bathing, similar to this piece.

This composition provides evidence of Degas's geometric drafting skills. He commonly used diagonal lines to show body structure and zigzag lines to add presence to items in his backgrounds. In this print, diagonal lines are the basis for the principal axis of the figure, which includes the spine, legs and especially the arms. The action of the bather is geometric in its portrayal of the balancing act necessary for her position, as she uses the sponge in her hand and is framed by the circular tub. Her hand and feet are the most detailed elements of the piece.

The main significance of these depictions stems from the overall statement that Degas was making with such new portrayals of the female nude. When first publicly displayed, his bathers received negative reactions. Many found them distasteful, and some determined they were completely revolting. Art critics followed with their own criticism of his newest topic. They called Degas' nudes, *portraits of prostitutes*; this reading being the main reason for their negative reception. The writer Joris-Karl Huysmans, for example, described Degas' bathers as a "piercing damnation of some women who enjoy the deviated pleasures of their sex, a curse which makes them violently irrational as they humiliate themselves announcing to all the

world the damp horror of a body that no bath can ever clean."[2] Another critic, Henry Fèvre complained that "Degas lays before us, with the great, sweeping shamelessness of the artist, the bloated, doughy, modern flesh of the prostitute."[3]

Others disagreed with this reading. His close colleague, Mary Cassatt (catalogue 55 and 56) warned that "Degas' art is after all for the very few. I cannot believe that many would care for the nude as I have. Those things are for painters and connoisseurs."[4] Some observers like Maurice Hermel aptly noted their importance in demonstrating "anatomical problems solved by an astonishing draftsman and rendered poetic by a colorist of the first rank."[5] He added, in response to the critical voyeuristic and misogynist reviews: "Whatever the subject, treated by a true painter, it speaks only to the artistic sensibility. The only way of being moral in art is by painting well. What really is immoral and despicable is duping people with intentions that are cunningly sentimental and discreetly pornographic."[6]

It was obvious now that Degas had taken a fresh new approach to the female nude. He had left the academic standard of women portrayed as goddesses (catalogue 13 and 21) and mothers (catalogue 4 and 7). Degas could have designed this woman in one of two ways. He may have planned her to be a simple middle class woman. The famous Parisian poet and critic, Charles Baudelaire (catalogue 41) said that Degas "loved the human body as a material harmony, as a beautiful architecture with the addition of movement."[7] Degas's bather reveals an intimate look into a candid moment of a faceless woman. With this direction many today interpret the scene in a broader modernist sense, as a bourgeois woman taking a bath, a fresh approach to depicting a *real* nude, in line with the larger subject of Impressionism: everyday people participating in common activities.

On the other side of the spectrum, however, many interpret her as a prostitute bathing in a brothel, between clients, in order to ward off venereal disease. Further evidence toward this view (aside from the critics' statements) can be found in the contemporary connection between frequent bathing and prostitution. Normal housewives did not bathe frequently and generally were not completely nude when they did.[8] Bourgeois women linked too much bathing to childbearing and skin problems. Common women washed their feet every few days, but many only bathed every few weeks.

The Parisian prostitute, however, bathed more than daily, another reason why frequent bathing had a negative connotation. The subject of prostitutes and bathing women might also have been suggested through Degas' interest in Japanese *ukiyo-e* (images of the *floating world* of everyday pleasure) woodblock prints. Some of his bathing scenes included fully clothed males observing these women and others verged on pornography (Degas' brother destroyed many such images after the artist's death).[9] Most contemporary critics therefore linked Degas' constant showing of bathers in the 1880s with brothels. Critic J. M. Michel aptly predicted that the beautiful Venuses of the old days were now replaced by this "Impressionist ideal" of modernity.[10]

[Joseph Scurto, *Class of 2008*]

[1] James H. Rubin, *Impressionism* (London: Phaidon, 2001), 214.

[2] Jean Sutherland Boggs, *Degas* (New York: Metropolitan Museum of Art, 1988), 446.

[3] Ibid., 443.

[4] Ibid.

[5] Ibid., 448.

[6] Belinda Thomson, *Impressionism: Origins, Practice, Reception* (London: Thames and Hudson, 2000), 188.

[7] "Edgar Degas," Artfact, http://www.artfact.com/features/artistLot.cfm?iid=otSLybz0 (31 October 2005).

[8] Rubin, 210.

[9] Ibid.

[10] Ibid., 211.

59

Albert Joseph Moore, R.A., R.W.S. (British 1841–1893)
Study for "Shuttlecock", final painting dated 1868–1870
Black and white chalk drawing
Signed t.r. in image with anthemion device
32.9 x 16.2 cm., 13-1/16 x 6-7/16" image
34.8 x 17.8 cm., 13-3/4 x 7" sheet
Paul A. Anderson Chair in the Arts Purchase, Augustana College Art
Collection, 2002.6

Albert Moore began his life surrounded by a family of landscape painters. He likely learned how to appreciate and study nature through their encouragement. As one of his students, Alfred Baldry, later recalled, Moore was an ardent admirer of nature, who was often distracted by the "flickering glints of daylight between overhead masses of leaves and interlacing branches."[1] During his youth, Moore attended a design school, and at the age of fourteen, he went to Kensington Grammar School where he took highest honors in mathematics as well as distinction in Classics. Three years later he began classes at the Royal Academy of Art in London.[2] His background and ability in math and design qualified him for employment as an architectural draftsman. During this time, he also studied art and architecture from many different cultures and historic periods.[3]

While working as a draftsman and involved in architectural circles, Moore met William Eden Nesfield, one of the most important architects of the time, and the two immediately became close friends. This was an especially important friendship for Moore because Nesfield introduced him to artifacts collected from various exotic lands. Persian items shared space with objects from such diverse cultures as India, Greece and Japan. Moore's exposure to this eclectic assortment helped him to define his own style, evidenced in the variety of objects and ideas he would later combine in his paintings.[4]

Moore synthesized many influences in his art. His Classical roots were evident in his detailed and structured compositions, emphasizing the mathematical linearity he also employed in his architectural studies. He had in fact copied many Classical works of art, including the famous *Elgin Marbles*, sculptures on the Classical Greek Parthenon temple in Athens that were brought to England by Lord Elgin in the early nineteenth century. Similar to these figures, Moore's females are clothed in *wet drapery*, with delicate folds that subtly reveal idealized bodies beneath.

Along with Classical sources, Moore revered nature, which resulted in his initial admiration for the powerful Victorian art critic, John Ruskin, who encouraged artists to replicate nature.[5] To this end, Moore generally worked from a live model for his studies. He, however, never fully adhered to slavishly copying nature, but ultimately moved toward the opposite camp of *Aestheticism*, which encouraged further interpretation. Advocates of *The Aesthetic Movement*, or *Art for Art's Sake*, believed that: "the sole purpose of art was beauty; form, composition, and color were only the means of getting there."[6] Artists thus had the liberty to manipulate nature in order to improve it. Opposing these ideas were those who felt, as Ruskin and many conservatives did, that true art was edifying if it followed nature.

Moore combined these competing influences into his own unique style. He copied the *patterns* he found in nature and adapted an architectural integrity to painting. Through his sketches, the structure within his art came to light. He often created geometric grids and laid out his paintings accordingly. The grids determined the positioning of figures and even where details, such as porcelain pots, should be placed. In his finished works, this structure can be seen in the geometric background, often overlaid with diagonal figures, that creates an overall harmony within the piece.[7]

In 1865, Moore forged another very important friendship. He became a

close colleague with American expatriate, James McNeill Whistler, perhaps the most vocal leader of *The Aesthetic Movement* in England. Both artists were fascinated by the possible aesthetic analogies between music and painting and were strong advocates for *The Aesthetic Movement*.[8] In this particular sketch, Moore has drawn a figure that is supposed to be playing badminton, but by looking at the dress and stance of the figure, it would be difficult to discern this recreational aspect, her quiet beauty being the more evident theme.

This *Study* is one of many preliminary sketches for Moore's painting, entitled *Shuttlecock* (1868–1870), which was commissioned along with another work, *Battledore*. In his biography of Moore, Baldry related that Moore "set his models for some hours to play the game of battledore and shuttlecock, watching them and sketching each attitude that struck him as presenting pictorial possibilities."[9] The finished paintings are very similar, depicting a single standing female, the same model for each, holding a shuttlecock and battledore, the equipment employed in this sport. In the chalk sketch, Moore's preoccupation with drapery is evident. The contrasting vertical and horizontal lines of the cloth seem to be the focus, rather than the figure whose head and foot are lightly sketched and whose arms are only suggested by means of a few dark lines.

Although such works may not look particularly intellectual in focus, aside from their careful depiction of classically draped, idealized females, they actually represent Moore's understanding of current scientific theory. At this time, he was experimenting with new ideas on the physics of light, using Michel Eugène Chevreul's *The Principles of Harmony and Contrast of Colours* (1839), which defined the color wheel.[10] In his *Shuttlecock* painting, Moore used the complementary colors of blue and orange. When blended, as with all complementary colors, they create gray, the third color in the painting.

Such paintings were not generally well-received when they were exhibited. The critics dismissed them as *decorative* and thus merely concerned with color and pattern, as in the decoration currently in vogue through the importation of Japanese prints, fans and screens. Like Whistler and Ruskin, Moore was caught between arguments about the nature of *high* versus *decorative* art used in design.[11]

This sketch clearly reflects the artist's love for Greek idealism gained through his thorough academic training. The drawing was done in chalk with beautiful detail and no smudging. Lone Classical Greek figures are generally the focus in Moore's works, better known for his oil paintings which are characterized by a high degree of finish. This work, as a study, better reveals the true artist as he searched for his essential form, demonstrating Moore's idealism at its very best.

[Meghan O'Brien, *Class of 2005* and
Errin Copple, *Class of 2005*]

[1] Elizabeth Prettejohn, ed., *After the Pre-Raphaelites: Art and Aestheticism in Victorian England* (New Brunswick: Rutgers University Press, 1999), 116.

[2] M. Therese Southgate, "The Cover," *Journal of the American Medical Association*, (1999): 214.

[3] Prettejohn, 120.

[4] Ibid., 121.

[5] Moore's early regard for Ruskin is ironic given that he later supported Whistler against Ruskin in his libel suit. Prettejohn, 118.

[6] Southgate, 214.

[7] Prettejohn, 127.

[8] Ibid.

[9] Quoted in Robyn Asleson, *Albert Moore* (London: Phaidon Press Limited, 2000), 112.

[10] Ibid., 114.

[11] Ibid., 118.

60

James Abbott McNeill Whistler (American 1834–1903)
Early Morning, 1878
Lithotint, IV/IV, edition of approximately 50
Signed b.l. in image with butterfly monogram
16.7 x 26.0 cm., 6-9/16 x 10-1/4" image
17.6 x 27.0 cm., 6-15/16 x 10-1/8" sheet
Paul A. Anderson Chair in the Arts Purchase, Augustana College Art
Collection, 99.22

*"The artist is born to pick and choose, and group with science, these elements, that
the result may be beautiful. . ."*　　　　Whistler, *"Ten O'Clock"* lecture, 1885

The gentle lithotint, *Early Morning* (1878), is a highlight in an exhibit concerned
with the advent of modernity in nineteenth-century art. Its artist, the eccentric
American expatriate, James Abbott McNeill Whistle was an inimitable figure
in his day. Throughout his career of painting and printmaking, he acted as
an individual, freely associating with various art movements of the late 1800s.
By combining, reinterpreting and refining different approaches to art, and by
breaking conventions with flair, he created a style that resists categorization.
This was preferable to Whistler, who frequently criticized art historians
and their tendency to *pigeonhole*[1] artists and their works. Thus, a broader
understanding of his artistic environment is necessary in order to appreciate
Whistler for his own nuances.

Whistler was born in 1834, in Lowell, Massachusetts, a humble beginning he
would later deny.[2] His father, a West Point graduate, had applied his own
artistic inclination to the practical career of civil engineering, surveying and
drawing topographical maps. His job moved the Whistler family around the
American northeast, through Europe and then to St. Petersburg, Russia, during
his son's childhood. During that time, the young James was tutored by his
mother, and after showing natural interest and ability in drawing, he began
lessons at the Russian Imperial Academy of Fine Arts.[3] Later, after his return
to America, he had a short enrollment at West Point, as his father desired for
him, and a brief stint with the U.S. Coast Survey, where he was exposed to the
techniques of copperplate printmaking while making detailed etchings of maps
and landforms.[4]

Despite the discipline and conformity of his academic and professional
training, and his practical-minded father's guidance, Whistler's drawing style
apparently emerged as inherently expressive and experimental. As he developed
artistically, he came into contact with inspiring print collections of master
etchers, William Hogarth (catalogue 14) and Rembrandt Van Rijn (catalogue
12) in particular, both based in the northern realistic and humanistic Dutch
tradition, which he would, in turn, explore himself.[5]

Whistler did not intend to live conventionally, and by the mid-1850s he had
installed himself in Paris, adopting the Romantic bohemian way of life. During
the next decades, Whistler traveled around Europe, making friends (and then
usually enemies) with many of the most prominent artists of the era. In his
association with the anti-academic Realism of radical French painter Gustave
Courbet, Whistler became familiar with the sort of theories which famed
French writer Charles Baudelaire (catalogue 41) had published in 1846 in his
On the Heroism of Modern Life.[6] Baudelaire called for the establishment of a
new school of art, one which embraced a straightforward, honest depiction of
life as an artist knew it, without the idealism and historicizing of the previous
generation. Whistler responded by sketching his family and mistresses, as well
the working-class people and decrepit buildings he found during his forays into
struggling urban neighborhoods, as he did in *Fumette, The Rag Gatherers* and
The Unsafe Tenement, three detailed, yet sketchy etchings from 1858.[7] Many
of his works at this time reflected the influences of Rembrandt's understated,
shadowy style. Whistler, who maintained a dedication to unifying all aspects
of his works of art, sometimes even used the heavy grey paper Rembrandt had
preferred.[8]

Whistler's interest in harmonious aesthetics, in coordinating all the elements of
a work, led him to explore the artistic manipulations possible with printmaking.
Once the image is etched into the metal plate, and the ink is wiped into the

depths created by the acid treatment, the areas meant to be blank must be
wiped clean of excess ink. Lighting effects can be accomplished by doing this
selectively, creating an effect of dramatic contrasts in tone called *chiaroscuro*.[9]
Whistler also varied the hue of his inks from dark browns to blacks, and the
quality and effect of his papers.

In 1878, Whistler began collaboration with the printer Thomas Way to use
the relatively untested technique of the *lithotint,* a form of lithography that
employed special solvent and pigment washes applied selectively by brush. The
result had the fluid gradations of hand-painted monochromatic watercolor,
a smoothness comparable to the luxury of velvet. *Early Morning* is one of six
lithotints Whistler completed for publication. It seems that Way first guided
Whistler to prepare, with a light acid etching, an overall half-tint base tone on
the stone. That base was re-worked with selective removal of the ground using
dilute acid or scraping, and with the addition of washes and crayon work. The
experiment with lithotint was not immediately successful; this image was only
resolved in the fourth state when it had been repeatedly lightened, probably by
Way or some of his employees.[10] Whistler delicately balanced the reductive and
additive processes to achieve the atmospheric effects of dawn.

Many of the design elements of *Early Morning* are shared among Whistler's
prints. The simplicity and subtle abstraction of form in this riverside landscape
was more typical of his later, more understated works, although early in his
career he made a departure from over-embellished Victorian print styles.
Throughout his life, but particularly during the 1870s, due in part to his costly
legal battle against his unfavorable art critic John Ruskin, Whistler faced
financial troubles. It has been suggested that such conditions pared down
Whistler's style, turning his interests to honing practical and affordable artistic
methods. Such capitalistic motives surely would have affected his creative
vision, bringing about aesthetic innovations, especially in the bookmaking
realm, when, in 1878, he published his witty grievances in his pamphlet,
Whistler v. Ruskin. The book was "remarkable for its understatement."[11]

Also notable for *Early Morning* is the hazy, passive, rather than didactic,
impression of the scene, expressing Whistler's preference for design over
content. The elegant balance between positive and negative space, between
the inked shorelines and the almost blank sea and sky areas in the distinctly
horizontal composition mimics the design virtues of Japanese woodblock prints
and porcelain, which Whistler collected throughout his life.[12]

These characteristics make the composition believable from both a two and
three-dimensional framework. The representation of foliage, the two men in
the foreground, the surface of the river and the buildings of the far shore are
still recognizable. The work has an illusionistic element, recreating a deep
space extending beyond its flat surface. Yet, the arrangement of the ink on
the page, including Whistler's stylized butterfly signature in the lower left
corner, is so balanced and smooth that the image can also be appreciated for
its two-dimensional aesthetic qualities. This value placed upon an experience
of balanced, beautiful composition rather than a manipulative illusion is a
hallmark of the transition into modern art, and James McNeill Whistler proved
himself to be a modern artist with such innovative prints.

[Carol Marquardsen, *Class of 2006*]

[1] Catherine Carter Goebel, *The Stinging Butterfly: Whistler and His Time* (Rock Island: Augustana College, 1993), 11.

[2] Ibid.

[3] Katharine Lochnan, *The Etchings of James McNeill Whistler* (New Haven: Yale University Press, 1984), 1-2.

[4] Ibid., 11-12.

[5] Ibid., 3 and 6.

[6] Ibid., 20.

[7] Ibid., 26-31.

[8] Ibid., 55.

[9] Ibid., 60-61.

[10] Nicholas Smale, "Whistler's Lithographic Techniques: Beauty and Business," *The Lithographs of James McNeill Whistler, Volume II: Correspondence and Technical Studies.* Martha Tedeschi, ed. (Chicago: The Art Institute of Chicago with The Arie and Ida Crown Memorial, 1998): 196-231.

[11] Avis Berman, "Whistler and the Printed Page," *American Art* (1995): 62-87.

[12] Goebel, 19.

61

William Nicholson (British 1872–1949)
James McNeill Whistler, 1897
Woodcut
Unsigned
24.5 x 22.6 cm., 9-5/8 x 8-7/8" image
27.3 x 25.0 cm., 10-3/4 x 9-13/16" sheet
Lent Courtesy of Private Collection

In 1897 William Nicholson, at that time an artist for *New Review* magazine, was commissioned by his editor to deliver a portrait of noted artist, James Abbot McNeill Whistler. The result was this stunningly elegant depiction of the contemporary tastemaker, generally considered one of Nicholson's greatest works.[1] The manner in which this piece portrays Whistler is very intriguing. His image, as it emerges for the viewer, is submerged in darkness, as if the black background completely absorbs him. Staged on a warm horizon, he holds his signature cane as he proudly displays his ribbon signifying the honor he received in being awarded the French *Legion d'Honneur.* The fine attire that he wears recalls his appearance in 1885 when he delivered his famous *Ten O'Clock* lecture.

Nicholson presented the artist wearing his trademark monocle and a pompous expression on his face, which is further emphasized through the dramatic use of chiaroscuro. Whistler's arrogant and refined appearance was fitting considering the brilliance he exuded. As Henry Landor, a good friend of Whistler, recalled: "His lightning rapidity of wit was almost incredible. He had a lash of the whip ready whenever anybody said anything…when [invited]…to meet the great genius…[people] arrived enthusiastic at so great an honour, and invariably departed detesting Whistler, for in the conversation he never spared anyone so long as he could say something brilliant."[2]

James McNeill Whistler acts as a tribute piece to Whistler's reputation as one of the leading artists of the *Aesthetic Movement*, an art era that emphasized the aesthetic beauty of art over any implied story or moral. Nicholson, along with many younger artists of the day, revered Whistler as a great master. Even as a teenager, Nicholson was infatuated with the artist and his paintings.

This admiration became reciprocal as Whistler ultimately became a mentor to Nicholson, encouraging his work and development as a painter. It is evident that Whistler was fond of the younger artist, when he wrote a sympathetic introductory note for an exhibition of Nicholson's works in 1900: "Out of opposing masses of black and tint of apparently the most clumsy shape emerge forms of the most convincing, and often beautiful, description. The result is gained by balance, by suggestion, and by the art of putting in. Mr. Nicholson states the few essential facts, and makes all else accessory."[3]

At the time of this portrait's publication, Whistler was at the height of his fame, being as well known as his work, if not more. Aside from his artistic talent, his outlandish behavior assisted in promoting his image and his art. Whistler had a penchant for effective use of the media, and the critics were clearly aware of his potential for selling newspapers and magazines. He was truly an original character, which made him a very memorable celebrity. Whistler supported this image with his 1892 release of his autobiographical book, *The Gentle Art of Making Enemies.* In this publication, he dedicated a chapter to venting frustrations based on his career (and certainly enlivened beyond reality) about the nature of art critics. The following excerpt in Whistler's own words reveals his unique personality and distinct form of intellect: "Let work, then, be received in silence, as it was in the days to which the penmen still point as an era when art was at its apogee. And here we come upon the oft-repeated apology of the critic for existing at all, and find how complete is his stultification. He brands himself as the necessary blister for the health of the painter…No! let there be no critics! they are not a 'necessary evil,' but an evil quite unnecessary, though an evil certainly."[4]

Nicholson, like many artists of his day, was inspired by Whistler's words and works. This English illustrator never lost his philosophical connection to Whistler. Nicholson's later paintings were even said to exude *Whistlerian* attributes, turning even the most rudimentary objects of a painting into works of art themselves. As demonstrated in this piece, he had an intuitive ability to capture this elusive artist and make the resulting ensemble into a memorable masterpiece.

[John Regan, *Class of 2008*]

[1] Sanford Schwartz, *William Nicholson* (New Haven and London: Yale University Press, 2004), 66.

[2] Stanley Weintraub, *Whistler* (New York: Weybright and Talley, 1974), 425.

[3] Catherine Carter Goebel, *Tracing Line Through Time: A Whistler Centenary Exhibition* (Rock Island: Augustana College, 2002), 105.

[4] James McNeill Whistler, "Whistler v. Ruskin: Art and Art Critics," *The Gentle Art of Making Enemies* (London: William Heinemann, 1892), 30.

James McNeill Whistler.

62

William Merritt Chase (American 1849–1916)
Red Snapper and Still Life, n.d. (could be as early as 1879, no later than 1915)
Oil on canvas
Signed b.r. in image "W. M. Chase"
74.3 x 91.9 cm., 29-1/4 X 36 1/4"
Anonymous Gift in Memory of Lewis J. Stone (Augustana 1965), Augustana
College Art Collection, 91.16.1

Red Snapper and Still Life is a wonderful example of late nineteenth-century American still life painting. The fish glisten as if the artist kept their surfaces wet while painting from them. The composition is not as busy as those in the European tradition that burst with foodstuffs and flowers, yet it is livelier than the subdued works of fellow American still life practitioner Emil Carlson (1853–1932). William Merritt Chase marketed himself as a vibrant personality, a refined gentleman who courted public attention. His studio at the Tenth Street Studio Building established an American trend for luxurious studio settings filled with exotic bric-à-brac.[1] Chase painted for the emerging upper middle class that was becoming affluent enough to collect art.

Born in 1849 to an Indiana family of modest means, Chase showed early talent and was sponsored in 1872 by a consortium of St. Louis businessmen to study abroad in Munich. He returned to the U.S in 1878 to join the newly-formed Art Students League faculty. His devotion has been recognized by art historian William Gerdts, who extolled him as the "single most important teacher of his generation, perhaps in all of American art education."[2] Previous practice in the United States restricted new students to drawing, usually from plaster casts, but Chase was renowned for allowing students to paint from *life* right away.[3] He also instructed through his own demonstrations of still life painting. He taught at many national and international locations, among them the Art Institute of Chicago and the Pennsylvania Academy of Fine Arts. He also established Shinnecock Summer School of Art near Southampton and the Chase School (now Parsons School of Design, New York).

Even though Chase left his midwestern origins for an adult life on the East Coast, he maintained contacts in St. Louis. *Red Snapper and Still Life* was probably listed in 1927 with Newhouse Galleries in St. Louis, Chase's agent.[4] It is certain that before 1947 it came to its first home in the Quad Cities, that of Dr. Struck of Davenport, Iowa.[5] Dr. Struck gave his fine collection to his daughter, Mrs. Dorothy Mundy, who circa 1964 sold this Chase painting to Dr. and Mrs. Alex and Martha Stone. They viewed the painting as a masterwork that had been under appreciated, feeling that American art historians had not explored much in still life articulation beyond *trompe l'oeil* illusion. Ronald G. Pisano, a scholar/connoisseur devoted to Chase, looked at this painting during a 1995 campus visit. He assessed it as a fine example of Chase's fish still lifes, painted to grace some affluent parlor of the time.

The objects assembled here allowed for a virtuoso tactile rendering of reflective surfaces of metal pots and slippery fish, with a contrast of several crimson fruits. Chase's still life approach, including the then fashionable umber coloring, was influenced by Hans Makart and Munich circles.[6] Chase excelled in rapid brushwork that both articulated a surface and reposed on the canvas as beautiful paint strokes, a verve matched only by his contemporary John Singer Sargent. Chase was known to finish a fish still life in one day, propelled by his use of siccatif (drier composed of metallic salts) and varnish as a medium that required quick execution to achieve the layered shimmer of the fish.[7] We can appreciate the varieties of paint layering, the contrasts between hard and soft surfaces and the architectural balance of circular forms set against horizontal directives. Pisano noted of Chase's appraisal of his fish paintings, "In his own estimation, these works were paintings of great artistic beauty, no less so than his paintings of beautiful women. In complimenting his wife on a sequined gown she was wearing one evening, Chase compared its radiance to the sheen of fish scales—a compliment that only an artist's wife...could appreciate."[8]

Although he produced many interior scenes and landscapes, and was immediately recognized for his accomplished portrait painting, there is evidence that Chase's fish still life paintings were his economic success, his

trademark. It is often cited how Chase was condemned with faint praise for his still lifes by fellow artist Kenyon Cox. "[Kenyon Cox] acknowledged his colleague's powers, calling him a 'wonderful human camera' and a 'seeing-machine' who cared for little save the 'iridescence of a fish's back' or the 'red glow of a copper kettle.'"[9] Sarah Burns adds, "Amos Stote reported that the 'works that have become known as "Chase's Fish Pictures" are classics from the artist's standpoint. It is rumored that he has a standing offer of $3,000 each for as many...as he cares to paint.'"[10] Otherwise, Chase struggled against a weak market for American paintings.

By 1881, some critics began to complain about the reliance of Chase and the "Munich school" on their clever brushwork.[11] As the divide widened between critics who valued formal concerns and those who preferred narrative content, Chase left to tour Europe. He was in contact with Impressionist-circle artists such as Mary Cassatt, and subsequently gravitated toward their brighter palette colors and landscape subjects. He spent much of the summer of 1885 in London with American expatriate James McNeill Whistler, whose portrait Chase painted. It is generally accepted that Chase then absorbed from Whistler a more reductive, abstract approach to his compositions.[12] Those aspects are quite apparent in Chase's landscapes. His still life scenes, however were always contrived arrangements, and it is difficult to gauge any stylistic evolution for dating purposes. Chase's *Still Life: Fish* of 1912, completed four years before his death, has the umber background, reflective copper pot and glistening fish, all painted with bravura brushwork. Thus it is difficult to date *Red Snapper and Still Life*.[13] In a 1915 interview, Chase revealed a life-long devotion, saying "I enjoy painting fishes: in the infinite variety of these creatures, the subtle and exquisitely colored tones of the flesh, fresh from the water, the way their surfaces reflect the light, I take the greatest pleasure....It may be that I will be remembered as a painter of fish...."[14] Today, Chase's Impressionist style landscapes have overshadowed the presence of his still lifes, but the latter were prized in their time, and their teaching value still resonates.

[Sherry C. Maurer, *Director of Augustana College Art Museum* and
Dr. Alex B. Stone]

[1] Ronald G. Pisano, *William Merritt Chase*. (New York: Watson-Guptill, 1979), 13. Bruce Weber has noted how fashionable bric-à-brac collecting had become by 1880 (pages 19-20), and the importance of the Studio for the still lifes as "the showplace for Chase's aesthetic beliefs" (page 24). Chase arranged objects in his studio to suggest still life compositions, to better direct a viewer's reception of his paintings (page 51). Weber in *Chase Inside and Out: The Aesthetic Interiors of William Merritt Chase* (New York: Berry-Hill Galleries, Inc., 2004).

[2] William H. Gerdts, *American Impressionism* (New York: Abbeville Press, 1984), 134-135.

[3] Pisano, 15 and 82. Pisano notes on page 15 that students left sites where Chase had taught to follow him to the Chase School.

[4] Letter to Sherry Maurer from Ronald Pisano, February 16, 1996. This letter notes that the painting was probably historically referred to under several different titles, such as *Fish and Still Life*. Pisano thought that the earliest reference for it, under a different title listing, was #26 (confused in measurements with #10) in a 1927 Newhouse Galleries catalog, *Paintings by William Merritt Chase, N.A., LL.D.* Pisano found *Red Snapper and Still Life* listed in Wilbur Peat's 1947 catalog *Chase Centennial Exhibition*, Indianapolis, Indiana, John Herron Art Museum, documented as having been in the collection of Harold K. Wakem, New York.

[5] Pisano's letter, listed above, referred to Dr. Otto Struck. *The R.L. Polk & Co. 1910 Davenport City and Scott County Directory* (Davenport: R.L. Polk & Co., 1910; researched courtesy of the Richardson-Sloane Special Collections Center, Davenport Public Library) lists physician *Dr. Kuno Herbert Struck*. Dorothy Verna Struck is identified as Dr. Kuno Struck's daughter in his obituaries of March 5, 1947, page one in both the *Davenport Daily Times* and *Davenport Democrat*. An e-mail of September 17, 2005 from MaryAnn Moore of the Davenport Public Library confirms that she found a record that Dorothy Struck was married to William James Mundy in 1958.

[6] Arthur Edwin Bye, *Pots and Pans or Studies in Still Life Painting* (Princeton: Princeton University Press, 1921), 201-202.

[7] Ibid, 203-204.

[8] Pisano, 82.

[9] Sarah Burns, *Inventing the Modern Artist: Art and Culture in Gilded Age America* (Danbury: Yale University, 1996), 127.

[10] Ibid, 16.

[11] Uncited contributor to *The Brooklyn Daily Eagle* in "The Third Annual Exhibition of the Society of American Artists," April 13, 1880, page 2, quoted in Barbara Dayer Gallati, *William Merritt Chase: Modern American Landscapes, 1886-1890* (New York: Brooklyn Museum of Art in Association with Harry N. Abrams, Inc., 1999), 24.

[12] Weber, 40-41.

[13] In the opinion of Sherry C. Maurer, *Red Snapper and Still Life* might have been painted prior to 1885 because it seems to retain enough of a three-point perspective compositional approach, and does not evidence as much of Chase's later compressed compositional tension.

[14] Pisano, 82.

63

Theodore Butler (American 1861–1936)
Winter Landscape, ascribed title, n.d.
Oil on canvas
Signed b.r. "T. E. Butler"
33.0 x 40.9 cm., 13 x 16-1/8"
Lent Courtesy of Mr. and Mrs. Michael Moss

The American Impressionist, Theodore Earl Butler (1861–1936) painted this beautiful *Winter Landscape.* The town is viewed from above, the typical *bird's-eye* perspective preferred by Impressionists. There seems to be a distinct foreground and background, but very little middle ground, evidence of the abstract influence of Japanese woodblock prints that were currently being imported (catalogue 57).

The piece evokes a sense of quiet, reinforced by the winter whites and soft tonality, which could be disrupted at any moment. Winter scenes were popular with the Impressionists because they offered opportunities to contrast clear and diffused light, an atmospheric challenge these artists embraced. They also effectively reduced forms to simplified shapes that worked well with the Impressionists' quick and loose brushstrokes. The atmospheric perspective, achieved through the beautiful background tones of blue and purple, produce an illusion of depth and ambience. One of Butler's goals was to try to capture the "Spirit of the Place,"[1] which he truly achieved in this painting.

Like most Impressionists, Butler painted *en plein air*, meaning outdoors, in front of the subject, rather than in the studio. This was now possible due to the invention of portable oil paints. Such painting better enabled artists to capture the immediacy of a certain time and place. Impressionists were also aided in this venture by the greater accessibility of snapshot-type photography in the later nineteenth century.

Butler was a native of Ohio. Before moving to France, he studied at the Art Students League in New York City. Like American expatriate artists of the previous generation, such as Mary Cassatt (catalogue 55) and James McNeill Whistler (catalogue 60), Butler ultimately went to France to pursue his artistic education and career. After training in various schools, he showed academic promise by receiving an honorable mention at the 1888 Salon exhibition in Paris.

In the late 1880s, he and his close associate, American Impressionist Theodore Robinson, ventured to Giverny,[2] a small village about forty-five miles northwest of Paris along the Seine River. Here they worked under the influence of great French Impressionist, Claude Monet[2] and became one of a group of artists called *American Givernois*.[3] Monet moved to Giverny in 1883 and made his home there until the end of his life. He created a total artistic environment through his water lily pond, Japanese bridge, gardens and home that attracted large numbers of artistic devotees.

Butler undertook permanent residence at Giverny in 1892, the year of Robinson's last season there (Robinson unfortunately died four years after returning to the United States in 1896).[4] Butler and Robinson were among the first Americans to paint under the direct influence of Monet. Butler ultimately became not only a close artistic colleague of Monet, but even a member of his family, marrying Monet's stepdaughter, Suzanne Hoschedé-Monet. The couple had two children, and Butler delighted in painting his family engaged in their daily activities. When Suzanne tragically died in 1899, he then married her sister, Marthe, who had cared for their children during Suzanne's illness.[5]

Winter Scene is most likely one of Butler's earlier Impressionist paintings, painted between 1888 and 1889. It is very close to the viewpoints captured by Robinson during this period, such as *The Valley of Arconville* (c.1888), *Winter Landscape* (1889) and *Bird's Eye View of Giverny, France* (1889).[6] Both artists depicted bird's-eye views of towns, which incorporated asymmetrical compositions, accentuated by cropped hills and geometric rooftops that punctuate the organic flow of the scene. Like Robinson, Butler did not include people and focused completely on the landscape. One of Robinson's scenes is also a snowy winter landscape. Due to their close artistic collaboration, and their parallel adoption of Monet's technique, one might well imagine that Butler and Robinson could have created these pieces side-by-side. Based on the untraced style of architecture depicted, however, it is clear that Butler's piece is not located in Giverny.[7] Yet the striking stylistic similarities in their views are instructive toward placing this painting within its appropriate artistic context.

Butler's talent and painting were often overlooked in favor of the more famous Impressionists of his era, such as Monet, Cassatt and Robinson. As this painting demonstrates, he was, nevertheless, an innovative artist of his time and a sensitive practitioner of the beautiful naturalism of Impressionism. He was the only early American Impressionist in Giverny who remained there throughout his career. In this position, he became an important "conduit for Americans in Giverny"[8] and thus facilitated the spread of Impressionism to America.

[Kate Felde, *Class of 2006* and
Catherine Carter Goebel, *Professor of Art History,
Paul A. Anderson Chair in the Arts*]

[1] "110 Years of American Art: 1830-1940." Spanierman Gallery, New York, 2001 http://www.spanierman.com/110years2001/110_pr.htm. (26 Jan 2005).

[2] William H. Gerdts, *American Impressionism,* 2nd. ed. (London and New York: Abbeville Press Publishers, 2001), 75.

[3] *"110 Years of American Art 1830-1940."*

[4] William H. Gerdts, *The Golden Age of American Impressionism* (New York: Watson-Guptill Publications, 2003), 22.

[5] Gerdts, *American Impressionism,* 75.

[6] See reproductions in Gerdts, *American Impressionism,* 69.

[7] William Gerdts, discussion at Augustana College, 29 September 2005.

[8] Gerdts, *American Impressionism,* 75.

64

Albert Goodwin (English/British 1845–1932)
Durham, 1892
Oil on canvas
Signed b.l. "Albert Goodwin/ 92"
65.5 x 141.5 cm., 25-3/4 x 55-5/8"
Purchase with Gift Through Paul Arnell, A Friend of Augustana College, and the Paul A. Anderson Chair in the Arts, Augustana College Art Collection, 2002.15

Albert Goodwin, R. W. S., was born in Maidstone, England in 1845. His father, a builder, and his mother, a staunch Methodist, provided a profound religious background for young Albert, which led him to be later described as a very "religious man."[1] Another strong influence on Goodwin was artist J.M.W. Turner, perhaps the most celebrated of all English Romantic landscape painters. His works inspired Goodwin, as evident in his painting, *Durham* (1892).

There are actually many similarities, artistically and otherwise, between Turner and Goodwin. They were both child prodigies who exhibited at the Royal Academy by the age of fifteen. As primarily landscape artists they had a similar approach to their subjects that was always highly imaginative. Both landscape painters seemed to enjoy experimenting with different techniques.[2] Like Turner, Goodwin used poetic presentations of his landscapes which often were combined with elements of Impressionism.[3] This particular similarity may have accounted in part for the admiration they both inspired from the prominent Victorian art critic, John Ruskin. Throughout their lives they both traveled widely, but retained a special fondness for the Alps. Goodwin turned out to be one of the "most interesting of Turner's artistic heirs,"[4] and in the painting, *Durham*, there are characteristics of mood and atmosphere reminiscent of the Romantic, Turner.

Ruskin became a close friend to Goodwin, and is given credit for encouraging him to study the works of Turner.[5] Ruskin also persuasded Goodwin to travel to Italy to paint some of the ancient Roman buildings and ruins.[6] This mission kindled his interest in architecture, a preoccupation reflected in his frequent choice of cathedrals as the subject matter for many of his paintings. Durham Cathedral, which he painted many times, was one of his favorites. This particular large oil on board version measures 23 x 55 inches.

Durham Cathedral, perched high above the River Wear, is considered "Britain's most magnificent Romanesque structure,"[7] and has stood at this location for over nine hundred years as a place of prayer and pilgrimage. Its associated castle, which stands to the right of the cathedral in the painting, was an ancient Norman fortress and former residence of the Prince Bishops of Durham.[8] Beautiful moors and rivers surround the cathedral city.

The viewer's initial reaction to the painting might be similar to that felt in viewing a startling drama filled with portent and suspense. The mood is created by the immense, unpredictable sky which covers the major portion of the painting. Goodwin's underlying statement seems to be that God through nature is all powerful and important. Everything else in the painting appears subordinate to these varied dramatic patterns of the sky. The dark, ominous clouds at the top of the painting break into a halo of clear light that forms over the cathedral, itself bathed in a soft mystical atmosphere of fog and soft impressionistic light.

A shepherd tending his flock nestles peacefully at the base of the cathedral's hill. They parallel the bank of the River Wear as it stretches diagonally backward into the painting. The river separates the majestic cathedral city from an ordinary group of peasants working in the field in the lower right corner. This river importantly provides, through perspective, both depth and breadth to the painting. It gradually diminishes into the horizon and directs the viewer's eye to the distant small white church, its steeple accentuated by a waning Turneresque sunset with the overhead sky punctuated by a scattering of crows.

Further study of this painting allows for a different feeling and interpretation. Having a biographical glimpse of the religious character of the artist, and knowing that this painting was done at a time of personal religious crisis, suggests a possible underlying intentional religious allegory. A visual "*Pilgrim's Progress*" starts with the peasants working for "their daily bread" at harvest, with the fire in the field forming an offering of thanks, like incense, with smoke wafting and mingling into the outer atmosphere. Beneath the circling crows (Christian symbols of death) stands the white church suggesting the message of everlasting life. The sky's subtle light over Durham Cathedral, linked with the sense of peace created below the cathedral hill by the scene of a shepherd and sheep by the side of the river, completes the allegory. Whether this painting of *Durham* by Albert Goodwin is read as a sublime, poetic, Turneresque landscape that exalts nature, or as a religious allegorical lesson from God, it is a memorable work by an artist who deserves more recognition than has been accorded him in the past.

[Paul A. Arnell, *Class of 2006*]

[1] Hammond Smith, *Albert Goodwin, R. W. S. 1845-1932* (Leigh-on-Sea: F. Lewis, Publishers Ltd., 1977), 12.

[2] Ibid., 25.

[3] Ibid., 26.

[4] Ibid., 25.

[6] Ibid., 20.

[6] Chris Beetles, *Albert Goodwin, R. W. S. 1845-1932* (London: Chris Beetles Ltd., 1996), 15-16.

[7] *Great Britain* (Oakland: Lonely Planet Publications Pty Ltd., 2005) , 622.

[8] J.J. Norwich, *England & Wales (New York: Alfred A. Knopf, 2000), 406.*

65

Henry Charles Clifford (British 1861–1947)
Boating Scene, ascribed title, n.d.
Oil on canvas
Signed b.r. "H. Charles Clifford"
38.8 x 46.3 cm., 15-5/16 x 18-1/4"
Lent Courtesy of Private Collection

Impressionism in Great Britain gained its greatest momentum after the French Impressionists already disbanded their final 1886 exhibition, and continued well into the twentieth century. Beyond their sources in the French movement, earlier English Romantic landscape paintings by John Constable (catalogue 30A) and Joseph Mallord Turner inspired and reinforced the inherent British love for nature. English painter, Henry Charles Clifford, is not a well-known artist, yet his *Boating Scene*, painted in oil on canvas, demonstrates significant similarities to the more recognized painters of the Impressionist movement. Born in 1861 in Greenwich, he exhibited as both a watercolorist as well as a landscape painter.[1] He died in 1947, but his work continues to be exhibited and appreciated today.

Impressionism was perhaps publicly defined in Paris in 1874 by the first exhibition of the *Society of Painters, Etchers and Engravers*. Although the members of the Society chose this formative and inclusive title, critic Louis Leroy dubbed them *Impressionists* soon after their opening. He found their works to be incomplete sketches and *impressions* of scenes, lacking the academic finish he preferred. They thus disrupted traditional practice, and instead of planning compositions based on the Old Masters, Impressionists attempted to capture the immediate effect of landscape, in order to create as Claude Monet suggested: "a spontaneous work rather than a calculated one."[2]

This group of avant-garde artists included such notables as Edgar Degas (catalogue 56 and 58) and Monet. They rebelled against the academy and its conservative, elitist focus on classicism. Like the Realists before them (catalogue 37, 38 and 39), they determined to paint modern life and the world of the everyday bourgeoisie, both in the city and the country. The Impressionists aimed at accuracy in their depictions, following recent scientific theories in the physics of light by painting in *plein air*, directly before nature, with portable oil paints. Artists like Monet thus strove to accurately capture their perceived view of the real world.

British Impressionism developed later, through the influence of Walter Sickert, who was a follower of American expatriate, James McNeill Whistler (catalogue 60) and Philip Wilson Steer, who continued Monet's practices.[3] Although sources in Whistler and Monet seem related, if judged by their looser and somewhat abstracted effects, the two artists actually developed philosophies which were diametrically opposed.

Whistler believed that "Nature contains the elements, in colour and form, of all pictures, as the keyboard contains the notes of music. But the artist is born to pick, and choose, and group with science, these elements, that the result may be beautiful."[4] In this manner, he rejected his Realist roots and embraced *Art for Art's Sake* toward the artist's right to improve upon nature. Monet, on the other hand, struggled to replicate nature and its initial impression, as his student Lila Cabot Perry related: "Monet's philosophy of painting was to paint what you really see, not what you think you see; not the object isolated as in a test tube, but the object enveloped in sunlight and atmosphere, with the blue dome of

Heaven reflected in the shadows."[5]

This Impressionist canvas captures a picturesque moment on a lovely summer day. The lower center focuses on six figures, separated into two groups of three. Two women supporting a young child approach a boat in the center, and within that boat sit two men and what appears to be a child between them, whose back is highlighted in red and who looks toward the approaching female figures. The fashionable white dresses appear light blue as they reflect the water below. The child frolics toward the stream, supported between the two maternal figures, and in line with the child in the boat. The painting reflects Clifford's interest in capturing the color, light and beauty of the English rural landscape.

While there are people in the painting, they appear secondary in importance to the landscape. Loose brushstrokes subtly depict the small figures as they emerge at the end of a very long pathway lined with trees in full bloom. The foreground opens onto the water with a cropped boat at right, as well as the center boat around which the activity take place. The stream bends and inspires viewers to imagine a far-off point toward which the boaters are prepared to embark. As in a photograph, the reflections of the trees are painted in the water. Judging from the length of the shadows, the time of day must be either late morning or afternoon.

The painting crops off the edges of the trees on both sides of the composition, *zooming* into the scene, like a close-up camera lens. While the date is unknown for this particular work, it reflects the Impressionist quest for the good life: the promise of a day filled with conversation and leisure. The linear perspective seems to break into two directions. It leads viewers up the path to the right, through the trees, into a world with which they might be familiar. And it also follows to the left, where they might find themselves in a boat venturing through the bend in the brook, toward something unexplored and yet unknown. The whole illustrates a world that is filled with opportunity and shades of green that seem to represent new life and abundance. The atmospheric perspective, which recedes to cool, grayish-blue colors in the distance, reflects recent theories on the physics of light.

Clifford's *Boating Scene* resonates from its own time period of the late nineteenth century into our present day. The soft brushstrokes that build on top of one another in the bottom left corner help the observer to seek out more peaceful moments in the rest of the scene. As with those by the famous Impressionists of this time, this work carries a consummate harmony between painter and viewer. It remains an esteemed image that takes us around the river bend into a world filled with Impressionist style and grace.

[Beth Luebke, *Class of 2005* and
Catherine Carter Goebel, *Professor of Art History,
Paul A. Anderson Chair in the Arts*]

[1] E. Bénézit, *Dictionaire des Peintres, Sculpteurs, Dessinateur et Graveur*, vol. 3. (Paris: Editions Gründ, 1999), 716.

[2] Herbert Read, ed., *The Thames and Hudson Dictionary of Art and Artists* (London: Thames and Hudson, 1984), 171.

[3] Kenneth McConkey, *British Impressionism* (New York: Harry N. Abrams, 1989), 12.

[4] James McNeill Whistler, "Mr. Whistler's 'Ten O'Clock,'" *The Gentle Art of Making Enemies* (London: William Heinemann, 1892), 142-43.

[5] Barbara Ehrlich White, *Impressionism in Perspective* (New Jersey: Prentice-Hall, Inc., 1978), 14-15.

66A

Emma Ruff (French b. 1884)
Le Jardin du Luxembourg [The Luxembourg Gardens], n.d.
Oil on canvas
Unsigned
33.0 x 41.2 cm., 13 x 16-1/4"
Lent Courtesy of Private Collection

Emma Ruff was born in 1884, toward the end of the Impressionist movement, but was clearly influenced by the French Impressionist masters of the previous generation. Little is known about Ruff's background, although her talent did not go unnoticed. She studied under academic artists, F. Lauth, M. Baschet and Henri Royer[1] and worked primarily in France, exhibiting at the Salon des Artistes Français in Paris. Her overall acceptance by the establishment is evidenced by the fact that this institution elected her a full member and bestowed upon her a silver medal in 1941. She was a painter of portraits, landscapes and genre scenes. *Le Jardin du Luxembourg* seems to bridge two of these categories as it depicts a genre scene within an urban landscape.

Ruff's style clearly reflects Impressionist roots. Her paintings are full of color and beauty, much like these works, yet there are some distinct differences. Her brushstrokes are much tighter, especially when depicting figures, a tendency also apparent in Impressionist Edgar Degas' beautifully drawn pieces. Most Impressionists, however, abandoned academic drawing in favor of capturing the immediacy of a given subject while standing before it, rather than through sketches constructed in the studio. The invention of portable oil paint tubes made this *open air* practice possible. Impressionist style was more *painterly* with its loose brushstrokes, quickly applied in an attempt to seize the subtle nuances of light and nature. The academic conservatives generally considered such works to be sloppy and *unfinished* and did not embrace the philosophy that in pursuit of capturing a *slice of life*, artists should simply *draw what they see*, rather than constructing through research in the studio.

Ruff's painting is oil on canvas. There are no existing records to indicate its exact date or if it was exhibited. It comes from a private collection and was likely meant to be paired with Ruff's other painting, *Le Jardin des Tuileries* (catalogue 66B). Ruff's style might properly be called *conservative Impressionism*. It was probably painted *en plein air*, in open air on site, rather than in the studio. Most of the composition is bright and colorful, and you expect to see a blue sky with puffy, billowing clouds, but instead it is a subtle color, tinted with shades of gray above, perhaps hinting at a more romantic side to the artist or simply reflecting an overcast day.

The composition depicts the Luxembourg gardens in Paris. This location is indicated by the two shaded pathways and the sculpture and fountain. The bronze *Fountain de l'Observatoire* lies at the southern part of the Luxembourg Gardens, close to the Paris Observatory. It consists of four women, representing the four corners of the world—Europe, Asia, Africa and America—who support a globe above their heads, while horses and dolphins spring from the base.[2] These beautiful gardens and their sculpture surround the Luxembourg Palace,

once home to Marie de' Medici (catalogue 11), but now the headquarters for the French Senate. During the nineteenth century, as well as in our present time, these gardens seemed to belong to the people of Paris. They remain a favorite meeting place for Parisians during the milder seasons of the year.

Ruff's painting includes many elements similar to works by other Impressionist artists such as Claude Monet, Pierre Auguste Renoir and Mary Cassatt. Monet's influence can be particularly felt when comparing this painting to his vibrant, painterly garden scenes where figures are generally secondary in importance to the landscape. His love for gardens led him to create his ultimate Impressionist environment for his home and gardens at Giverny. Both Monet and Renoir also included within their compositions children with toy hoops, a common sight during the century, where the child's goal was to run alongside the rolling hoop, keeping it in motion as long as possible through carefully paced touches of the stick.

Post-Impressionist Georges Seurat also seems to have influenced Ruff. As in his famous *A Sunday Afternoon on the Island of La Grande Jatte* (1884), Ruff's painting depicts an array of classes, particularly the bourgeoisie, participating in various leisure activities. Throughout the garden, people from different walks of life gather: a family, a soldier, a young couple, the wealthy and the working. It is a place to relax and to play. Beyond the trees and the fountain, the *mansard* roofs which visually defined modern Paris tower over the gardens, evidence of the many recent changes sweeping away old Paris and replacing it with modern boulevards and buildings. But here in the park, one could still catch a glimpse of nature and retreat to a simpler world, seemingly far away from, but actually within the more complex city.[3]

Women artists were not common in nineteenth-century France, but Impressionists Mary Cassatt (catalogue 55) and Berthe Morisot were likely important role models for ambitious female painters of the next generation. Like Cassatt and Morisot, Ruff focused here on women and children: particularly the group in the right foreground, which includes an upper bourgeois mother and her daughter, faithfully attended by the girl's nursemaid who arranges her hair. The mother, with her expensive dress, fancy hat and walking stick, is content to watch her child and allow the nanny to interact with her, typical of society's expectations at the time. Beyond this obvious focus, more subtle touches exist, such as two children playing hide-and-seek at the right edge of the painting. One child peeks from behind the trees and a boot is all that remains visible of another child who enters the forest. This element suggests that Ruff might have relied on photography, as did many Impressionists, to help capture fleeting, split-second effects that they then translated into paint. It also reflects a sense of humor as well as a modern philosophy that children ought to have fun and be carefree.

[Courtney Olson, *Class of 2008*]

[1] E. Bénézit, "Ruff, Emma," *Dictionnaire Critique et documentaire des peintres, sculpteurs, dessinateurs et graveurs de tous les temps et de tous les pays par un groupe d'écrivains specialists français et étrangers*, vol. 12 (Paris: Gründ, 1999), 87.

[2] The fountain was constructed in 1873 by Gabriel Davioud. "History of the Paris Observatory," *L'Observatoire de Paris*, 2005, http://www.obspm.fr/histoire/paris/paris.en. shtml (25 July 2005).

[3] Gary Tinterow and Henri Loyrette, *Origins of Impressionism* (New York: Harry N. Abrams, Inc., 1994), 142-143.

181

66B

Emma Ruff (French b. 1884)
Le Jardin des Tuileries [The Tuileries Gardens], n.d.
Oil on canvas
Unsigned
33.0 x 41.2 cm., 13 x 16-1/4"
Lent Courtesy of Private Collection

In *Le Jardin des Tuileries*, as in *Le Jardin du Luxembourg* (catalogue 66A), Ruff depicted a scene from everyday life, an afternoon at the popular Parisian park. An attentive young man in soldier's uniform converses with the object of his attention, a young lady, possibly the distracted nanny for the children playing in the sand below. Upper class and bourgeois Parisians stroll through the park in the background but are not necessarily the focal point. Small in scale and generally scattered throughout the painting, they share the spotlight with the gardens. The background apartment buildings are distanced through the use of atmospheric perspective, the cooler colors effectively convincing the viewer that they actually recede in space beyond the flat picture plane.

Located in the heart of Paris, the Tuileries have a long history, having been first constructed under Catherine de Medici as private gardens next to the palace. They were later opened in the center to form an axis that projected outward, culminating in a boulevard leading to the Arc de Triomphe. This famous monument (not pictured) is echoed at the opposite end of the garden, by the smaller triumphal arch, seen in the upper right of the painting, framed before the Louvre Palace and Museum. Above the trees jut the Louvre pavilions, located behind the gardens.

When the city underwent its nineteenth-century renovation by Napoleon Bonaparte, and the palace was declared a public art museum, this became the grand axis of Paris that was used as the base for the new ground plan.[1] People could escape the hectic city life in the parks and gardens, if only for a short while, and effectively get back to nature. Both young and old, wealthy and working class came to wander in these beautiful gardens.

This piece is very Impressionistic in the sense that Ruff used small dots of color to create a larger picture, revealed upon closer examination of the flowers and trees. Characteristic of Impressionism, the overall conception becomes more comprehensible when viewed from a distance. Impressionists were fascinated with light and tried to capture it on canvas, which led to images that appear almost fractured. They aimed not to paint a particular object, but instead to paint the light reflecting off that object. In doing so, they employed new theories on the physics of light, published by Eugène Chevreul, whose recent scientific theories established the color wheel, still accepted today. Shadows were no longer considered black but became the darker complementary colors to light, such as blues and purples opposite the warmer colors of orange and yellow. Light was broken into a myriad of hues and shades depending on the time of day, the weather and the angle of light.

In *Le Jardin des Tuileries*, the scene has an Impressionistic quality, similar to Claude Monet's many garden scenes. The flowers were created by seemingly quick flicks of paint and the looser brushstrokes that characterize the rest of the piece. Moving away from the painting, the brushstrokes are blended by the viewers' eyes into creating a bigger picture and an overall warm atmospheric effect. Ruff, although not necessarily an Impressionist, was definitely influenced by this style.

As the nineteenth century came to a close, many artists who began with Impressionism, tired of its single-minded goal toward the scientific capturing of a moment.[2] Groups began to evolve from these origins to experiment with different styles. At the 1910 exhibit, *Manet and the Post-Impressionists*, various artists, such as Paul Cézanne, Vincent Van Gogh, Paul Gauguin, Henri Matisse and Pablo Picasso, were first joined together by the term Post-Impressionism. Impressionism formed the common ground that linked them and would continue to inspire generations of artists because of its enduring influence as the "first movement to assert the creative autonomy of the artist in regard to subject matter, technique and style. More than anything else, it was this insistence on autonomy that linked the various aesthetic impulses we now identify with Post-Impressionism."[3] Ruff, undoubtedly, felt the influence of these giants in art history.

Le Jardin des Tuileries can be considered a transitional piece, from Impressionism to a more modern style of painting. While Ruff used Impressionist technique and color within her trees and flowers, she also painted, in a more finished academic manner, such elements as the park bench and the people in the foreground, as well as the figures and apartments in the background. Her style is not idealized, but convincingly depicts a realistic scene of a lovely afternoon in a nineteenth-century Parisian park.

[Beth Gilmartin, *Class of 2008*]

[1] Tom Turner, "Jardin des Tuileries," Garden Guide, 2005, http://www.gardenvisit.com/ge/tuil.htm (7 July 2005).

[2] Diane Kelder, *The Great Book of Post-Impressionism* (New York: Abbeville Press, 1986), 14.

[3] Kelder, 15.

67A

Henri-Edmond Cross (nee Henri Delacroix, French 1856–1910)
Au Jardin [At (the) Garden], ca. 1895
Preparatory color pencil drawing for *Les Champs-Elysées*
Unsigned
9.8 x 9.0 cm., 3-7/8 x 3-5/8" image
15.3 x 11.6 cm., 6 x 4-5/8" sheet
Paul A. Anderson Chair in the Arts Purchase, Augustana College Art
Collection, 2001.25

67B

Henri-Edmond Cross (nee Henri Delacroix, French 1856–1910)
Les Champs-Elysées, published in **Pan IV**, No. 1, "The Color Revolution"
52, 1898
Five-color lithograph
Stamped b.l. below image at margin edge "*Henri-Edmond Cross, In Den
Champs-Elysees* Pan IV 1./ *Fünffarbige original lithographie*"
20.3 x 26.2 cm., 8 x 10-5/16" image
28.2 x 36.9 cm., 11-1/16 x 14-1/2" sheet
Paul A. Anderson Chair in the Arts Purchase, Augustana College Art
Collection, 2000.61

Henri Delacroix was born in France and due to poor health and a short life, had a relatively small output of art. He trained in Lille and Paris, first creating earth-toned Realist portraits and still life paintings. He soon adopted a shortened English version for his name, changing it to Henri-Edmond Cross, in order to avoid confusion with the great Romantic painter, Eugène Delacroix (catalogue 34). In 1884, he co-founded *La Société des Artistes Indépendants*, through which he met many of the Neo-Impressionists with whom he would associate. He fully converted to the movement in 1891, the year that Georges Seurat, its founder, died.

Cross became involved in the second phase of the Neo-Impressionist art movement, along with Paul Signac, Charles Angrand, Camille Pissarro, Maximilen Luce and Albert Dubois-Pillet. The *pointillist* style of the Neo-Impressionists was composed primarily of tiny dots, typically painted in primary colors in order to optically generate secondary colors. This application of brushwork was very important to pointillists.

Seurat, the most famous of the pointillists was seen as the "real force," "leader" and "the greatest discoverer of the unknown."[1] A critic for the journal *L'Art moderne* declared him: "the Messiah of a new art" in 1886.[2] Seurat himself referred to this new style as "scientific Impressionism," in contrast to the "romantic Impressionism" of Claude Monet and his generation of artists.[3] The term *pointillism* derived from the uniform touches of paint employed, called *points* in French.[4] During his career, Cross evolved from tiny pointillist dots to larger more mosaic-like brushstrokes, akin to *Fauvism* (French Expressionism), which grew out of pointillism and Post-Impressionism. The critic, Félix Fénéon, invented the term *Neo-Impressionism* to describe Seurat's masterpiece, *A Sunday Afternoon on the Island of la Grande Jatte* when it was exhibited at the eighth and final Impressionist exhibition in 1886.[5]

This print entitled *Les Champs-Elysées* (1898) is a beautiful Parisian scene reflecting the French *joie de vivre* (joy of living) along the fashionable Champs-Elysées. This street was one of the major boulevards constructed in the newly remodeled modern Paris, lined with fashionable shops and restaurants. It was considered a very chic area by the bourgeoisie. Since it linked the Arc de Triomphe and its turnaround with the Tuileries Gardens and the Louvre (catalogue 66B) at the opposite end, it was utilized as a major thoroughfare for strollers and carriages.

In this image, Cross focused on the landscape. A nurse and child are seated in the foreground, simplified into abstracted shapes. In the background, there are many additional figures, including other seated women and a pair of horses pulling a carriage. The vertical tree trunks balance the curvilinear masses of rounded figures in order to produce compositional unity.

The choice of colors Cross employed is very interesting, as the dominant yellow hue initially catches the viewer's eye. The mosaic-like pattern of the dots is very noticeable and is based on recent scientific theories on the physics of light by physicist, Michel-Eugène Chevreul as well as publications on the science of aesthetics by Charles Henry. The use of complementary colors to create shadows and to make objects protrude emerged from such cutting-edge modernist approaches. The bright shades suggest the warm sunlight shining on the women on this idyllic day. Cross added shades of blue to intensify the grass and the trees. Although he mainly used primary colors throughout the piece, the yellow still manages to dominate.

A very rare opportunity presents itself in comparing this five-colored lithograph with one of its preliminary sketches (catalogue 67A), entitled *Au Jardin* (At the Garden). The drawing shows a more detailed study of a woman seated, in nearly the same position and angle as the finished print. The sketch, however, is more detailed and three-dimensional as defined through subtle color gradations and sensitive additions in colored pencil. It is interesting to note that Cross first worked from such beautifully rendered naturalistic studies, which he then abstracted into overall shapes and patterns, arranging the parts into a balanced composition and finishing it in the pointillist technique. This comparison demonstrates his steps in abstracting nature. At this point in his development, however, his pointillist application was broadening from the multiple tiny dots of his early career toward the larger abstracted shapes, which would influence *Fauves* like Henri Matisse.

Since Seurat was such an influential role model and leader for the pointillist movement, it is not surprising to see similarities between works by Cross and Seurat. *Les Champs Elysées* looks very similar to Seurat's *A Sunday Afternoon on the Island of La Grande Jatte* (1884-1886) and *Bathing Asnières* (1883-1884). Both artists used the pointillist style, and were similar in the manner in which they simplified some of the women's bodies into flattened geometric masses. Also complimentary is their use of pointillism to create light and shadow as well as their choices for colors. It is very easy to see the influence Seurat had on Cross's work and artistic style and in turn, the effect both would have at the end of the nineteenth century toward inspiring the next generation to experiment further toward ultimate abstraction.

[Kelly Volkert, *Class of 2007*]

[1] John Rewald, *Seurat* (New York: Henry Abrams, 1990), 134.

[2] Russell T. Clament and Annick Houze, *Neo-Impressionist Painters* (London: Greenwood Press, 1999), xv.

[3] Ibid., ix.

[4] Ibid.

[5] Ibid., xiii.

67A

67B

68

Ivan Ivanovitch Kowalski (Russian, active in France, 20th century)
Park Scene, ascribed title, 1909
Oil on canvas
Signed b.r. "Ivan Ivanovitch Kowalski '09"
46.0 x 33.1 cm., 18-3/16 x 13-1/16"
Paul A. Anderson Chair in the Arts Purchase, Augustana College Art
Collection, 2004.15

Ivan-Ivanovitch Kowalski was a Russian born painter who was active in France. He painted this *Park Scene* in 1909, likely near Paris. Kowalski was known for his paintings of landscapes in watercolor and pastel. He was also captivated by the changes in the seasons and capturing them on the canvas.[1] During the turn of the century, the period in which he worked, Post-Impressionism was advancing from artists who essentially had one foot in nineteenth-century Impressionism and the other in twentieth-century modernism. In particular, Neo-Impressionist Georges Seurat clearly had a powerful impact on Kowalski.

The focal point of this piece is the beautiful tree in the foreground, the largest and most dominant element in the composition. Judging from the bright bold colors of its foliage, we can assume that the season is autumn. The deep burgundy, dark orange, gold and wine colored leaves create a colorful fall canopy that overshadows the numerous figures beneath. The pathway, accentuated with falling leaves, effectively leads the eye into the scene. The location is likely a public park or arboretum.

Seurat had developed an Impressionistic brushstroke that varied with texture and movement, similarly apparent in Kowalski's *Park Scene*. The unfinished appearance of the painting leads to the conclusion that this painting is Impressionist, however, the dotted technique further indicates the Post-Impressionist *pointillist* technique of Seurat and his followers, such as Henri-Edmond Cross (catalogue 67B). Seurat exhibited his new, more standardized version of Impressionism at the eighth and final exhibition of the Impressionists in 1886, labeled *Neo-Impressionism*.

In the background of the painting, Kowalski focused on various genre groupings, dominated by children. The girl seated beneath the large tree, in the center of the path and composition, creates an important focal point to the painting. She is dressed in contemporary apparel with a large white hat that further accentuates her position. The most arresting aspect of this girl is her mask-like face. Her skin seems very pale due to the manner in which the light strikes her face, suggesting a frozen countenance, like a porcelain doll.

This element suggests a slight Symbolist influence, as evident in works like Fernand Khnopff's *Un Masque à la tenture mauve* (catalogue 82), a pastel created two years earlier in 1907. Masks would become important modernist symbols of primitivism, especially with the early twentieth-century fascination for African masks (catalogue 80 A and B). They also lent a sense of mystery, and suggested false impressions that *mask* true feelings in modern society. Kowalski's use of a mask is subtle and barely suggestive here, yet it is disturbing and alludes to such interpretations. One might infer, perhaps, that as a Russian whose homeland was feeling the early stages of Revolution, the artist suggested discomfort in a world about to dramatically change.

In this *Park Scene*, Kowalski teeters between systematic application of Impressionist technique, based in scientific theories of color and light, and systematized pointillist application toward a Symbolist subjective response to nature, echoed in the young girl's gaze toward her audience. Children were generally revered in the nineteenth century and their daily activities celebrated, from blowing bubbles (catalogue 46) to regular chores of bathing and manicures (catalogue 55). In both of these examples, the audience is voyeuristic as the subjects are unaware of our presence. There are also, however, examples of imaging children where their presumed eye contact with the audience adds further meaning. One might note tintype portraits (catalogue 45), a young girl pausing while reading poetry (catalogue 47) and a child looking out from a balcony (catalogue 48) that demonstrate such direct interaction. This eye-contact communication is somewhat disarming and invites greater emotional investment on our part.

Beyond this riveting figure, the background is filled with wonderful vignettes of children gathered at what appears to be a carnival or some type of celebration. There are balloons and a large band with a crowd gathered around it. The whole effect is like a rich tapestry woven with painterly brushstrokes. The background effectively frames the overall scene, through atmospheric perspective, with a line of trees that horizontally parallels the pictorial space. This scene seems to represent the country version of Parisian park scenes by artists like Emma Ruff (catalogue 66A and B).

The *Park Scene* also exhibits the transition from Impressionism to Post-Impressionism. Like many conservative Impressionists, Kowalski abstracted the landscape more than the people who inhabit it. He also felt the impact of *Japonisme*, as demonstrated in the asymmetrical composition and bold cropping. Like Seurat's *A Sunday Afternoon on the Island of the Grande Jatte* (1884-86), the defining piece for pointillism, flattened figures are sprinkled along a strong diagonal park scene. In Seurat's painting, however, the audience's candid observer status is preserved. Here, however, the anonymous elements in the background are contrasted with the foreground child who invites further interaction, thus blending Impressionist and Post-impressionist elements into an original statement of transition.

Post-impressionism was becoming more acceptable by the early 1900s. Upon examining Kowalski's *Park Scene*, we see threads of many styles and ideas coming together at a pivotal artistic moment. It seems reasonable to conclude that, like many of his generation at the beginning of the twentieth century, he was torn between tradition, nature and interpretation. Many of the original Impressionists were even questioning its original adamant adherence to science and nature, and were seeking a more interpretative response to the modern world around them. Impressionist Camille Pissarro summarily noted this change when he wrote: "The unity which the human spirit gives to vision can only be found in the studio. It is there that our impressions—previously scattered—are co-ordinated...in order to create the true poem of the countryside."[2]

[Stephanie Walz, *Class of 2007* and
Catherine Carter Goebel, *Professor of Art History,
Paul A. Anderson Chair in the Arts*]

[1] E. Bénézit, *Dictionaire Critique et documentaire des peintres, sculpteurs, dessinateur et graveurs de tous les pays par un groupe d' écrivains specilists français et étrangers*, vol. 8 (Paris: Gründ Paris, 1999), 18-19.

[2] Thomas Parsons and Iain Gale, *Post-Impressionism: The Rise of Modern Art: 1880-1920* (Toronto: The Gallery Publishing, 1999), 42.

69

Henri de Toulouse-Lautrec (French 1864–1901)
Moulin Rouge - La Goulue - Tous les Soirs - Les Mercredis et Samedis Bal Masqué [Moulin Rouge - "The Glutton" - Every Evening - Masked Ball on Wednesdays and Saturdays], 1896 edition of Maindron's *Les Affiches illustrées*
Color lithograph, small format version
Signed b.l. in image "H.T. Lautrec" and b.r. in image "*Anonces Américains Ch. Levy 10, Rue Martel, Paris*" and below image in printed text at b.l. "*G. Boudet, Editeur*" and b.c. "*Les Affiches illustrées*" and b.r. "*Imprimerie Chaix*"
20.1 x 14.0 cm., 7-15/16 x 5-9/16" image
31.7 x 22.4 cm., 12-1/2 x 8-7/8" sheet
Purchase with Gift in Memory of Dr. Thomas William Carter, Augustana College Art Collection, 2005.8

Henri de Toulouse-Lautrec's celebrity was not achieved through exhibitions in galleries or commissions from private collectors, but through a single commercial piece publicizing Montmartre's most infamous cabaret, the *Moulin Rouge*. *Moulin Rouge: La Goulue* (1891), a poster reaching nearly six feet in height on public exhibition along the Paris streets, elevated Lautrec and *la Goulue* to overnight celebrity status. As Lautrec's contemporary, Francis Jourdain recalled: "I still remember the shock I had when I first saw the Moulin Rouge poster…carried along the Avenue de l'Opéra…[which] so enchanted [me] that I walked alongside it on the pavement."[1] As the official chronicler for this popular institution, through his posters as well as smaller journal illustrations such as this one published in 1896, Lautrec exploited the popularity of the Moulin Rouge and established his own position as one its immortals.

Moulin Rouge: La Goulue was the embodiment of *fin-de-siècle* Parisian society. Paris in the 1890s was coming to terms with a rapidly industrialized world. Avant-garde artists of the previous generation had focused on Impressionist renderings of nature, attempting to capture the world as directly viewed by the artist, adding little or no individual interpretation. Impressionists might thus be considered artistic sociologists for the middle and lower classes. Such painters as Edouard Manet and Edgar Degas included common subjects in many of their memorable works.

Degas, in particular, deeply affected Lautrec who profoundly admired and respected the older artist and often sought his advice and approval. Lautrec related in 1891 that "Degas has been most encouraging, and told me that the work I did this summer was quite good. If only I could believe it."[2] Furthermore, painter Edouard Vuilliard recalled one of Lautrec's extravagant dinner parties, after which the artist proudly presented a work by Degas, exclaiming "'There's my dessert!' He could envisage no greater favour to bestow on his guests than the sight of a work by Degas."[3] It is no surprise, then, that an artist like Degas who focused his research on women who were artists (catalogue 56), ballet dancers and prostitutes (catalogue 58) would inspire his *pupil* to paint and befriend the performers at the Moulin Rouge.

Bringing to light such subjects of urban culture was a modernist aspect of what was known as the *decadent critique*.[4] With censorship laws relaxed, subjects with overt sexual connotations rapidly emerged. The Moulin Rouge became an effective stage-set for performers like *la Goulue* who epitomized this climate. Fellow dancer, Yvette Guilbert, related her initial impression of this flamboyant performer:

La Goulue, in black silk stockings, one foot—shod in black satin—raised in her outstretched hand, made the sixty yards of lace on her petticoats swirl around and, when she coquettishly took her bow, displayed her drawers with a heart mischievously embroidered in the middle of her tiny behind: bunches of pink ribbon were gathered at her knees, and the prettiest froth of lace cascaded to her dainty ankles alternately hiding from view and exposing her lithe, nimble, and alluring legs. With the lightest touch of her foot she would send her partner's hat flying and her black satin skirt spread out five yards around her in the shape of an umbrella.

It was a magnificent sight. La Goulue was pretty and amusing to watch in spite of a certain vulgarity, blonde, with a fringe hanging down to her eyebrows. Her chignon, piled high on the top of her head like a helmet, originated in a single coil firmly twisted at the nape of her neck to ensure that it should not fall down while she danced. The classic *rouflaquette*—or ringlet—dangled from her temples over her ears, and from Paris to New York, by way of the dives of London's Whitechapel,

all the wenches of the period imitated the style of her hair and the coloured ribbon around her neck.[5]

A member of her audience, Henri Vernier, described the atmosphere and enthusiasm which enveloped *la Goulue* during such performances:

A noisy crowd milled around in the brightly lit haze of reddish dust raised by the quadrille dancers, which settled on the lights and on the gilded ornaments, clouded the mirrors and the pictures already dimmed by cigar-smoke…The male dancers whirled about quite independently of their partners whose skirts, festooned with lace, swirled around, revealing through flimsy underclothing glimpses of delicately rose-tinted flesh. At the back of the hall, on a platform surrounded by a handrail, the orchestra played with tremendous zest. The sonorous voices of the soberest of men could be heard through the pink haze crying, "Higher, La Goulue, higher still!"[6]

Moulin Rouge: La Goulue embraces what was *modern* for the 1890s. The world which for centuries was agrarian was becoming commidified. The rapidly industrializing city needed an outlet for its workers. The café culture of Paris was at its peak. The former outlying suburb of Montmartre, the artists' district, had recently become an official quarter of Paris, with further latitude granted to media and art. And no artist more shrewdly combined the two than Lautrec, who effectively defined his persona in the process.

Lautrec's graphic work also reflects the contemporary interest in *Japonisme*. With the opening of trade with Japan by mid-century, European collectors sought blue and white porcelain, carefully wrapped for safe transport in *ukiyo-e* woodcut prints (catalogue 57). Artists were impacted by the bold approach of such images and consequently, innovative printmakers such as James McNeill Whistler (catalogue 40 and 60) and Paul Gauguin (catalogue 78), combined flat planes of color, linear shapes and genre scenes (often of the lower classes) in their own images. Lautrec similarly adopted such *Japonisme*, forming his own unique stylistic synthesis while utilizing the modern mass media approach available through reproductive color lithography.

He astutely combined the commercial textual message with large flat outlined forms, here featuring the characters of Valentin le Désossé (the boneless one) in the right foreground, cast in purple shadow and Louise Weber, nicknamed *la Goulue* (the glutton), spotlighted at center. Lautrec felt *la Goulue* was wondrous in her "zest for life" and she "considered him as her own particular painter."[7] The crowd and the organically designed orb lights are boldly abstracted into *Art Nouveau* silhouettes.

It has been suggested that Japanese shadow plays influenced the layout of this image. Highly in vogue in the cabaret halls, these plays used cutout or cast iron forms placed at different distances in front of a light that had the enabling quality of eroticism through suggestion, a theatrical aspect that can be seen in this piece.[8] The foreground includes Valentin while La Goulue is pushed further back at center, yet highlighted as she teases the crowd with her raised skirts. The bourgeoisie, depicted as a black mass defined by elaborate coiffures and top hats, provide a backdrop as well as targets for her performance, since she was famous for kicking off the hats of her spectators. The yellow lamps appear to take on a personality and importance of their own, one particular lamp on the far left seems to illustrate a time sequence as it spins.

As to the sociological modernity of this piece, we see the blending of class structures in a way that was unheard of prior to the café-concert. The echelons of society who earlier condemned the poor and prostitutes were now becoming their greatest patrons and admirers. La Goulue dances center stage for her spectators in a seemingly frigid manner, without a smile, doing perhaps what was essential to her survival in an industrial, urban and overtly self-indulgent modern society.

[Dana Kau, *Class of 2005* and
Catherine Carter Goebel, *Professor of Art History,
Paul A. Anderson Chair in the Arts*]

[1] Philippe Huisman and M. G. Dortu, *Lautrec by Lautrec* (Secaucus: Chartwell Books, 1964), 91.

[2] Ibid., 88.

[3] Ibid., 89.

[4] Richard Thomson, Phillip Dennis Cate and Mary Weaver Chapin, *Toulouse-Lautrec and Montmartre* (Washington, D.C.: National Gallery of Art, 2005), 5.

[5] Huisman and Dortu, 92.

[6] Ibid.

[7] Huisman and Dortu, 82.

[8] Thomson, Cate and Chapin, 7.

LES AFFICHES ILLUSTRÉES

G. BOUDET, Éditeur   IMPRIMERIE CHAIX

70

Henri de Toulouse-Lautrec (French 1864–1901)
Repertoire de Jane Avril [titled without accents], published by Antoine Bosc
circa 1893
Lithograph in olive green ink
Signed b.r. in image "H.T. Lautrec" and "*Paris, A. Bosc, Editeur. 8. Rue
Rochechouart....*"
27.7 x 22.5 cm., 10-7/8 x 8-7/8" image
34.2 x 26.7 cm., 13-1/2 x 10-1/2" sheet
Lent Courtesy of Private Collection

Although it might be argued that *la Goulue* (catalogue 69) had her followers early
on, it is certain that it was artist Henri de Toulouse-Lautrec who established Jane
Avril as a celebrity in Montmartre. As she later recalled: "It is to Lautrec that I
owe my fame, which dates from the appearance of his first poster of me...My
dreams were so far removed from reality! I have fluttered my way through our
epoch without revealing an inkling of the depths of my innermost soul."[1] She
was the pale, elegant, ethereal performer whose enigmatic demeanor intrigued her
receptive audiences. Lautrec's friend, dealer and biographer, Maurice Joyant
appropriately described her: "She dances like a delirious orchid"[2] within the
hothouse environment of the Parisian café-concert.

"Of all the pleasures of Paris—the dance halls, circuses, cabarets, and brothels—it
was the café-concert and its stars that cast the greatest spell on Toulouse-
Lautrec...the café-concert in the 1880s and 1890s was at the vortex of several
trends that signaled modernity at the end of the century: art, publicity, and
celebrity."[3] "The role played by the café-concert in Lautrec's life resembled that
played by Versailles in the life of Lebrun, Saskia in the life of Rembrandt....It
provided the background of his life, the subject of his work, and his public."[4] The
art of the poster also reflected the contemporary shift from artists creating works
commissioned by elitist patrons towards *public* works such as advertisements for
the cafés and cabarets that they frequented. These images now serve as visual
records of the microcosm of Montmartre in fin-de-siècle Paris.

Toulouse-Lautrec was the finest of these illustrators, all masters in the rendering
of human emotion through their adaptations of modern life though *Japonisme*.
With the opening of the East to trade, Japanese woodblock prints (catalogue 57)
came into vogue in European collectors' circles. Characterized by bold areas of
flat color, curvilinear forms and the depiction of genre scenes, the stylistic and
iconographic qualities of the printed media became the preferred method for
highly trained fine artists. Lautrec was by far the most illustrious of these
chroniclers of modern life and his favorite muse was Jane Avril. This single-color
lithograph depicting *Repertoire de Jane Avril* demonstrates Lautrec's mastery of
caricature and line as well as the popular use of his artworks as illustrations for
textual media such as this songbook.

Repertoire de Jane Avril was the cover for a music book, written and edited in Paris
by A. Bosc. A similar print titled *La Goulue* (1894) was also produced for A. Bosc
and printed in limited edition by Kleinmann in a set of fifty. The image of *Jane
Avril* was not commissioned specifically for Bosc, but for a series of images (now
belonging to the Baldwin Collection) entitled *The Café Concert* which was

composed a year prior to Bosc's adaptation in 1893.[5]

What is most noteworthy, perhaps, about this piece was Lautrec's foresight into
the gamut of public imagery. At a time when most artists would not have given
thought to copyright, Lautrec capitalized on the immense public appetite for his
reproduced works. He specifically gave Parisian publishers unlimited rights of
reproduction so long as they added text to the image. For songwriters, Lautrec's
art was chic and complimentary to their bohemian songs and poems. The
agreement for Lautrec, on the other hand, capitalized on reproduction as a means
of distributing his works at no cost to himself whilst simultaneously fueling
interest in collector's editions of the prints *sans* textual additions.[6]

This particular illustration is organically composed of curvilinear forms in
monochromatic olive green ink. The form of Avril is meticulously constructed to
produce a character which is both delicate and fluid. Lautrec walked a careful line
in depicting Avril's celebrated sensuous dance, always alone with lateral
movements of her legs, while maintaining a façade of cool detachment. As
described by contemporary writer Arthur Symons, her combined elegance with
latent sensuality gave her an "air of depraved virginity."[7]

While publicly displaying her, Lautrec allowed her the privacy she desired.
Despite the fact that she raises her skirt and reveals her stockings, in sinuous
billowing curves, her face remains aloof, her eyes appear closed, her delicate
features separated from the voluminous arcs of her hat and dress. Lost in the
presence of the cursive form of Avril is a second character, implied by our role as
spectator (and presumably Lautrec's before us), as we gaze upward toward the
floating figure, delicately lighting on the stage as a butterfly on a flower.

This subtle play on human relations can be understood when considering
Lautrec's own tumultuous relations with women such as Avril, who were his
collaborative stars of the café-concerts and perhaps the subjects of his unrequited
love. He, and by extension, *we* are spectators toward this provocative
phenomenon. The abstracted lights above her accentuate her spotlighted
importance. The flattened perspective and bold reductive composition evidence
his roots in *Japonisme*. Avril tips forward toward her admirers, yet at the same
time, is paradoxically flattened against the page. The elegant curvilinear line is
symptomatic of the popular *Art Nouveau* style of the time, infusing all the arts,
fine and decorative (catalogue 71, 72, 73, 74, 75 and 82). Yet in the case of Lautrec
and Avril, their friendship and understanding reached very deep and far beyond
mere artistic considerations. Jane Avril was a loyal friend to Lautrec throughout
her life, keenly aware that, during the course of her career, she "had many a lover,
but only one painter."[8]

[Dana Kau, *Class of 2005*]

[1] Phillippe Huisman and M. G. Dortu, *Lautrec by Lautrec* (Secaucus: Chartwell Books, 1964),
108.

[2] Ibid.

[3] Richard Thomason, Phillip Dennis Cate and Mary Weaver Chapin, *Toulouse-Lautrec and
Montmartre* (Princeton: Princeton University Press, 2005), 137.

[4] Huisman and Dortu, 108.

[5] Ibid, 274.

[6] Julia Frey, *Toulouse-Lautrec. A Life* (London: Viking, 1994), 392.

[7] Thomason, Cate and Chapin, 139.

[8] Huisman and Dortu, 108.

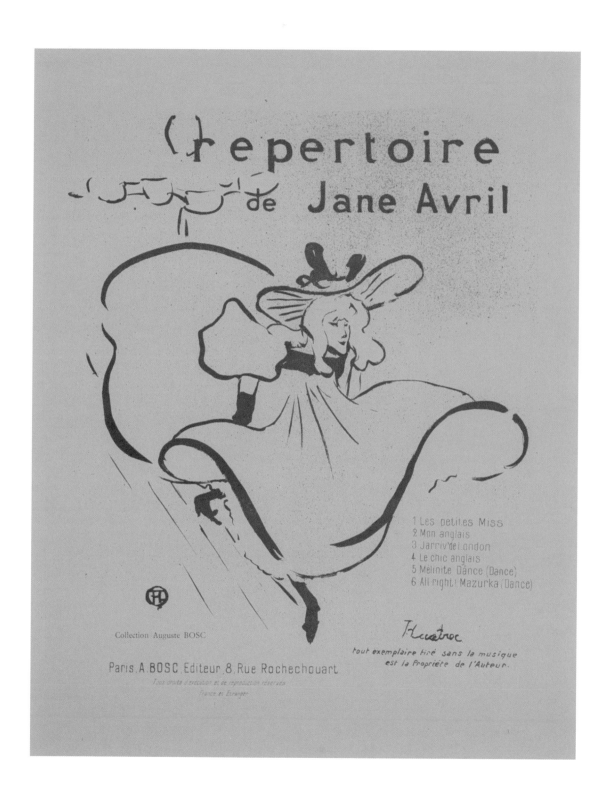

71

George Van der Straeten (Belgian 1856–1928)
Art Nouveau Female Figure, ascribed title, attributed to late 19th century
Cast bronze
Cast signature at back on base "Van der Straeten"
65.4 x 21.5 x 24.7 cm., 25-3/4 x 8-1/2 x 9-3/4"
Lent Courtesy of Private Collection

Born in Belgium in 1856, George Van der Straeten remains an enigma due to the lack of surviving records about his life and work. As a noteworthy sculptor, working primarily in bronze, Van der Straeten's known works consist primarily of busts and sculptures of figures.[1] During the nineteenth century, sculpture varied greatly in style and subject and ranged from public commissions to private works. Sculpture did not progress in quite as traceable a stylistic line as painting, and sometimes only subtle differences are evident between works of espoused Neoclassical artists and Romantic ones.[2] Since many commissions were large and expensive and often had to satisfy the tastes of a committee, they tended to be more conservative in style, even by the end of the century. Smaller, decorative sculpture, however, reflected a more experimental spirit. Van der Straeten's sculptures clearly found their source of inspiration in the popular *Art Nouveau* movement of his time.

Van der Straeten's sculpture is as innocent as it is beautiful. The young woman bending over a cluster of flowers has her hair tied back in a knot atop her head and is dressed in a French Regency style dress. Although displayed with flowers, this piece was likely part of a fountain. The grotesque face at the base has a hole in its mouth that could spurt or drain water. The girl clutches her dress and bends down as if to take a drink without getting wet. She wears a look of contemplative innocence laced with subtle sensuous overtones. Her gaze does not fall on the cistern, but beyond it, probably into the fountain. What is interesting is that while the whole of the sculpture is bronze, the cistern, with its colored patina, looks remarkably like stonework. Depending on the interpretation of what was meant to fill the opening, she is either leaning forward to smell a flower or to take a drink of water.

Van der Straeten worked in the Art Nouveau style. The curvilinear line that makes up the girl's face, figure and dress, as well as her elongated form, place her firmly within this artistic movement. The artist depicted a youthful flirtatious beauty perching upon a ledge. No greater hidden story or meaning seems to

form the subject of this work, beyond what the viewer might interpret. Art Nouveau artists rebelled against tradition and, like their predecessors in the *Aesthetic Movement*, believed that art needed no explicit meaning. Beauty itself was enough. This aesthetic goal, they also professed, could be attained through a harmonious combination of art and craft.[3]

In accordance with the philosophy of Art Nouveau, Van der Straeten here raised a serviceable object, a fountain (or planter), to the level of art. What should be remembered is that this is actually meant to be a working piece, and the flowers or water would be added to accentuate the place of the sculpture within nature. As a functional artwork, the shape was already partially determined. Yet the appearance of the girl is indicative of Van der Straeten's desire to create beauty, a goal he convincingly achieved through her elegant, curving pose.

Van der Straeten was also inspired by the paintings of the French Rococo master Antoine Watteau.[4] With the soft, delicate quality inherent in the Rococo style, Watteau painted the people of the eighteenth century in genre scenes as they undertook everyday pursuits. His influence on Van der Straeten can be seen in the choice of a female subject and her pleasing portrayal. Although envisioned over a century later, Van der Straeten's depiction of a young woman bending over a fountain or flowerbed is reminiscent of Watteau's women enjoying leisure activities, such as dancing, walking or sitting in the park.[5]

Van der Straeten achieved a masterful balance of line, form and meaning. If viewers were to look at the pillar on which this girl stands in a more meaningful perspective related to its time, they could see that this is no goddess situated on a pedestal for eternity: it is rather a young woman dressed in simple clothing, performing a commonplace action. There is thus an elevation of a mortal woman to a higher plain, flush with the beauty and impetuousness of youth and intriguing to a modern audience, in her time as well as our own.

[Andrew Gustafson, *Class of 2005*]

[1] E. Bénézit, *Dictionaire Critique et documentaire des peintres, sculpteurs, dessinateur et graveurs de tous les pays par un groupe d' écrivains specilists français et étrangers,* vol. 13 (Paris: Gründ Paris, 1999), 292.

[2] Maurice Rheims, *19th Century Sculpture,* trans. Robert E. Wolf (New York: Harry N. Abrams, Inc., Publishers, 1977), 8.

[3] Peter Selz and Mildred Constantine, eds., *Art Nouveau: Art and Design at the Turn of the Century* (New York: The Museum of Modern Art, 1975), 8.

[4] Bénézit, 292.

[5] See for example his *Assemblée dans un parc,* in Donald Posner, *Antoine Watteau* (Ithaca: Cornell University Press, 1984), 176.

72

Henryk [II] Kossowski (Polish 1855–1921)
Woman in Profile with Peacock Feather Tidy, ascribed title, attributed to
late 19th century
Cast bronze
Cast signature on tray "Kossowski"
3.9 x 26.2 x 18.5 cm., 1-1/2 x 10-1/4 x 7-1/2"
Paul A. Anderson Chair in the Arts Purchase, Augustana College Art
Collection, 2001.38

Very little is known about artist Henryk Kossowski. His pieces, however, were
recognized and appreciated in his time. Born in 1855 in Poland, he worked
primarily in Paris. A second generation artist, his most notable achievements
include an honorable mention at the Paris Salon and a bronze medal in the
Universal Exposition.[1] Kossowski's tidy, *Woman in Profile with Peacock Feather*,
is made completely from cast bronze and exhibits influences from many
different sources, most predominantly the *Art Nouveau* movement. Judging
from the dates of Kossowski's honorable mention in 1883, and his bronze medal
in 1900, as well as the period when this style was popular, it is logical to date this
piece to the late nineteenth century.

Art Nouveau was born out of the *Aesthetic Movement* and the *Arts and Crafts* or
Decorative Arts movement. Like *Aestheticism*, or *Art for Art's Sake*, a philosophy
promoted by American expatriate artist, James McNeill Whistler (catalogue 61),
Art Nouveau rejected the need for meaning in art and looked instead to beauty
as the primary objective. Aestheticism, however, did not rely on the
manipulation of images, such as the long, abstracted, curvilinear lines that
defined the Art Nouveau style. It also exhibited a lesser degree of decadence
than Art Nouveau, which often obsessed on imagery of the sensuous *femme
fatale*.

As this tidy demonstrates, Art Nouveau also combined beauty with function in
the creation of *decorative arts*, artworks that were meant to be used. This
concept stemmed from the Arts and Crafts movement, which took place at the
turn of the nineteenth-century and stressed the need for a total art that
combined both the *high* and designed arts. In 1897 Alexander Koch, a German
architect, wrote of "the need of a complete integration of all artists, architects,
sculptors, painters, and technical artists. They all belong intimately together in
the same place, each thinking individually, yet working hand in hand for the
larger whole."[2] This innovative idea that great art was a synthesis of the
functional and the beautiful, and that function could beget beauty, was
embraced throughout much of the European and American art world.[3]

As reflected in the tidy's asymmetrical composition and simple, expressive
quality of line, Art Nouveau was clearly influenced by the late nineteenth-
century fascination with Japanese art. Like the Aesthetic Movement, it drew
heavily from this new culture. It also emulated Celtic art, with its interlacing
knots and patterns, derived from medieval sources such as illuminated
manuscripts.[4] Art Nouveau artists desired to bring art to more than just a small,
elite audience, by producing pieces such as this bronze which could be cast from
a mold in multiple numbers. Such works were thus more affordable and could

be found in many middle-class homes. Kossowski probably used bronze for this
piece because of its durability, flexibility and traditional elevated sculptural
status. The fact that this sculpture is made from cast bronze therefore meant
that Kossowski could make copies as he wished, as long as the mold remained
intact. Yet by nature of the medium, Kossowski could maintain a sense of
craftsmanship, which was also important during the period.

Upholding female beauty and utilizing sinuous lines typified the Art Nouveau
style. This piece is immediately defined as a woman's face in profile with loose,
fluid tendrils of hairs that ultimately transition into a large peacock feather that
almost completely encircles the entire composition. This feather curves upward
and out, providing a practical lip to contain any dresser-top items the tidy might
hold. The bottom right corner, where there is no feather, has been sloped down
in order to provide a visual and functional point of entry into the piece. Here
we can also clearly see Kossowski's engraved signature.

She is portrayed in a classical profile accentuated by a slight smile, a typical
enigmatic Art Nouveau expression. This celebration of female beauty and the
use of the peacock feather, one of three symbols of the Aesthetic Movement,[5]
connect this piece to earlier ideas. Her hair is slightly tussled in a sensual
suggestion as it flows uninterruptedly into the peacock feather, making it
difficult to pinpoint where the feather begins and her hair ends.

Peacocks, especially the tail feathers, derived from the Japanese-influenced
Aesthetic Movement and became one of the primary Art Nouveau motifs.[6]
Such images became popular with the public with the rise in interest in Japanese
exports. The peacock as a recognizable image of the Aesthetic Movement came
to symbolize pride and beauty.[7] A well-known example of this *Japonisme* (as the
phenomenon of Japanese inspired western art came to be called) was Whistler's
infamous *Peacock Room*, unveiled in London in 1877. Most American and
European artists would have been familiar with this room, through coverage in
the popular press, and its various interpretations of the peacock motif.

The organic subject matter, blending both the elegant beauty of nature and the
provocative aesthetics of the woman's face, seems to comment on both the
fragility and immortality of beauty. It also reminds viewers of the
corresponding qualities that might be found between nature and humanity. Its
functional charm places this piece as a bridge between the long curvilinear lines
of Art Nouveau and the Aesthetic Movement from which it was born.

[Wilder Anderson, *Class of 2005*]

[1] E. Bénézit, *Dictionaire Critique et documentaire des peintres, sculpteurs, dessinateur et
graveurs de tous les pays par un groupe d' écrivains specilists français et étrangers*, vol. 7 (Paris:
Gründ Paris, 1999), 957.

[2] Quoted in Peter Selz and Mildred Constantine, eds., *Art Nouveau: Art and Design at the
Turn of the Century* (New York: The Museum of Modern Art, 1975), 7.

[3] Elizabeth Aslin, *The Aesthetic Movement: Prelude to Art Nouveau* (New York: Excalibur
Books, 1981), 33.

[4] Selz and Constantine, 12.

[5] The lily, sunflower and peacock feather were the identifying symbols for this movement.

[6] Selz and Constantine, 14.

[7] Ibid.

73

Artist unknown
Art Nouveau Style Inkstand, ascribed title, attributed to late 19th century
Cast bronze
Unsigned
6.4 x 23.8 x 23.8 cm., 2-1/2 x 9-3/8 x 9-3/8"
Erick O. Schonstedt Inkstand Collection number 343, Augustana College
Art Collection

The features on this *Art Nouveau* inkstand lead to an assumption that it was created in the late nineteenth century or early twentieth century. It was most likely made in France, where depictions of the female nude were more prevalent and accepted than in countries like England or the United States. This piece was cast in bronze, making it much heavier than it appears, and has a delicate, copper-colored patina which adds a rich dimension to the overall piece. There are three parts to this inkstand: the central container that holds the ink itself, the circular tray beneath it and the lid with raised relief at the top that serves to protect the ink from evaporation.

Inkwells and inkstands have been a historic part of the *decorative art* world for many centuries, reflecting the changing preferences of many cultures and individuals for whom they were made.[1] The terms *inkwell* and *inkstand* are interchangeably used in references today, but the terminology may need further definition. Early forms of ink containers used by scribes included inkhorns and ink pots. The *inkwell* was a vessel for ink storage, into which a pen could be dipped, that was usually located on or in a desk. The container identified as the *inkstand* seemingly also included a tray to support additional accoutrements, such as a taper holder to melt wax for an envelope seal, a sander to size the paper, or a resting surface for a pen.[2] Originating in Egypt as simple forms of clay or stone, inkwells made their way around the globe with the increasing rate of literacy. They gained popularity in the sixteenth century as aristocrats began to write their own letters, rather than dictating to scribes. Inkstands, while functional as a part of daily life, also became exquisite works of art in themselves and ultimately, important status symbols. The variety of media and forms is astounding. Materials range from precious metal, porcelain, tortoise shell and animal horn to blown and pressed glass. Imaginative forms portrayed include a vast array of motifs such as pomegranates and carriages, to name only a few. Inkwell production was profitable until the 1880s, when the invention of the fountain pen and its consequent modern efficiency, competed with such output.[3]

This particular inkstand was most likely created around the turn of the nineteenth century. It depicts a swirling array of poppy flowers and their elongated stems surrounding the actual inkwell in the center, on which rests a female nude figure reclining within a blossom. The style is Art Nouveau, evidenced by the sinuously swirling plants and the celebration of feminine beauty. At the turn of the nineteenth century, Art Nouveau became very popular while artists searched to redefine art through a synthesis of artistic crafts.[4] Uninspired by overused historical art and traditions, craftsmen sought to join in a revolution for modernity. One artist declared that "modern life alone must be the sole starting point of our artistic creation, all else is archaeology."[5]

They looked to nature for inspiration, attempting to portray not simply a *copy* of nature but rather an interpretation of an *idea* from nature, a symbolically organic representation. The style of Art Nouveau is characterized by curling and twisting lines, constantly in motion, flowing across surfaces. Beautiful young women with long hair, swans, peacock feathers, lilies and all arrangements of entwining nature filled their imaginations.[6] This inkstand tray is defined by tendrils, flower stems, from poppies. There are four poppy flowers on this piece with brushes of tendrils throughout the tray. These tendrils form patterns of curving lines, bringing texture to the piece. An idealized nude female rests gracefully upon the lid as a crowning motif within the poppy blossom.

Along with French Art Nouveau, there is also Japanese influence in this piece. Japanese art had an enormous impact on the western world. For centuries the country and its markets had been virtually closed to westerners, but in 1856 they again entered Japan and reopened trade. When the restrictive shogunate government fell thirteen years later, Japanese export products flooded the European market.[7] Woodblock prints, bronzes, porcelain and lacquered items were the most popular. The radically different approach to art met with enthusiastic approval from western artists who were looking for fresh inspiration, away from Renaissance tradition. They sought to synthesize such Japanese stylistic characteristics as flat, two-dimensional perspective, simplification of nature, asymmetrical compositions and bold color schemes into their own modern viewpoints. Japanese influence thus swept across the European art world.[8]

French avant-garde artists were particularly affected and quickly reacted by producing *Japonisme*, art that reflected these new Japanese techniques. One such medium, known as *black ink painting*, was characterized by a modernist '*less is best*' approach, creating as much as possible with minimal use of lines. The thickness and curve of a particularly well-executed line could serve to capture an entire subject. This influence can be seen in the emphasis on swirling lines on the inkstand.

An interesting element in this particular piece is the poppy motif. The poppy had been used in symbolic representations throughout history. In ancient Greece, it was the attribute of *Hypnos*, the god of sleep, as well as *Morpheus*, the god of dreams, and *Night*, owing to its ability to induce sleep.[9] The reclining position of this figure seems to invite such a classical reading. Yet it might also suggest an interpretation more relevant to its own time. The opium poppy, another popular Asian export to the west, was prevalent at the time for both its medicinal and narcotic benefit, known to provoke particularly vivid dreams. This meaning also seems to be supported by the imagery. Such complex readings make this piece particularly inspiring; since there is only limited information about this inkstand, the viewer is offered more latitude to interpret its meaning within its historic and contemporary contexts.

[John Sexton, *Class of 2006*]

[1] Judy Penz Sheluk, "Inkwells: A Necessity for the Literate," *Antique Trader's Collector Magazine and Price Guide*, (2004): 5.

[2] Michael Finlay, *Western Writing Implements in the Age of the Quill Pen*, (Cumbria, U.K.: Plains Books, 1990), 35-38. Also, "Inkstand Basics," *All's Well*, http://pages.cthome.net/allswell/Basics/Inkstand, (1 November 2005). Augustana College holds a large collection of inkwells and inkstands assembled by Erick O. Schonstedt. Sherry C. Maurer was consulted for this information.

[3] Sheluk, 20.

[4] Peter Selz and Mildred Constantine, eds., *Art Nouveau: Art and Design at the Turn of the Century* (New York: The Museum of Modern Art, 1975), 8.

[5] Ibid., 11.

[6] Ibid., 14.

[7] Colta Feller Ives, *The Great Wave: The Influence of Japanese Woodcuts on French Prints* (New York: The Metropolitan Museum of Art, 1974), 11.

[8] Ives, 11.

[9] James Hall, *Dictionary of Subjects and Symbols in Art* (New York: Harper & Row, 1974), 250.

74

Louis Comfort Tiffany (American 1848–1933)
Favrile Inkwell, 1899
Blown glass and hinged brass lid
Signed with incised initials on underside "L.C.T." and "K 1901"
8.2 x 12.5 x 12.5 cm., 3-1/8 x 5-1/4 x 5-1/4"
Erick O. Schonstedt Inkstand Collection number 202, Augustana College
Art Collection

An object of modest size but beguiling surface, this ink container has the golden glow of Tiffany *Favrile* glass. Louis Comfort Tiffany's Favrile glass works combined inspirations from Venetian glass techniques and decorative styles of ancient Egyptian and Near Eastern arts. It is thus interesting to compare this piece to the two Roman glass objects in the Augustana College Art Collection (catalogue 3A and 3B). The Eastern Mediterranean cosmetic tube and the West Roman bowl altered with aging and chemical changes; the encrustations and iridescence developed long after the glass was produced. While not original, this aging has a visual allure that was approximated in *modern* later nineteenth-century glass.

Although the term *Favrile* was also applied to Tiffany's work in jewelry and other media, it was the Favrile *glass* that became a decorative staple of well-bred American homes from 1900 to 1915. Many artistic style revivals were circulating in the 19th century but Tiffany formed a new synthesis of influences. The sources for his inspiration can be traced to his association with Tiffany and Company, the luxury goods business of which his father, Charles Lewis, was the founder and principal owner.[1] The son was befriended by the Company's renowned silver designer, Edward C. Moore, who was one of the first major American collectors of Islamic and Asian arts (his huge collection was ultimately bequeathed to the Metropolitan Museum of Art). Designers such as Moore, for the honor of their employer, competed with virtuoso entries at the great universal expositions of the time. Moore brought home an 1889 gold medal for his *Saracenic* silverwares.

In 1869, the 21-year-old Louis Comfort returned to New York after studying in Paris and traveling to more exotic locations abroad. During that same year, his father's company began to import and sell items from the studio of Venetian glassmaker Antonio Salviati. Three years later, the son began to explore glassmaking, and in 1880 he attempted to start his own glassworks with the help of a Salviati-trained glassblower.[2] The setback of several fires that destroyed his plants repeatedly delayed the younger Tiffany's entry into the production of blown glass. At the 1893 World's Columbian Exposition in Chicago, Louis Comfort Tiffany, with his Tiffany Studios, won recognition for his stained glass and glass mosaic work.

Even as the Exposition was opening, Tiffany founded the Stourbridge Glass Company with the help of Arthur J. Nash, a talented English glassblower formerly employed with the Thomas Webb Company. According to Tiffany scholar Robert Koch, it was Nash who suggested as a company trademark an old English word *fabrile* in order to convey a sense of craft and craftsmanship. In 1894 Tiffany's company filed for a *Favrile* trademark to apply to any of its goods.[3] Finally, in the 1895 Tiffany and Company sales catalog, the *Blue Book*, the store debuted offerings of "'Tiffany Favrile Glass made by a new process, and blown under the personal supervision of Mr. Louis Comfort Tiffany' at prices from ten to fifty dollars."[4] Simultaneously, the premier French purveyor of things Art Nouveau, Samuel Bing, showed the new works in his Paris gallery.

The entry in this catalog on the Art Nouveau inkstand (catalogue 73) explains the difference in meaning between the terms *inkwell* and *inkstand*. The entry for

catalogue 92 notes the trend to value handwork over mass production. Tiffany blazed a path in attempting to produce affordable objects of luxury style, such as desk sets with inkwells and inkstands. "Tiffany firmly believed that 'beauty in the home has little or nothing to do with the amount of money spent.'"[5]

When Louis Comfort Tiffany inherited his father's estate and took on the family business in 1902, he was able to market free-blown glass holloware in great quantity. Most of Tiffany's pieces were marked with a registration system. This inkwell is initialed and marked with a letter "K" that dates it to 1899.[6] The hinged brass lid fastens down on a lobed blown glass bottle type that appears in Tiffany works around 1889. The lobed base recalls Edward C. Moore's *Elephant Foot* loving cup made for the 1889 Paris Exposition.[7] Different golden yellow colors suffuse this inkstand, luminous and kaleidoscopic with ripples that catch and change in the light with glints of turquoise, pink and bronze. This piece both reflects and refracts light, with two types of surfaces. The sheen is both the gold iridescent glass that Tiffany claimed to invent, and also the opalescent glass that was so popular in his windows and glassware. The top surface of the container is reminiscent of crème brûlé, and the overall effect is as delightful as dessert.

Tiffany saw beauty derived from the inspiration of nature, not from any advance in technique, however much his glasswork is now admired for technical accomplishments. He esteemed color over all other visual qualities. He vowed "...color is of the first importance. In many flowers their form is distinctly a secondary consideration, which comes after the satisfaction we feel in their colors—those hues that glow and flicker and strike the sight like the embers, the little many-jets and the steadier flames of a drift-wood fire."[8] Pieces were free blown and molds were not used. Tiffany equated beauty with the unique quality of a handmade object, with a modern aesthetic that embraced the ventures of accident and chance of the process. One of the major thesis points of John Loring's 2002 book is to show that Tiffany had a crucial presence in overseeing and directing the work of the artisans he employed, and as such really was a key factor in the art of his products. He meshed well with his collaborators until about 1913, when European modernist movements were introduced in the New York Armory Show. The reductive aspects of that new wave of style countered the richness of Tiffany's aesthetic. Although he tried to adapt, he had to hire different designers, and World War I further diminished the demand for his offerings. In 1920 the glass production was reorganized under Nash's son as Louis C. Tiffany Furnaces, Inc., and Tiffany's interest in the business was sold to A. Douglas Nash in 1928, drawing to a close a vivid chapter in American decorative arts.[9]

[Sherry C. Maurer, *Director of Augustana College
Art Museum and Permanent Collection*]

[1] John Loring, *Louis Comfort Tiffany at Tiffany & Co.* (New York: Harry N. Abrams, 2002), 12-16.

[2] Loring, 240-241. Tiffany made at least three failed attempts to create a blown glass factory due to destruction of his property by fire. Each fire disaster brought business failure that required refinancing from Tiffany's father.

[3] Robert Koch, *Louis C. Tiffany's Art Glass* (New York: Crown Publishers, 1977), 10. Koch states (page 9) that Nash would have held equal partnership with Tiffany if the Stourbridge Glass Company had not burned in 1892. When the plant was re-built, it was re-named Tiffany Furnaces, a subdivision of Tiffany Glass Company, later named the Tiffany Glass and Decorating Company.

[4] Loring, 131.

[5] Ibid., 179.

[6] Koch, 40.

[7] Loring, 236.

[8] Koch, 38.

[9] Loring, 46-49, and 138.

75

Emile Gallé (French 1846–1904)
Art Nouveau Style Vase in Plum and Yellow, ascribed title, attributed early
20th century
Cameo blown glass
Signed b.r. "Gallé"
18.5 x 8.9 x 7.5 cm., 7-1/4 x 3-1/2 x 3"
Lent Courtesy of Private Collection

Technology was greatly expanding in the late nineteenth century. Thomas Edison's invention of the electric light in 1879 and Henry Ford's production of the first automobile in 1893 were indicative of a new era of science and machines.[1] The advances in technology were spreading rapidly even to the most remote locations. In Nancy, France, innovative artist Emile Gallé (1864–1904) took the medium of glass design to a new level. Through modern methods fused with tradition, he diversified the medium beyond mere functionality by showing its capacity to express the aesthetics of nature.

The innovations that Gallé contributed to the Art Nouveau movement came through his manipulation of *cameo*, a technique dating back to ancient Rome. Cameo glass comprises two or more separate colored layers of glass. The top layers are acid-etched, a technique used to remove areas of overlaid glass, in order to create designs in relief on the cameo glass vessels. Gemstone engravers originally developed the cameo technique. Glassmakers adapted it by blowing and fusing together layers of different colored glass and then hand-cutting, acid-etching or sand-blasting away the background layer(s) to create a design that stood out above the surface.[2]

The cameo technique reached new heights in the hands of Emile Gallé. He transformed formal two-color vases into complex, multilayered compositions. Using combinations of cutting and carving by hand, along with acid-etching, he created organic designs from as many as five layers of colored glass. Gallé also eliminated the sharp color contrasts, preferring to cut away colors at various levels in order to create shading, subtle color gradations, atmosphere and perspective. His inventive talent lay in his ability as an alchemist to conjure up new colors with which to tint his glass. Although Gallé's ability to manipulate glass was ahead of its time, his true artistic genius rested in his union of the functionality of the glass vessels to the poetry of nature.

Gallé had a close relationship with nature, as a philosopher and as a poet, and he found within the plant world the inspiration for his totally unique glass creations. He felt that beauty was truth and truth lay in nature. He believed that our very existence depends on the abundance of plants, and his decorative principles were thus wholly founded on a close study of nature. In this new era of science and machines, Gallé wanted to get back to the simplicity of nature. The elements of nature that had the most significant impact on Gallé came from the new influence of *Japonisme*.

Japanese art displayed in major European exhibitions from the 1860s onward is generally credited with inspiring the Art Nouveau movement. Contemporary French art critic, Philippe Burty, first used the term *Japonisme* in 1876 to describe the fashion for all things Japanese that pervaded French art and design in the second half of the nineteenth century. Japonisme provided Gallé with inspiration, encouraging him to push the boundaries of contemporary glass both in terms of shape and content. He had enjoyed running through the summer fields in Nancy, spotting wild flowers, and sketching their colors and shapes. It was such early experiences with nature that led to his fascination with similar botanical motifs in Japanese art.

Through studying Japanese aesthetics, Gallé developed an expressive power of line, and learned how to abstract a flower, yet still retain its essence. He also adopted from this foreign culture a reverence for natural forms, focusing in particular on their varied colors and shapes. His creations were characterized by abstracted beautiful flowers that were not rigid and straight, but displayed graceful curves. An irregular whiplash motif dominates his designs, typical of the Art Nouveau style in general. Orchids, not the sunflowers of the Aesthetic Movement, were the order of the day. Instead of constructing vases that were simply and predictably decorated with flowers, the entire vase itself became the flower through the subtle blend of shape and color.[3]

Many of these organic Japanese influences can be seen on this particular vase. One of the first points of interest is the winding spiral tree which takes up more than half of the vessel. The curvilinear form is typical of the Art Nouveau movement. Although the line is dramatic, the vase does not lose its organic shape. There is a strong sense that this is not a tree from his local environment, but is reminiscent of an asymmetrical element derived from a distant Japanese garden. By incorporating this exotic addition, the vase gains a mystical, poetic quality which invites the viewer to be contemplative.

Gallé wanted his glass vessels to connect with his audience so that they might become one with nature. In this manner, he felt that individuality could still be maintained in contrast to the modern urban pace which emphasized conformity. The technique and medium demonstrated here are typical of Gallé's general oeuvre. The cameo glass vase is acid-etched to create a layer of multi-colors that enable the various elements—flowers, trees and the stream—to stand out amidst a mountainous landscape, seemingly shifting and changing in a given light, akin to the subtle moods of nature. In such translucent manner, Gallé has effectively captured the subtle nuances of life.

[Paul Arnell, *Class of 2006*]

[1] William Warmus, *Emile Gallé: Dreams into Glass* (New York: Dover Publications, 1984), 11.

[2] Philippe Garner, *Emile Gallé* (New York: Rizzoli, 1977), 92-100.

[3] Tim Newark, *Emile Gallé* (London: Quintet Publishing, Ltd., 1989), 28-31.

76

Edgar Melville Ward (American 1839–1915)
Gathering Oysters, Low Tide, circa 1874–1880
Oil on canvas
Signed b.r. in image "Edgar M. Ward"
55.3 x 68.5 cm., 21-7/8 x 27"
Purchase with Gift of a Friend of Augustana College, Augustana College
Art Collection, 2003.3.2

It seems that, for nearly 200 years, Brittany has been "an inexhaustible source of inspiration" for painters.[1] Paul Gauguin was one of the many artists to escape from the busy city life of Paris to find solace in the rich and vibrant landscapes, the colorful costumes and the traditional and religious way of life in Brittany. Many other well-known painters such as Gustave Courbet, James McNeill Whistler, John Singer Sargent, Claude Monet, Emile Bernard and Henri Matisse were captivated by this region that refuses to surrender to modernity. Bernard commented, "It is a permanent Impressionist exhibition here...when the weather is fine: it's Monet all over again...It's enough to make you mad."[2] Brittany was considered *the* place for artistic experimentation, from the elite to the beginner, Realist to the Expressionist, Brittany was an exceptional source.[3]

Another lesser-known artist who fell in love with Brittany's beauty was American expatriate, Edgar Melville Ward (1839–1915), generally described as a genre painter. He was born in Ohio and trained at the National Academy of Design in New York. His brother, American sculptor, John Quincy Adams Ward, shared his brother's artistic abilities.[4] Edgar Ward studied with academic French painter, Thomas Gérôme (a former student of Neoclassicist Jacques Louis David), along with future American Impressionist, J. Alden Weir, who accompanied him to Pont-Aven to paint the environs in the Realist technique.[5] Ward is best known for his *Coppersmith* painting; however his beautiful technique is illustrated here in this lesser known painting, *Gathering Oysters, Low Tide*,[6] possibly dating to the 1870s when Ward was working in Brittany with Weir. American artists actually "discovered"[7] this area as a welcome respite from the accelerated pace of Parisian life. The artist colony at Pont-Aven flourished for twenty years before the arrival of perhaps its most famous visitor, Post-Impressionist Paul Gauguin. His influence might be felt in the Breton work of his follower, Emile Dezaunay (catalogue 77), which displays a more Post-Impressionist interpretive freedom.

As previously mentioned, this is a genre painting, which means that it portrays scenes from everyday life in a realistic or romanticized way. Such works typically show ordinary people participating in commonplace events. They were very popular with the bourgeoisie (middle class) and were favorite subjects for artists in Brittany, many of them similar to Ward's.

Oyster gathering, or harvesting, was an important job in the inlet called *Cancale Harbor* in Brittany. The bustle of this activity created a great subject for artists.[8] In fact, painters John Singer Sargent and Eugéne Feyen became famous for this genre; Sargent even created a series of paintings depicting locals gathering oysters in *Cancale*. It was this group of works for which he was recognized at the Salon of 1878.[9] These paintings are probably more closely related to Ward's *Gathering Oysters, Low Tide*, and further reinforce its dating to the 1870s, most likely between 1874 (his arrival with Weir) and 1878 (Sargent's exhibition of similar women in parallel compositions).

Stylistically, this is a brilliant and visually stimulating painting. There have been many accounts from artists about the illuminated sky or the fascinating sea of Brittany's landscape.[10] The color is beautiful, ranging from the intense blue-green of the water and sky and the bright red skirt, balanced by the neutral sandy color of the beach. The painting is Realist in manner, however the bright colors may reveal an early Impressionist influence. In this painting, the vibrant colors of Brittany's scenery are beautifully captured. These women are obviously peasants in their traditional costumes, which enticed so many artists of the time. The eye never wanders from the well-orchestrated composition: the woman on the right is balanced by the other oyster gatherer, who is bending down in a circular pattern. One cannot help but wonder, what is the object of the woman's gaze? She seems to be captivated by someone or something off in the distance. Perhaps she is weary of her peasant lifestyle and longs for change. One can only speculate, but it is possible that she is dreaming of a more glamorous and exciting city life, ironically, the very life that artists like Ward and Gauguin chose to flee.

Modernist, Henri Matisse later reminisced about his stay in Brittany, "And soon I was seduced by the brilliance of pure colours. I returned from my trip with a passion for the colours of the rainbow."[11] This painting epitomizes those very colors that Matisse and so many others experienced and relished while in this region. Artists like Ward longed for the charm and diversity of landscapes that this timeless environment offered: a place where they could find nature, spirituality and perhaps even themselves.

[Laura Kurczodyna, *Class of 2007*]

---

[1] Denise Delouche, "Painters in Brittany". Brentagne Nouvelle Vague, http://www.brittanytourism.com /eng/bretagnedespeintres/02_mer.cfm . (2005)

[2] Ibid.

[3] Ibid.

[4] The Columbia Electronic Encyclopedia, 6th ed., Columbia University Press, 2005. http://www.infoplease.com/ce6/people/A0851458.

[5] Beacon Hill, 13.

[6] Previously published in Beacon Hill, No. 64, 47.

[7] David Sellin and James K. Ballinger, *Americans in Brittany and Normandy: 1860-1910* (Phoenix: Phoenix Art Museum, 1982), 11.

[8] Delouche.

[9] Sellin and Ballinger, 137.

[10] Delouche.

[11] Ibid.

77

Emile Dezaunay (French 1854–1938), printed by Eugène Delâtre (French 1864–1938)
Messe en Bretagne [Mass in Brittany], ca. 1895
Etching, aquatint and roulette, 4-color plate, impression apart from the edition of 50, one of five proofs, edited by Edmond Sagot
Unsigned
32.1 x 42.1 cm., 12-5/8 x 16-9/16" image
43.6 x 61.8 cm., 17-3/16 x 24-1/4" sheet
Augustana College Art Exhibits Purchase as a Memorial Honoring William L. Beer, from Betty L. Beer, 97.11

Born in France, Emile Dezaunay began his artistic career under the tutelage of the Symbolist painter, Pierre Puvis de Chavannes. He later trained under Maxime Mauffra who introduced him to French Post-Impressionist, Paul Gauguin. At the time, Gauguin brought artists together to Bridge Swallow-Hole, Bretagne, in order to discuss and introduce his new technique. Gauguin considered the region "primitive" and embraced the "simple life" there.[1] Dezaunay was among several artists who studied under Gauguin in Brittany, where he developed his etching skills and an understanding of Gauguin's *Synthetism*, which he later applied to his own work, *Messe en Bretagne* (Mass in Brittany). Synthetism aimed at achieving beautiful and powerful artwork through the fusion of nature, artistic training and medium.[2]

Gauguin's theory challenged earlier Impressionist beliefs that one should paint nature just as it appears. Gauguin instead advised his followers that "the synthetist artist must dominate rather than be submissive to nature"[3]. He further suggested: "Paint in your room; finish it outside."[4] His main ideology was to create a direct and bold composition through simplicity and concentrated color.[5] This artistic approach was one of the most prevalent ideas in art during the latter part of the nineteenth century.[6] The Synthetism evident in Gauguin's pivotal work, *Vision After the Sermon: Jacob wrestling with the Angel*, 1888, clearly influenced Dezaunay's style seven years later in *Messe en Bretagne*. Dezaunay is sometimes categorized as a Neo-Impressionist painter, following the *pointillist* manner of Georges Seurat and Henri-Edmond Cross (catalogue 67A and 67B). This print, however, empasized the Synthetist embellishment of the "formal aspects of representation, line, colour, and value."[7]

Dezaunay's scene depicts *fin-de siècle* (end of the century) religious practice in Brittany at a peasant devotional site. The people of Bretagne had a very rigorous and full religious life. The young women wear aprons and head coverings, part of their everyday dress, each region distinguished by a unique female head covering. The subject of the painting, according to the title, is a religious service. Young women in traditional costume dominate the foreground while the church and graveyard loom large and imposing in the background. The women appear to be socializing; some whispering to each other, others appear disinterested. One particular young woman leans against a crucifix, her eyes closed and turned away from the church and the doorway which appears dark with doors shut. The juxtaposition of the church, the young women and the graveyard seems to be making a statement about the closeness of life and death, as well as the role of religion in both. The young women are extremely vague and generalized. Only two faces are shown, in profile and without much detail.

As a Symbolist, Dezaunay suggests meaning, but does not explain, inviting viewers to interpret. This work might also imply the idea of youth being wasted upon the young. Surrounded by death and spirituality, the women are perhaps no closer to faith in this setting than they would be in their own homes. The differences between the directly observed views of Breton peasants by American artists like Edgar Melville Ward (catalogue 76) in the 1870s, and Dezaunay's French Synthetist vision created twenty years later, are instructive. Ward focused on labor and a straightforward style that bridged Realism and Impressionism. Dezaunay, on the other hand, simplified and heightened nature, with religious overtones, effectively straddling Synthetism and Symbolism.

As with Gauguin's work, there seems to be much implied meaning in Dezaunay's impression. We might wonder if he meant to invite his audience to examine the nature of piety, in a region that was considered "the most devotedly religious of all the French provinces."[8] Or perhaps he merely embraced Gauguin's ideal of a simpler, more primitive way of life. Whatever the case, Dezaunay's blend of Synthetism and Symbolism are so remarkably close to the work of Gauguin that it is difficult to speak of him without recalling the imprint of the original modern artistic *savage*, Gauguin.

[Mikeda Cannon, *Class of 2007*]

[1] Lawrence and Elizabeth Hanson, *Noble Savage: The Life of Paul Gauguin* (New York: Random House, 1955), 79.

[2] Richard Bretell, *Modern Art 1851-1929: Capitalism and Representation* (Oxford: Oxford University Press, 1999), 26.

[3] Ibid.

[4] Hanson, 81.

[5] Ibid., 82.

[6] Bretell, 26-27.

[7] Ibid., 26.

[8] Lewis Spence, *Legends and Romances of Brittany* (New York: Fredrick A Stokes Co., 1917), 377.

78

Paul Gauguin (French 1848–1903)
Manao tupapau (**Watched by the Spirits of the Dead**), 1894–1895
Woodcut
Unsigned
17.3 x 12.8 cm., 6-3/4 x 5" image
25.1 x 17.7 cm., 9-7/8 x 7" sheet
Purchase Through Paul A. Anderson Chair in the Arts and Art Exhibits,
and Gifts of Dan Churchill, George and Pat Olson, Al and Lynne
DeSimone, and Dr. Kurt Christoffel, Augustana College Art Collection,
2004.8

Paul Gauguin was one of the most influential late nineteenth-century artists
who pointed the way in the establishment of modernism. He began as a
Sunday painter-stock broker in Paris and came to be considered one of the
founders of modern art, along with fellow Post-Impressionists, Paul Cézanne,
Georges Seurat and his long suffering friend, Vincent Van Gogh. His
mother's Peruvian Incan roots have generally been cited as the source for his
passion for primitivism, which led to his moving from Paris to Panama,
Martinique and Brittany (where he co-founded the *Symbolist Synthetist* style
which influenced artists like Emile Dezaunay [catalogue 77]) and ultimately
settling in Tahiti. His goal through this restlessness, as he wrote to his wife,
was to "live like a savage…I am taking my paints and my brushes with me,
and there I will steep myself [in nature] far from all men."[1]

Gauguin was clearly reacting to the perceived decadence of 1890s Paris, aptly
recorded by Henri de Toulouse-Lautrec (catalogue 69 and 70) in his scenes of
Parisian nightlife at the famous nightclub, the *Moulin Rouge*. The modernist
promise of the city and its environs, captured by Impressionists Eugène
Boudin (catalogue 42) and Charles Pécrus (catalogue 43), gave way to feelings
of disillusionment as the Impressionist movement broke down with the final
of eight exhibitions in 1886. By the 1880s, Gauguin had already proposed
that unlike the Realist/Impressionist quest for nature, he was developing a
more interpretive approach, founded on the assumption that: "Art is an
abstraction."[2]

This woodcut is a variation on the theme of the *tupapau* (Spirit of the Dead)
which Gauguin had already treated in 1892 in an oil painting with the same
title during his first sojourn in Tahiti. Among several other versions of the
tupapau figure were two *(Te po [Night]* and *Manao tupapau)* of a series of ten
woodcuts which Gauguin made in 1893–4 for use as chapter illustrations in
Noa Noa, his projected travel account of his first stay in Tahiti. This 1894–5
woodcut is similar to the original oil painting in that it depicts an
(abbreviated) nude female figure lying on her stomach and peeking fearfully
from the shelter formed by her upstretched fingers; the enigmatic figure of the
tupapau looms behind her. In both oil painting and woodcut, the *tupapau* is
a forbidding, hooded figure with a piercing almond-shaped eye seen against a
shadowy background, although in the woodcut the *tupapau* is perhaps more
menacingly placed almost directly behind the head of the nude woman. The
boxwood block on which the woodcut was created contained two other scenes

(Maori Woman in the Forest and *Standing Maori Woman)*, which probably
explains the need to abbreviate the female figure in *Manao tupapau*.

Gauguin's woodcuts are innovative in both technique and subject. Though he
may have drawn on a long tradition of French woodcuts or on a growing
interest in Japanese woodcuts (catalogue 57) in fin-de-siècle France, Gauguin
was a precursor of the revival of woodcuts in the early twentieth century.[3]
Charles Morice, Gauguin's collaborator in the production of *Noa Noa*,
proclaimed his woodcuts a "revolution in the art of wood-cut."[4] Technically,
he tended for example to reverse the "traditional relationship of positive
(white) and negative (black) areas in the woodcut," with the result that prints
have the "appearance of photographic negatives."[5] He also concentrated less
on clear-cut lines than creating for decorative or expressive purposes "broad,
contrasting areas" such as the dark background which suggests the
"mysterious world of Polynesian myths and legends"[6] in the present piece.

As regards subject matter, Gauguin was no less a revolutionary. One might
compare Gauguin's female figure (seen full length in the original oil-painting
and in abbreviated form in the woodcut) with Edouard Manet's *Olympia*
(1863), since in each case the figure is a reclining female nude. However,
Gauguin's stated intentions in his letters and journals underline the
differences between the Realist Manet and the primitivist, Post-Impressionist
aspects of Gauguin's art. They suggest perhaps a greater affinity with artists
like Pablo Picasso (catalogue 100) who drew much of his early inspiration
from African masks (catalogue 80A and 80B) and the Expressionists of the
early 20th century (catalogue 81, 83, 84, 85 and 97). His interest in *Manao
tupapau* (a subject he returned to again and again) was not for a "beautifully
painted nude" like Manet's famous work or a "simple study of an Oceanic
nude," but rather he wished to "imbue it with the native feeling, character
and tradition."[7]

Manao tupapau recalls the return to Romantic dreams and beliefs toward the
unknown, as earlier recorded by Francisco Goya in his *Sleep of Reason
Produces Monsters* (catalogue 27). Specifically, this woodcut, like the 1892 oil
painting, evokes the superstitions of a primitive culture through the Tahitian
myth of the ubiquitous presence of the *Spirits of the Dead* among the living
and the terror inspired in the latter by these *tupapau*. As theorist and poet
Charles Baudelaire (catalogue 41) proposed: "What is pure art according to
the modern concept? It is the creation of a suggestive magic…the world
outside the artist, and the artist himself."[8]

[Roger Crossley, *Professor of French*]

[1] Robert Goldwater, *Paul Gauguin* (New York: Harry N.Abrams, [1972]), 13.

[2] Ibid., 44.

[3] Ibid., 49.

[4] Christopher Becker, ed., *Paul Gauguin: Tahiti* (Stuttgart: Staatsgalerie, 1998), 120.

[6] Goldwater, 114.

[7] Ibid., quoted from Gauguin's letters.

[8] Goldwater, 44.

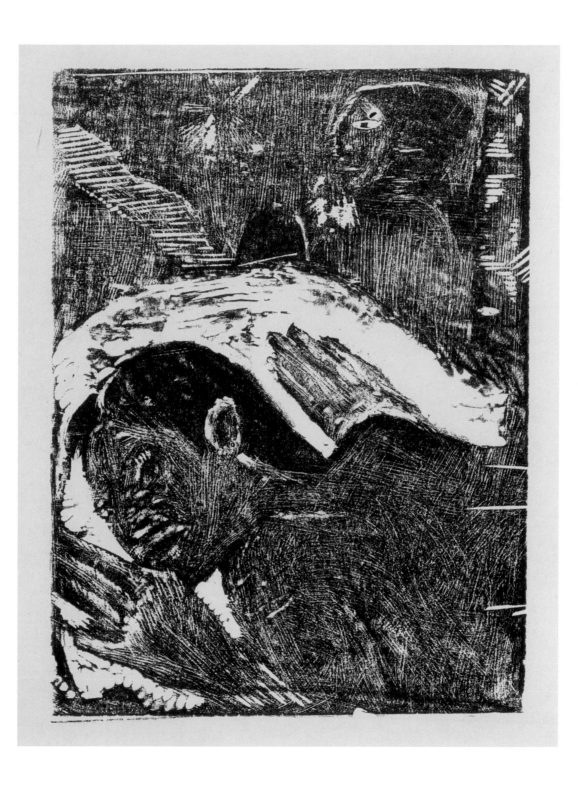

79

Ignace-Henri-Jean-Théodore Fantin-Latour (French 1836–1904)
Immortalité [Immortality], 1898, issued for ***L'estampe Moderne***
Lithograph hinged to backing sheet
Signed b.l. in image "Fantin"
34.7 x 24.7 cm., 13-5/8 x 9-3/4" image
40.7 x 30.8 cm., 16 x 12-1/8" backing sheet
Gift in Memory of Dr. Thomas William Carter, Augustana College Art
Collection, 2002.10

Immortalité is a work that stylistically parallels artist Henri Fantin-Latour's life. In this beautiful piece, Fantin combined elements of Neoclassicism, Romanticism and Symbolism, but overall, it is based on a very personal imaginative expression. Although Fantin practiced many different styles throughout his career, self-expression was the basis for his work. Even in constructing group portraits, he used his feelings about his sitters to promote social statements as well as propagandistic ideas. He was prolific, painting everything from Realist portraits and still lifes to imaginative Romantic evocations of angels and dreams. *Symbolism* was very important to Fantin's later romantically-styled images, speaking to the viewer's imagination by including classical characteristics as well as suggestive iconography.

Neoclassical elements are apparent in the classical idealism of this female figure, appropriately clothed in *wet drapery* and standing in a typical *contrapposto* position. By this time, Fantin had abandoned his Realist roots, for a more traditional academic approach. Yet his Neoclassical style was infused with romantic mystery and emotion. The dreamy atmospheric effects achieved through lighting and texture recall earlier Romantic etchings such as Francisco Goya's *Sleep of Reason Produces Monsters* (catalogue 27). The sources for Fantin's allegorical figure can be traced to Christian angels or classical *nikes* (winged victories). The careful balance of Neoclassicism and Romanticism might be appropriately termed *Neo-Romantic*.

Aside from the use of this style, this piece is primarily an expression of the Symbolist Movement. Through the allegorical subject matter, *Immortalité* expresses Fantin's feelings about the importance of the imagination, in a world relying on observed nature through photographic arts (catalogue 44, 45 and 49). The subject is almost thrust upon her viewers, asking them to think, imagine and interpret. Fantin considered his masterpieces to be those that focused on Symbolist ideas. The medium of lithography lent itself to such subtle interpretations and was also pursued by his close friend and colleague, American expatriate, James McNeill Whistler (catalogue 60). Both artists achieved reductive poetic qualities, closely allied to sensations created by music.

The structure of this work consists of a central idealized female figure with expansive wings. The image evokes a dreamlike aura within a heavenly black and white atmosphere. Rays of light create a miraculous effect as they radiate downward from the upper left corner, originating from an unknown source. Her outstretched wings fade into the background depth. The figure is frontally illuminated, establishing her as an independent light source, reinforced by the star-like form above her head. She holds the "palm branch of immortality" in her right hand, dropping the flowers of "memory" with her left.[1]

This particular image closely resembles Fantin's earlier oil painting, *Immortalité: à Eugène Delacroix*, exhibited in the 1889 Paris Salon. It also repeated motifs used in funerary monuments at Montmartre cemetery. Montmartre, the artists' district in Paris, was immortalized at this time through the works of Henri de Toulouse-Lautrec depicting the famous nightclub, the *Moulin Rouge* (catalogue 69 and 70). In Montmartre's cemetery, however, the grave of Henri Mürger included the figure of "youth scattering the petals from the roses of memory."[2] Mürger, one of the original Romantics, inspired the next generation of artists to live the bohemian life in Paris, through his popular novel, *Scènes de la vie de bohème*. During the 1850s, following Mürger's example, Fantin, Whistler and Alphonse Legros established their own avant-garde organization, the *Société des trois* (Society of three),[3] and Delacroix (catalogue 34) was one of their heroes. Mürger's book was later transformed into Puccini's important opera, *La Bohème*.

The close association of this image with the Romantics—painter Delacroix and writer Mürger—established Fantin's allegiance to the mysterious world of the imagination, rather than to scenes of modern Paris that surrounded him. Perhaps he typified the modernist crisis of the *fin-de-siècle* (end of the century), in the realization that observed reality was likely not enough, as many wished for deeper elements that lay beneath the surface. Fantin himself stated: "art is mixed up with too many human concerns...this kills me because it prevents me from being the artist I dream to be."[4] Although many contemporary critics appreciated the "nobility" of Fantin's aims, at least one questioned his motivation: "*Immortality*. One wonders whether it was not his own that Fantin wished [here] to achieve."[5]

[Katie Gedrimas, *Class of 2007 and*
Catherine Carter Goebel, *Professor of Art History,*
Paul A. Anderson Chair in the Arts]

[1] Douglas Druick and Michel Hoog, *Fantin-Latour* (Ontario: National Museums of Canada, 1983), 316.

[2] Ibid.

[3] Catherine Carter Goebel, *Tracing Line Through Time: A Whistler Centenary Exhibition*, (Rock Island: Augustana College, 2002), 1.

[4] Druick and Hoog, 98.

[5] Ibid, 316.

80A

Artist unknown, Ivory Coast, Africa
Yawaré Mask (for a hairdresser), n.d.
Carved, painted wood
Unsigned
48.5 x 16.5 x 9.2 cm., 19-1/2 x 6-5/8 x 3-1/2"
Gift of Betty L. Beer Franklin, Augustana College Art Collection, 2004.18.2

80B

Artist unknown, Africa
Figural Mask, n.d.
Carved wood
Unsigned
45.0 x 16.5 x 12.0 cm., 17-3/4 x 6-1/2 x 4-3/4"
Paul A. Anderson Chair in the Arts Purchase, Augustana College Art Collection, 2004.22

African masks are a type of primitive art, so why might they be included in an exhibition on modern western art? Artists throughout history have consulted sources from the past in order to inspire new works of art. Before the twentieth century, for example, eighteenth-century Neoclassicists revived the Classicism of ancient Greece and Rome. In the nineteenth century, Impressionists (catalogue 56) and Post-Impressionists (catalogue 69) reached further to draw inspiration from Japanese woodblock prints (catalogue 57).

With the establishment of modernism, the world was becoming more complex and many artists responded with greater abstraction, initiated by avant-garde innovators like James McNeill Whistler (catalogue 60). Some reacted by searching for more formative and primeval pasts, rooted in the mystery and genesis of civilization. Post-Impressionist Paul Gauguin, for example, pursued primitive truth amongst the natives of Tahiti. His *Manao tupapau* (Watched by the Spirits of the Dead) (catalogue 78) reflects such primitivism both in subject as well as in its use of an intentionally rough woodcut medium. The background spirit, with her long nose and angular eyes, creates a mask-like effect.

Although contact with Africa can be traced as far back as Roman times,[1] it was not until the early twentieth century that African masks truly reached out to western artists. Masks in general, however, were already part of the modern European consciousness. German Expressionist, Franz Marc (catalogue 84) commented that "Everything has appearance and essence, shell and kernel, mask and truth. What does it say against the inward determination of things that we touch the shell without reaching the kernel, that we live with appearance instead of perceiving the essence, that the mask of things so blinds us that we cannot find the truth?"[2] Masks as emblems of false impressions were a legacy to the twentieth century from Symbolism, as seen in such works as Fernand Khnopff's *Un Masque à la tenture mauve* (catalogue 82).

It is difficult to establish precise dates for African masks, but many works were created in the period before European influence was established in the mid-nineteenth century. Masks have appeared in a wide variety of places as early as the beginning of humankind. Used for hunting ceremonies and magic rituals, they can be traced as far back as the Stone Age. Today, the power and iconography of African masks have lost much significance, as they are often seen by non-African cultures as a means toward physical disguise, rather than an actual lens into African culture. However, in Africa, many tribes still use them for everyday activities and they reflect their rich traditions.

Masks are created through a specific process. Since they hold such a magical essence, the creation of one has precise rules and rituals. The religious head of the village, who directs every ceremony in which the mask will appear, must authorize the carving. Once a sculptor is given permission to carve a mask, he chooses a material to use, usually wood since it was easily available. A specific type of wood is prescribed for each type. Young wood is always used because it is easier to cut and less likely to dry out and split while being carved. Once the

right tree has been found, the sculptor cuts out a piece of wood and works in an isolated spot until completing the mask. The tools used are a hand axe, a curved knife for hollowing out the inside of the wood, some knives for detailed work and a punch to make holes. Rough leaves, strips of animal skin, sand, stones or pieces of bone are also used to polish the mask's surface. If a mask is to be darkened, either vegetable dyes from leaf pulp are used, or the mask is scorched.

The *Figural* and *Yawaré* masks are typical of Ivory Coast forms with their oval life-sized human faces and the zigzag patterns running along each side of the face.[3] A conventional approach is shown in the large forehead, emphasized eyebrow arches, the slit or wide opened eyes, well-defined cheekbones, the slender nose with flared nostrils and the mouth with parted lips. Sometimes, as in the *Figural Mask*, a human figure stands atop the mask in order to make it particularly impressive.[4] Through the ages, African masks have varied in function and meaning. Many masks are still associated with religious ceremonies, concerned with spirits of the dead or curing sickness. Other masks are used on festive occasions to portray mythological events.

Each mask possesses a spiritual meaning but the major function is psychological and relates to the purpose of escaping oneself. A mask allows one to create a new world beyond the reality of present life. More common types of masks include ones constructed for social status, funeral ceremonies and for protection. In order to immortalize an ancestor, masks were created and passed down by descendents. Masks worn to honor ancestors are powerful because it is believed that they can bring higher status to the new owner. Another type of mask relates to protection. The running mask, for example, is worn by the fastest runner in the village, responsible for keeping watch and raising alarm in case of danger. A burial function is also common when a respected member of the tribe dies. When this happens, other members gather to honor him and the mask is used during the ceremony to send away the spirit of the dead man from the village. The *Yaware Mask* served this purpose; the comb-like crown shows that it was dedicated to a hairdresser. Lastly, some masks are used to entertain with songs, dances and comedy, while others tell stories of heroes with epic poetry. No matter what type of mask is present, all masks are respected and feared because they appear as expressions of supernatural beings.

Because of the high status of masks, only men are permitted to wear them. The ownership of masks is restricted to powerful individuals or families. To be permitted to wear a mask, one must be designated and trained. Masks and the spirits they represent greatly impact African culture. They provide entertainment and social status for a community, enabling African cultures to express themselves spiritually and provide a meaning for life.

In terms of the development of modern art, African carvings acted as a springboard for elements of the two major schools of early twentieth-century art: Cubism and Expressionism. Upon first seeing the African exhibit at the Ethnographic Museum at the Trocadéro in Paris in 1907, Picasso edited his pivotal piece, *Les Demoiselles d'Avignon,* because of the "profound emotion of the shock."[5] Art critic Guillaume Apollinaire (catalogue 87) introduced Georges Braque to Picasso at this time, who proclaimed in response to this painting: "You paint as if you wanted to force us to eat rope or drink paraffin."[6] Yet "the work of Picasso's so-called *Negro Period* has none of the aloofness, the reserved containment, of its African prototype; its lashing rhythms remind us that Picasso looked to his masks as emblems of savagery, of violence transferred into the sphere of culture."[7] African art and its influence, with its conceptualized imaging, thus provided the genesis for the major modernist collaboration which resulted in the birth of Cubism (catalogue 90).

[Katrina Kainz, *Class of 2007 and*
Catherine Carter Goebel, *Professor of Art History,*
Paul A. Anderson Chair in the Arts]]

[1] Jean-Baptiste Bacquart, *The Tribal Arts of Africa* (London: Thames and Hudson, 1998), 10.
[2] Frederick S. Levine, *The Apocalyptic Vision: The Art of Franz Marc as German Expressionism* (New York: Harper & Row, 1979), 14.
[3] Ladislas Segy, *Masks of Black Africa* (New York: Dover, 1976), 68.
[4] Robert Bleakley, *African Masks* (New York: St. Martin's Press, 1978), 2-4.
[5] Thomas Parsons, *Post-Impressionism: The Rise of Modern Art: 1880-1920* (Toronto: The Gallery Publishing, 1999), 176.
[6] Ibid., 177.
[7] Robert Hughes, *The Shock of the New* (New York: McGraw-Hill, Inc., 1991), 21.

80A

80B

81

Paula Modersohn-Becker (German 1876–1907)
Sitzende Alte [Seated Old Woman], ca. 1900 (English title translation
kindly provided by Sonja Knudsen, Augustana College German
Department, 1999)
Etching and aquatint printed in dark brown, state three of three
Signed b.l. below image in graphite by artist's husband "F. P. Modersohn-
Becker/O. Modersohn."
18.8 x 14.5 cm., 7-3/8 x 5-9/16" image
33.8 x 25.5 cm., 13-1/4 x 10" sheet
Paul A. Anderson Chair in the Arts Purchase, Augustana College Art
Collection, 2000.60

While working at the Worpswede colony in Germany, a rural mecca that
many cutting edge painters, musicians and writers called home, Paula
Modersohn-Becker quietly and prolifically created a niche all her own.
Tragically, she suffered a heart attack in 1907, ending her life and career at the
early age of thirty-one. It must have been a shock even to her husband and
colleague—Otto Modersohn, a prominent artist in his own right—to find
such a wealth of sketches, paintings and etchings. Despite near obscurity
during her lifetime, Modersohn-Becker managed to leave behind
approximately four hundred paintings and one thousand sketches and graphic
works.[1]

As the twentieth century progressed, Modersohn-Becker received more and
more recognition as a precursor to the German Expressionist Movement.[2]
While there certainly appears to be ample evidence for such a claim, she has
transcended this label with her intriguing iconography and the incorporation
of not only German, but French influences (namely Post-Impressionists Paul
Cézanne, Paul Gauguin and Vincent van Gogh).[3] Modersohn-Becker's
iconography is often interpreted as a close reflection of the turn-of-the-
century Women's Movement, although she never overtly identified it as such.[4]
In addition to her undeniable fondness for feminine subjects, her disposition
was toward portraits and depictions of the Worpswede peasantry. Both of
these themes are evident in the etching, *Sitzende Alte* (Seated Old Woman).
Given this general description of Modersohn-Becker's work, it is useful to
note that her career was always dynamic, even in its aforementioned brevity.
Thus, when discussing *Sitzende Alte*, it is important that it be placed within
its proper, more specific context.

Early in 1900, Modersohn-Becker made a trip to Paris where she developed a
great enthusiasm for Cézanne after visiting an art gallery.[5] Likewise, she
would have been aware of Gauguin's *Synthetism* and primitive woodcuts
(catalogue 78) as she made her foray into etchings. The impression that these
two French masters made on her likely contributed to the bold, flat simplicity
of form we see in this figure, as well as the artist's initial attraction to the
more natural, rustic spirituality of peasant life.

Modersohn-Becker incorporated these French Post-Impressionist influences
into her roots at the Worpswede, combining "aesthetic and iconographical
preoccupations" with the beauty of simple people in nature (and a return to
nature in general).[6] Through these two influences, she contributed a unique
nexus of French and German modernity. However, she went even further by
making her works "harsh and heavily shadowed, to show ugliness and

awkwardness."[7] *Sitzende Alte* is a perfect example of this. The woman's
clothing is black and her face is shrouded in shadow. The deepest contrast is
the white of the woman's abnormally large hands. The entire figure is so
dramatically outlined that it appears to be cut from the more nondescript
landscape behind it, rather than a natural part of it. She went in a decidedly
different direction in her work such as the 1903 etching, *Mother and Child*,
where the scene of a mother breastfeeding her young child is portrayed as a
very natural act, more a part of the landscape at large rather than the focus of
the composition.

Indeed, the strikingly distinct figure of the old woman, with her
disproportionately large hands and shadowy face, suggest French stylistic
associations. Yet it is the intensity and complexity of emotion in this piece
that help to justify the argument of considering Modersohn-Becker as a
precursor to German Expressionism. The woman's stoic posture is
illuminated only by a light that reflects off her mouth and hands. It is also a
light that inexplicably does not seem to be falling on the landscape in the
background. This only adds to the sense of disjunction from the world
around her. Her two hands, though merely resting on her knees, jump out of
the composition, their grotesque size suggesting that they have carried heavy
burdens over the years. Perhaps a more indicative interpretation of this piece
could be found by putting it into its proper context using Modersohn-Becker's
own words:

> I have been depressed for days. Profoundly sad and solemn. I think the time
> is coming for struggle and uncertainty. It comes into every serious and
> beautiful life. I knew all along that it had to come. I've been expecting it. I
> am not afraid of it. I know it will mature and help me develop. But everything
> seems so serious and hard, serious and sad to me. I walk through this huge city,
> I look into a thousand eyes. But I almost never find a soul there. We
> acknowledge each other with a glance, greet each other, and then continue on
> our lonely way. But we have understood each other. Kindred souls embraced
> for an instant.[8]

This passage was a journal entry from Paris at the end of April 1900.
Although not intended to accompany this particular piece, Modersohn-
Becker penned this at around the same time she created *Sitzende Alte*. It
seems as though Modersohn-Becker could look at the old woman and see not
only a "kindred soul," but one who had survived the "struggle and
uncertainty." In response to the sadness that Modersohn-Becker was
evidently feeling at the time, perhaps she could look to the fortitude of the old
woman as a gritty reminder that her hands, too, would be big enough.

[Scott Metzger, *Class of 2006*]

[1] Gillian Perry, *Paula Modersohn-Becker: Her Life and Work* (New York: Harper and Row, 1979), 2.

[2] Olga S. Opfell, *Special Visions: Profiles of Fifteen Women Artists from the Reniassance to the Present Day* (Jefferson: McFarland and Co., 1991), 122.

[3] Perry, 4.

[4] Ibid., 39.

[5] Paula Modersohn-Becker, *Paula Modersohn-Becker: The Letters and Journals* (New York: Taplinger Publishing Company, 1984), 147.

[6] Perry, 4.

[7] Opfell, 126.

[8] Modersohn-Becker, 183.

82

Fernand-Edmond-Jean-Marie Khnopff (Belgian 1858–1921)
Un Masque à la tenture mauve [A Mask with Mauve Shades], 1907
Color crayons
Signed b.c. "Fernand Khnopff"
27.7 x 18.4 cm., 10-7/8 x 7-1/4" image
28.5 x 19.0 cm., 11-3/16 x 7-1/2" sheet
Gift of Mr. and Mrs. Michael Moss, Augustana College Art Collection,
93.48.1

Faces dominate the works of Fernand Khnopff, particularly enigmatic feminine faces. Khnopff was a leading artist of the Symbolist movement which emerged during the late nineteenth century. Symbolism was founded on the idea that images hold a power over the mind and convey meaning without being completely specific or rational.[1] The movement was inspired by the work of French poets such as Stéphane Mallarmé and Paul Verlaine[2] and may be traced in the late works of French artists Henri Fantin-Latour (catalogue 79) and Paul Gauguin (catalogue 78).

Un masque à la tenture mauve (A Mask with Mauve Shades) exhibits a mesmerizing image of a red-haired woman staring at the viewer against a patterned background. In her right hand she holds a scepter with a blue orb surrounding a small nude female figurine. This object draws one's attention to the bottom portion of the composition. The background of the piece is demarcated by equally spaced rectangles on either side of her head, resembling ancient coffered ceilings.

Introspection and thought are major themes and products of Khnopff's work.[3] His pieces are known for their sexual appeal and mystery. He was a harbinger of issues concerning the unconscious mind, prior to Sigmund Freud. Freud elucidated the theory that the mind is a complex system and helped to define the concepts of the unconscious, sexuality and repression.

Khnopff used photographs as sources, taking the immediate impression, then altering the background, coloring or other components. These helped to provide the foundation on which he projected his Symbolist images. He was intrigued by the power of photography to freeze images in time. Furthermore, he recognized that the segments of the composition that are cut off by the lens draw attention to those very portions. Notice in this work that the woman's head is cropped slightly above the forehead, hiding most of her luxuriant red hair from view, resulting in bringing greater attention to her countenance.

There are many Victorian Pre-Raphaelite qualities seen in the type of ideal women found throughout Khnopff's work.[4] They are strong, with delicate features and long red hair that generally frames a gaze that is hauntingly familiar. Khnopff's feminine subjects all appear to be based on his sister, whose beauty was his obsession.[5] The Pre-Raphaelites began portraying women with "fatal Medusan beauty which was later characteristic of the Symbolist femme fatale."[6] Khnopff and the Pre-Raphaelites also demonstrated a preference for naturalistic detail. The flatness of the composition and cropping were influenced by Japanese prints (catalogue 57).

Color is an important aspect of this work and an essential part of Khnopff's theory on art, possibly inspired by Post-Impressionist Georges Seurat's adaptation of *synaesthetic* color theories.[7] A predecessor to sensory experience, this theory promoted the idea that color unites the composition and contributes to the subconscious meaning of the image for the viewer. Khnopff was very interested in the poetic nature of color, and he combined it with form to create introspective and evocative moods.[8]

Khnopff sought eternal themes in his works, choosing subjects which embodied such intangible concepts as time, love, death, fate, consciousness, religion and philosophy.[9] The meaning of this drawing as a whole is difficult to discern, however certain aspects of it can be examined in various contexts, which was precisely what Khnopff intended. He did not aim for the meaning to be easily grasped, nor did he want his images to leave the viewer as soon as the composition was out of sight. The enigmatic image that Khnopff portrays was intentional and reflective of the aims of the Symbolist movement.

The Symbolists frequently depicted a new conception of women, which showed them as *femme fatales* (fatal women). This particular woman's teeth, which are clearly white, symbolize her upper class status and contribute to her erotic, yet menacing beauty.[10] The blue surrounding the orb had numerous connotations for Symbolists at the time. It was considered the color of death, truth and chastity, and was also associated with the spiritual figures of Jupiter, Krishna, Christ and Amon.[11]

Using the word *mask* in the title of the piece allowed Khnopff more symbolic freedom and further confuses the meaning for the viewer. He began using this term in his titles with a series of works, beginning in 1891. The *mask* term may apply to the fact that the forehead is missing, and may physically represent the withdrawal of her mind. This also brings more focus on the face, particularly the lips. Khnopff himself described that: "The expression of the mouth is the truest; there it is almost impossible to dissimulate."[12] The connotation of a mask with the myriad of other uncertain symbols accomplishes a goal for which Symbolists strove: to challenge the viewer to interpret the work, not for its superficial imagery, but to reflect more deeply on its underlying meaning.

[David Freeman, *Class of 2006*]

[1] Edward Lucie-Smith, *Symbolist Art* (London: Thames and Hudson, 1985), 15-24.

[2] Barrymore L. Scherer, "Enigma Variations," *Art and Auction* (2000): 111.

[3] Barry Friedman et al., *Fernand Khnopff and the Belgian Avant-Garde* (New York: Barry Friedman Ltd., 1983), 6.

[4] Friedman et al., 9.

[5] Sherer, 115.

[6] Sam Hunter, John Jacobus and Daniel Wheeler, *Modern Art* (New York: Prentice-Hall, 2004), 36.

[7] Cynthia Wiedemann Empen, "Symbolism and Psychological Modernism in Fernand Khnopff's *Un Masque à la Tenture Mauve*" (Unpublished Manuscript, 1995), 6.

[8] Ibid., 5-11.

[9] Friedman, 8.

[10] Robert Delevoy, Catherine De Croes and Gisell Ollinger-Zinque, *Fernand Khnopff* (Brussells: Lebeer-Hossman, 1987), 147.

[11] Empen, 10.

[12] Helene Laillet, "The Home of an Artist: M. Fernand Khnopff's Villa at Brussels," *The Studio* LVII (1912): 202.

83

Käthe Kollwitz (German 1867–1945)
Death, Mother and Child (*Tod, Frau und Kind*), 1910, from Becke
edition ca. 1945
Etching and drypoint
Unsigned; written in plate b.r. "*Druck v. O. Felsing Berlin _____*" and
blind stamp b.r. corner of sheet "*A.V.D. Becke/ Munchen 22*"
39.6 x 39.4 cm., 15-3/4 x 15-1/2" image
55.6 x 59.3 cm., 21-7/8 x 23-5/16" sheet
Augustana College Art Department Purchase, 69.24

The turn of the twentieth-century began a whole new era for the world of art. Nineteenth-century styles such as Impressionism and Post-Impressionism which had swept across Europe, led to abstraction, Cubism and Expressionism as the new century opened. Somewhere in the middle of these "-isms" stands the brilliant German artist, Käthe Kollwitz. She defined her artistic goal: "I know, of course, that I do not achieve pure art...But still it is art...I am content that my art should have purposes outside itself. I would like to exert influence in these times when human beings are so perplexed and in need of help."[1] Her powerful images are filled with iconography and emotion, defining her as a pioneer in German Expressionism. She aimed to not only capture the immediacy of the moment like the Impressionists, but also to portray the real and honest emotion found in her subjects.

Kollwitz was a unique individual and truly a free spirit, reflected in her statement that: "...bisexuality is almost a necessary factor in artistic production...the tinge of masculinity within me helped me in my work."[2] This lifestyle choice may have empowered Kollwitz by being different than typical women of the time. She used her art as a medium for personal expression as she depicted overworked, underpaid and poverty stricken women. After attending art school in the field of painting, she discovered printmaking and aggressively pursued this medium.

Death, Mother and Child (1910) is presented with animated and seemingly emotional lines and shading. There is dramatic use of light in the piece, accompanied by fluid lines that seem to link the faces of the mother and her child, creating a sense of bonding more intense than would have been found in works by the previous generation, such as the scenes by Mary Cassatt (catalogue 55). Both Cassatt and Kollwitz focused on the relationship between mother and child. However, Kollwitz, a mother herself, demonstrated the bond in a more emotionally wrenching direction through themes of death and suffering[3] in contrast to Cassatt's more comfortable approach to domestic routines.

Kollwitz aimed to reach beyond Victorian sentimentality, as she stated: "I have never been able to see beauty in the upper class educated person; he's superficial; he's not natural or true; he's not honest, and he's not a human being in every sense of the word...The working-class woman shows me her hands, her feet, and her hair... she presents herself and the expression of her feelings openly, without disguises."[4]

This statement describes not only why Kollwitz focused on lower class subjects, but also the importance she placed on illustrating real emotion, common women and genuine suffering. What made Kollwitz so unique was her ability to build on realistic ideology by portraying the true problems and feelings of her time. She was one of the first to express such ideas and to portray the strength of the modern woman and mother in a deeply empathetic manner.

Death, Mother and Child captures the moment when death overpowers the strong bond between mother and child. During this era of war and poverty, the idea of "holding on" to your loved ones, through death and suffering, was a prominent theme in Kollwitz's work,[5] incorporating emotions evoked by real problems. The woman is likely a self-portrait of Kollwitz. She used her own son, Peter as a model for the child, a disturbing premonition perhaps of his later death in World War I at the age of twenty-one."[6] The theme of a mother with her dead child was explored by the artist throughout her career, first appearing in *Woman with Dead Child* (1903). When Kollwitz showed a similar image to her close friend, Beate Bonus-Jeep, Kollwitz recorded her reaction: "It was pure passion itself, the force, sleeping contained in the mother animal, that yielding itself to the eye, is fixed here by Käthe Kollwitz, someone to whom it is given to reach beneath the ultimate veils."[7]

Also known as *Parting*,[8] *Death, Mother and Child* is filled with iconography alluding to separation and death. Half of a skeleton bone cuts through the middle, dramatically symbolizing Death as it separates the bond between mother and child. The composition looks intentionally unfinished, reinforcing the importance of immediacy in its expression. The sketchiness of the etching also emphasizes the frantic emotion. The viewer is uncertain why death is here and what will happen next. Both the style and dramatic lighting give the piece further interpretive potential. Yet there is one part of the piece that is undeterminable. As the hand reaches around the child's neck, it is unclear to the viewer whether or not it is pushing the child closer to the mother, or if it is another symbol of death pulling the child away. As with many modernists, the direct interpretation of Kollwitz's work is often inconclusive, leaving the decision up to the viewer as to what its ultimate meaning might be.

Käthe Kollwitz's images reflect her own life in every way. Even if her subject was not personally experienced, she drafted and composed with such emotion that she was deeply affected by whatever she sketched. She later stated: "While I drew and wept along with the terrified children I was drawing, I really felt the burden...."[9] Staying true to herself and illustrating the importance of a woman's opinion in a male-dominated society must have been a constant struggle. The power emerging from the faces of the women she immortalized clearly reflects her own strength in an era overshadowed by war, poverty and death.

[Katie Gedrimas, *Class of 2007* and
Catherine Carter Goebel, *Professor of Art History,
Paul A. Anderson Chair in the Arts*]

[1] Martha Kearns, *Käthe Kollwitz: Woman and Artist* (New York: The Feminist Press at the City University of New York, 1976), 173.

[2] Ibid., 58.

[3] Elizabeth Prelinger, *Käthe Kollwitz* (New Haven: Yale University Press, 1992), 39-40.

[4] Kearns, 81-82.

[5] Ibid., 82.

[6] Prelinger, 43.

[7] Ibid., 42.

[8] Ibid.

[9] Kearns, 164.

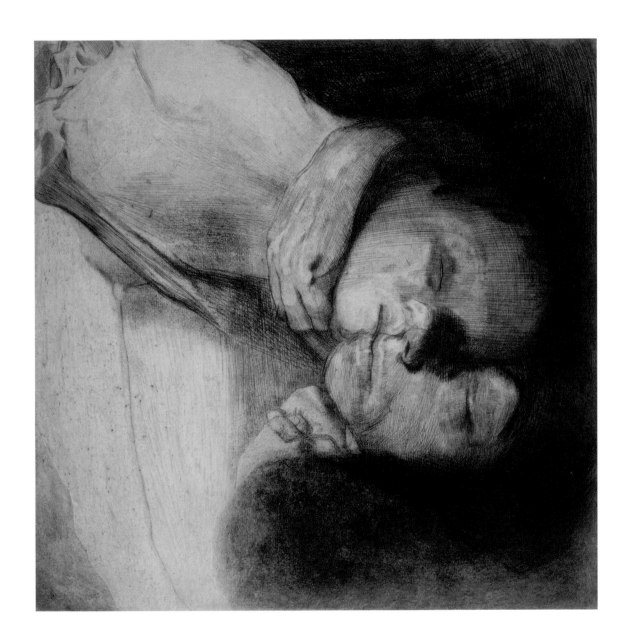

84

Franz Marc (German 1880–1916)
History of Creation II, or, **Story of Creation II**, 1914
Woodcut in black, yellow and green
Unsigned by artist; signed b.l. below image in graphite by Marc's printer
"Gedr. F. Voigt"
23.9 x 20.4 cm., 9-3/4 x 8-1/16" image
50.2 x 35.0 cm., 19-3/4 x 13-3/4" sheet
Paul A. Anderson Chair in the Arts Purchase, Augustana College Art
Collection, 2000.58

Franz Marc displayed deep introspective qualities early in life, causing his family to nickname him "the little philosopher."[1] His father, a Romantic painter, likely encouraged his art as well as his strong interest in theological studies. As a young boy in Munich, he began his education in theology with aspirations of becoming a pastor. By 1898, however, Marc had abandoned this vocation in order to study philosophy at the University of Munich. By 1900 he had changed his focus once again, this time to art.[2]

At the Munich Academy, Marc studied drawing and later moved on to painting. While attending the academy he pursued a more traditional style. Following a trip to Paris in 1903, however, Marc developed an interest in Impressionism. This influence, accompanied by the impact of *Jugendstil*, the German version of *Art Nouveau*, led Marc to a more contemporary use of color and a two-dimensional simplification of color and line.[3]

Another trip to Paris in 1907 further influenced the development of Marc's style. This time he came under the influence of Post-Impressionists Paul Cézanne, Paul Gauguin and Vincent van Gogh. Marc began to exert a more accentuated and energetic linear quality as well as more animated and Symbolist color, stemming from the influence of Van Gogh. Around the same time, he increasingly turned to nature for inspiration, specifically animals. In Marc's opinion animals had a spiritual significance. He believed that animals were in some way more natural and thus purer than people. Marc decided that he could use animals to symbolize his own spiritual feelings.[4]

Over time, Marc continued to assert his personal style through his choice of subject and color. By 1911 he had established subjective symbolism for his color use. Marc viewed certain colors to represent different ideas; blue for spirituality and maleness, yellow for femininity and sensuality and red for terrestrial materiality.[5] While he continued to define his personal style, Marc joined with Vasily Kandinsky to form *Der Blaue Reiter* (The Blue Rider) of German Expressionism. This group, germinated within the Expressionist movement and was composed of a variety of artists who emphasized a conceptual approach to their work rather than the formalist ideas of Cubism.[6]

Following the formation of *Der Blaue Reiter*, Marc and several other artists, including Kandinsky (catalogue 85) and Erich Heckel (catalogue 97), began a project to represent the books of the Bible through illustrations. Marc chose the *Book of Creation* as his contribution to the project.[7] In 1914 he conceived two woodcuts toward this project, *Story of Creation I* and *Story of Creation II*. Both works are characterized by their use of flowing forms and kinetic lines. The animals and plants depicted in these pieces are embryonic in nature, demonstrating the idea of a beginning rather than an ending. The presence of animals was meant to portray the conceptual post-apocalyptic world, which is free of the *impure* man.[8]

Specifically in *Story of Creation II*, we see the moment when God commands:

"Let the earth bring forth living creatures," just before its actualization. An embryonic image of some sort of feline creature emerges toward the upper right, beneath the sun. To the left emerges what seems to be a horse or a deer, and in the lower center, there is the genesis of an unidentifiable figure. These images appear to emerge from within the composition. Both the heavens and the earth seem to flow together and converge in the center of the work. Plant life below germinates. We thus see creation occurring in one turbulent moment.[9] The scene is likely foretelling the recreation that would follow the apocalypse.

An interesting dichotomy exists in the upper portion of the composition with the presence of both the sun and the crescent moon. As declared in Genesis, night and day are parts of overall creation, but the crescent moon takes on further meaning in the work of Expressionists. The members of this movement saw the crescent moon as a representation of the apocalypse. Marc began using this symbol as early as 1912 in works such as *Two Horses* and *Blue Horses*. In 1913 this motif began to demonstrate an association with images of chaos and destruction.[10] Use of the crescent moon in Marc's works shows a progression that begins with the prediction of the apocalypse followed by the apocalypse in progress and ends with the portrayal of a new beginning as seen in *Story of Creation II*.[11]

In this same year, Marc wrote: "The world gives birth to a new age: there is only one question: has the time yet arrived in which the old world will be dissolved? Are we ready for the *vita nuovo*? This is the most anxious question of our day."[12] In this same year, when Germany declared war on France, he volunteered for military service. By 1916, he was involved in the Battle of Verdun, which he described on March 2nd: "For days I have seen nothing but the most horrifying things that a human mind could imagine."[13] Two days later, Franz Marc was killed in battle.

Marc was a complex individual who sought deep, universal answers. As he wrote: "Truth is always on the move. It is always somewhere, never in the foreground, never on the surface."[14] Such works demonstrating a new beginning were possibly his predictions of what was to follow the completion of the First World War. Unfortunately, he would never see if his post-war predictions would come true. Marc's tragic death ended both his life as well as his promise for additional artistic contributions to further the art of modernism.

[Beth Cloud, *Class of 2007*]

[1] Frederick S. Levine, *The Apocalyptic Vision: The Art of Franz Marc as German Expressionism* (New York: Harper & Row, 1979), 20.

[2] Mark Rosenthal, *Franz Marc* (Berkeley: Prestel, 1989), 8.

[3] Ibid, 8-9.

[4] Ibid, 13.

[5] Ibid, 18.

[6] Peter Selz, *German Expressionist Painting* (Berkley: University of California Press, 1957), 206.

[7] Bernard S. Myers, *The German Expressionists* (New York: Frederick A. Praeger, 1957), 228.

[8] Levine, 139-140.

[9] Ibid., 139-142.

[10] Ibid., 123-126.

[11] Ibid., 137.

[12] Ibid., 138.

[13] Ibid., 172.

[14] Ibid., 14.

85

Vasily (or Wassily) Kandinsky (Russian 1866–1944)
Kandinsky Das Graphische Werk [The Graphic Work of Kandinsky],
n.d., from **Kandinsky Das Graphische Werk** by Hans Konrad Roethel,
included in limited edition of 1500 numbered copies, published by M.
Dumont Schauberg, ca. 1970, Köln
Color linoleum cut or woodcut
Unsigned by artist; printed text below image b.l. "Hans Konrad Roethel"
and b.r. "Dumont"
32.8 x 29.7 cm., 12-15/16 x 11-3/4" sheet
Anonymous Gift in Memory of Lewis J. Stone (Augustana 1965),
Augustana College Art Collection, 93.45.38

*. . . the ground-note of black is a silence with no possibilities. . . . a kind of
neutral background against which the minutest shades of other colors stand forth
clearly.* [1]

So wrote Vasily Kandinsky in his densely theoretical 1912 manifesto
Concerning the Spiritual in Art, just a year before he created the three block
woodcut for *Three Riders in Red, Blue and Black*. The colors, each printed
independently, do indeed "stand forth clearly," while the three riders of the
title are hardly discernible among the blots of red and blue. At first glance
this work appears to be completely abstracted, especially when considered
alongside Kandinsky's truly free-form *improvisation* and *composition* painting
series of the same era. In the medium of printmaking as illustrated here, the
thick stamped black lines are energetic, rhythmically curving, breaking and
framing the page, carved in such a way as to allow a noise of unincorporated
black flecks to create a texture. The riders and their horses, along with some
bordering foliage, are mere outlines, and are recognizable (although barely)
despite their distorted simplicity.

The symbolic use of the horseback rider, as well as the aesthetic elements of
dominating black lines paired with gregarious primary colors, can be seen in
many of Kandinsky's early prints created during his formative years in
Munich with Franz Marc (catalogue 84) as a member of the *Blue Rider*
Movement. Kandinsky later recalled the genesis of their avant-garde title:
"the name *Blue Rider* came to us around the coffee table in Marc's house at
Sindelsdorf; we both loved blue, Marc horses, and I riders. So the name came
by itself. And made Maria Marc's coffee taste even better." [2] As part of the
overall German Expressionist Movement of the early twentieth century,
Kandinsky and Marc pursued the "ultimate goal of Expressionism…literally
to 'lose its own mind,' to seek an identification with forms of precognitive
existence as a manifestation of its collective desire to reenter the world of
'unconscious consciousness,' the world in which being is not encumbered by
the weight of rationality, the world in which all life proceeds on the most
primitive, the most instinctual of levels." [3] Both artists worked in woodcut, a
traditional German printmaking medium, traceable to such brilliant
Renaissance masters as Albrech Dürer (catalogue 6), thus reflecting national
pride and tradition. It also demonstrates a return to primitivism, earlier
explored in Symbolist Tahitian woodcuts by French Post-Impressionist, Paul
Gauguin (catalogue 78).

One particularly comparable work, created for the cover of *The Blue Rider
Almanac*, published in 1912, shows Kandinsky's forms with a more explicitly
organic finish, evoking the sense of a dense natural forest. The featured rider
is the image of Saint George on horseback, the city emblem of Kandinsky's
home town. Published within the *Almanac* were examples of their artistic
sources, such as Henri Rousseau, Paul Cézanne, Pablo Picasso and the earlier
styles of primitive and medieval art. [4] The collection speaks of the
movement's deeply spiritual brand of German Expressionism, the larger trend
of the early twentieth century, founded on an interest in escaping the violent
and irrational political climate of the day.

Kandinsky was born in Moscow and is "generally considered the pioneer of

abstract painting." [5] He had trained to be a lawyer, but at the age of thirty
pursued art in Munich, followed by a year of study in Paris in 1906. He
returned from this artistic journey with a style largely based on Henri Matisse
(catalogue 87 and 88) and the French Expressionist Fauves. His simplified
forms and bright colors were also influenced by the Russian traditions of
painted religious icons and folk art. By 1910, Kandinsky had created his first
fully abstract work and in the following year, he and Marc co-founded the
pivotal *Der Blaue Reiter* (Blue Rider) branch of German Expressionism. [6] He
published his influential book, *On the Spiritual in Art* in 1912. In it, he wrote:
"So the abstract idea is creeping into art, although, only yesterday it was
scorned and obscured by purely material ideas. Its gradual advance is natural
enough, for in proportion as the organic form falls into the background, the
abstract ideal achieves greater prominence." [7]

With the dawn of the twentieth century, early modernists inherited the
disillusionment and decadence of the 1890s. They reacted with various
movements in pursuit of answers to the confusion resulting from challenges
to the traditional elevated position of humankind. "German Expressionism
was an art movement born of intense psychological despair…[the
Expressionist] sought to return to his origins, to cast off the shackles of
reason and self-awareness and to revert toward the bonds of unity he saw
existing between nature and its instinctual inhabitants." [8] In an age
dominated by new revelations and theories from such intellectual luminaries
as Sigmund Freud and Albert Einstein, Marc suggested that their consequent
goal was "to reveal unearthly life dwelling behind everything, to break the
mirror of life so that we may look being *(Sein)* in the face." [9] Like the German
Romantics and the French Symbolists before him, Kandinsky also explored
the instinctual aesthetic relationships between art and music.

Such a collection is truly a slim sample of the varied influences affecting
Kandinsky's style as it developed in the first few decades of last century.
Kandinsky himself had written of his experience in viewing one of the
paintings from French Impressionist Claude Monet's *Grainstack* series, which
explored the atmospheric affects of weather and shifting sunlight on an
arbitrary landscape. Of his reaction, Kandinsky wrote: "Deep inside me was
born the first faint doubt as to the importance of an 'object' as the necessary
element in painting." [10] Out of this thought grew the theories Kandinsky
would explore for the rest of his artistic career, experimenting with the limits
of true form and pure color on a flat plane, their associations with musical
sounds and the ability of such aesthetics to connect with and resonant in the
soul. He argued for the importance of freedom for modern artists, caught
within the dynamics of an increasingly complex and dangerous environment,
further emphasized by the approach of World War I: "The more abstract is
form, the more clear and direct is its appeal…There is no *must* in art, because
art is free." [11]

[Carol Marquardsen, *Class of 2006* and
Catherine Carter Goebel, *Professor of Art History,
Paul A. Anderson Chair in the Arts*]

[1] Vasily Kandinsky, *Concerning the Spiritual in Art* (New York: George Wittenborn, 1947), 60.

[2] Frederick S. Levine, *The Apocalyptic Vision: The Art of Franz Marc as German Expressionism*
(New York: Harper & Row, 1979), 63.

[3] Levine, 3.

[4] Sam Hunter, John Jacobus and Daniel Wheeler, *Modern Art* (New York: Prentice Hall,
2004), 116.

[5] Herbert Read, ed., *The Thames and Hudson Dictionary of Art and Artists* (London: Thames
and Hudson, 1984), 178.

[6] Ibid.

[7] Robert Goldwater and Marco Treves, *Artists on Art: from the XIV to the XX Century* (New
York: Pantheon Books, 1972), 449.

[8] Levine, 3.

[9] Ibid., 14.

[10] Hunter et al., 119.

[11] Goldwater and Treves, 450.

KANDINSKY

Das graphische Werk

Hans Konrad Roethel

DuMont

86A

Giorgio de Chirico (Italian 1888–1978)
Stazione Ferroviara (also titled **Station Ferroviara**), dated 1920
Oil on canvas-wrapped cardboard
Signed b.c. "g. de chirico" [sic]
Approx. 23.0 x 30.5 cm., 9 x 12"
Lent Courtesy of the Lohrey Family Limited Partnership

Giorgio de Chirico was the leader of the Metaphysical art movement and the acknowledged inspiration (although he fervently denied it) for Surrealist painters. He convincingly portrayed a dreamlike world just within the borders of the imagination. Unlike most modern artists who were only appreciated later in life, de Chirico found success early in his career, yet as his style progressed, the seemingly fickle art world no longer approved or understood. His innovative approach was highly influenced by the philosopher Friedrich Nietzsche, who defined art as the "real metaphysical activity of man," and the Symbolist painter, Arnold Böcklin, in his depictions of dreamscapes.[1]

De Chrico most likely created *Train Station Ferroviara* (catalogue 86A) and the *Piazza d'Italia* (catalogue 86B) as meticulous studies for larger paintings to be completed at a later time.[2] An exclusive patronage contract with the art dealer Paul Guillaume required that all of de Chirico's works created between 1913 and 1917 went to Guillaume. In return, de Chirico received a monthly stipend of one hundred francs.[3] Although such an arrangement supported the artist financially, it severely limited his income as well as his ability to broaden his range of patrons. It also resulted in an interesting dating discrepancy in these two paintings. Since they are described as having been painted in 1921 in an accompanying note written by the artist, judging from the style employed in these pieces, de Chirico may have assigned them inaccurate later dates in order to conceal that they were not sent to Guillaume. When they were recently restored, the conservator found an unusual white under-painting on both pieces, probably the zinc oxide that de Chirico used to prime his canvases during this earlier period.[4] Since the style and chemical analysis indicate that these works were made between 1913 and 1917, an interesting theory on the acquisition of these paintings has been suggested: that his mother, on going to de Chirico's apartment to pick up the artwork he left behind while he was in the army, possibly slipped these two smaller paintings under her voluminous skirts.

Stylistically, *Train Station Ferroviara* was painted at the height of de Chirico's Metaphysical Period. Called *Metaphysical* because it portrayed a world beyond that of the physical, this art depicted a dream world, ironically rendered in realistic detail. Scenes that could only be constructed in the mind, such as this strange landscape, were put forth on canvas. All the typical de Chirico components of this time are in place—the geometric arches and colonnade, black train and long shadows. De Chirico portrayed an almost uneasy emptiness with a sense of mysterious foreboding. The deserted city has that quality of a parallel world, where everything looks normal but is far from it. The deep shadows fall at different angles, further altering one's sense of logical reality. Time appears frozen as the puff of smoke lingers in the air above the train. Even the colors, the sharply contrasting blue-green of the sky with the mustard-tan ground, lend to the viewer's discomfort upon examining the piece.

The general locations depicted in these paintings reflect de Chirico's love of Italian architecture and city monuments around the Mediterranean. Ferarra and Turin were two such towns from which he drew inspiration for his *metaphysical* works. Turin was the city Nietzsche loved and Ferrara was the location where de Chirico was stationed with the Italian army from 1915-1918. It was here that he first met Carlo Carrà with whom he would start the Metaphysical group in Italy.[5] The movement was rather short-lived, essentially lasting less than a year before de Chirico, seeking greater classicism, decided to change his style. However, although not then defined as *metaphysical*, his work from 1912-1917 is now considered to be in this style.

[Errin Copple, *Class of 2005*]

[1] Francesco Poli, "Giorgio de Chirico: From Avant-gardist to Maverick: Seventy Years of Metaphysical Research," in *De Chirico and the Mediterranean*, ed. Jole de Sanna (New York: Rizzoli International Publications, Inc., 1998), 66.

[2] Donor/lender Derek van Lohrey, interview by Errin Copple, 9 June 2005.

[3] Angelo Visone, "Biography," *De Chirico and the Mediterranean*, ed. Jole de Sanna (New York: Rizzoli International Publications, Inc., 1998), 280.

[4] Giorgio de Chirico, *The Memoirs of Giorgio de Chirico*, trans. Margaret Crosland (New York: Da Capo Press, 1994), 234-235, and Derek van Lohrey.

[5] Poli, 69-70. He and Carrà grew close after spending several months together in a military hospital, detained for nervous disorders. This friendship would soon break with de Chirico accusing Carrà, probably quite accurately, of copying his ideas and art.

86B

Giorgio de Chirico (Italian 1888–1978)
Piazza d' Italia (also titled **Italian Plaza—with Beacon**), dated 1921
Oil on canvas-wrapped cardboard
Signed b.c. "g. de chirico" [sic]
24.2 x 33.7 cm., 9-1/2 x 13-1/4"
Gift of Lohrey Family Limited Partnership, Augustana College Art
Collection, 2005.22

The landscape of *Piazza d'Italia* was drawn from de Chirico's second *metaphysica*l Italian city of inspiration, Turin. Turin was especially important to de Chirico because of its close association with Nietzsche—it was the city Nietzsche loved and the place in which the philosopher suffered from madness the year of de Chirico's birth. The geometry of the streets, piazzas and porticos provided ample sources of inspiration for the young artist's imagination.[1]

The piazza, a metaphysical blend of reality, stands nearly vacant, and long shadows fall at uneven angles. The cloudless sky changes from a deep turquoise to a dirty yellow, almost tan, and the bare ground reflects putrid shades of green and orange in the dirt. A frozen tableau is again created by the motionless train and the calculated geometry of the archways and columned portico. The insertion of a lone figure, however, adds a new dimension to the scene, raising feelings of isolation and abandonment for the observer. Within the piece, such elements lead to questions of the enigma of life and the purpose of human existence in this world.[2] This inhabitant appears restricted to the limits of the physical world except in his mind.

The disturbing quality depicted by de Chirico reflected a deeper social unease. Although drafted into the Italian army, de Chirico and his brother (who was also an artist as well as a musician) reacted negatively to the war. They were strongly anti-modern, yet they were in contact with many avant-garde groups such as the Futurists. De Chirico wrote articles for the first Dada magazines (*Dada I* and *Dada II*), but differed in viewpoint from the other groups in his concept of a metaphysical space.[3]

Through contributions to the post-war journal *Valori Plastici* (Plastic Values), he and his brother helped to spread the influence of the Metaphysicists beyond Italy. Giorgio wrote many articles professing his wish for a return to classicism in art, although his was a return mixed with modern art influences. Guillaume Apollinaire (catalogue 87), the contemporary French poet and art critic, saw de Chirico's paintings as a reaction to the politics and modernity sweeping through the world, writing, "He constructs harmonious and mysterious compositions in tranquility and meditation. A plastic conception of the politics of the times. The strangeness of the plastic enigmas proposed by Mr. de Chirico escapes most spectators. In order to describe the fatal character of modern things, this artist makes use of the most modern of expedients: surprise."[4]

Striking parallels can be seen between the dream world of Metaphysical art and that of the Surrealists, and indeed De Chirico was considered at the time to be the *Father of Surrealism*, with Apollinaire first calling his work *surréel* in 1917.[5] De Chirico was greatly admired by many of the Surrealists, even considered an inspiration for their works. He officially joined the group in 1922 at the insistence of its leader André Breton. However, De Chirico's work by this time had begun to change. He had always professed a wish to return to classicism, often studying and copying works of that period and the fifteenth-century Renaissance masters. His art reflected this shift as he attempted to become a classical painter, although he would still cycle back to his metaphysical art.[6] Breton and the Surrealists considered his new style of painting inferior, and Breton referred to him as a *lost genius* in a magazine article published in 1926.[7] This last act completed his ultimate break with the group and caused him thereafter to vehemently reject the title *Father of Surrealism*, refusing to acknowledge any artistic connection.

De Chirico's art from these later decades has been largely ignored by critics and historians who perhaps believed, as the Surrealists did, that he had wasted his potential after his promising early career (or quite simply because they do not know how to categorize him).[8] A master at creating dreamlike, yet realistic scenes, it is de Chirico's deserted cityscapes, frozen in time, for which he is best remembered. Believing that art should be purged of the familiar and commonplace, he once wrote, "A really immortal work of art can only be produced by means of a revelation."[9] It is clearly such revelation which has inspired these important works.

[Errin Copple, *Class of 2005*]

[1] Angelo Visone, "Biography," *De Chirico and the Mediterranean*, ed. Jole de Sanna (New York: Rizzoli International Publications, Inc., 1998), 278.

[2] Francesco Poli, "Giorgio de Chirico: From Avant-gardist to Maverick: Seventy Years of Metaphysical Research," *De Chirico and the Mediterranean*, ed. Jole de Sanna (New York: Rizzoli International Publications, Inc., 1998), 68.

[3] Poli, 72.

[4] Poli, 66.

[5] Quoted in Visone, 280.

[6] Ellen E. Adams, "Dealing Late de Chirico: The Julien Ley Gallery, 1936-37," in *Giorgio de Chirico and America*, ed. Emily Braun (New York: Hunter College of the City University of New York, 1996), 76. From 1925-1930, De Chirico went through his second metaphysical period, this time incorporating mannequins, trophies, horses, gladiators, landscapes in rooms and furniture in valleys. Later in his life when his classical works were floundering in the market, De Chirico copied many of his earlier "popular" metaphysical works, dating them during that period and selling them.

[7] Quoted in Visone, 282.

[8] Adams, 79.

[9] Quoted in Poli, 66.

87

Henri Matisse (French 1869–1954)
Apollinaire VI, 1952, from the **Apollinaire Suite** printed by Fernand
Mourlot for the book **Apollinaire** by André Rouveyre, published by
Raisons d'Etre, Paris
Lithograph, artist's proof
Signed b.r. below image in graphite "Henri Matisse"
22.9 x 15.5 cm., 9 x 6-1/8" image
33.1 x 25.3 cm., 13 x 10" sheet
Gift of Mr. and Mrs. Frank Lufrano, Augustana College Art Collection,
94.10

Guillaume Apollinaire was a prominent Parisian art critic and writer of the
early twentieth century. He and modern artist, Henri Matisse, had a
mutually beneficial professional relationship. Although they worked in
different fields, the two often influenced each other. Together they helped to
define major aspects of modern art. Matisse's portrait, *Apollinaire VI* (1952)
survives as testimony to the abiding sympathetic response to modernism that
they shared.

Apollinaire was born in 1880 in Rome. Throughout his life he kept his
parentage a secret but alluded to his father's holding a position as a high
ranking clergyman. With a young single mother, he grew up in boarding
schools with his brother and for a short time worked as a banker in Paris.[1] He
became a writer, penning poetry and submitting articles to newspapers which
commented on avant-garde art. In his position as an art critic and
philosopher, Apollinaire came into contact with Matisse and many other
influential artists of the period, including Pablo Picasso and Georges Braque.

Upon their meeting, Apollinaire interviewed Matisse for an article which he
published in 1907 in *La Phalange*, concluding that: "We are not in the
presence of some extremist venture; the distinctive feature of Matisse's art is
its reasonableness."[2] Apollinaire also indicated his frustration with the
public for not accepting and supporting Matisse. From this point on, the two
maintained a warm friendship, commenting positively about each other's
work until the outbreak of World War I when Apollinaire volunteered for the
French National Army. While in action he was hit in the head with a large
piece of shrapnel and dismissed, returning home and dying soon after.

Although Apollinaire died in 1918, Matisse later sketched this lithographic
portrait in 1952 in memory of his departed friend. When André Rouveyre
wrote his book entitled *Apollinaire*, he asked Matisse to do several
illustrations of the close friend they had in common. This piece is one of the
six that Matisse ultimately drew for this production, entitled the *Apollinaire
Suite*. Each is different. Matisse began with near abstraction and ended in
this version with a more complete view. The resulting lithographs were
printed in an edition of approximately three hundred.[3]

During Apollinaire's lifetime, he defended Matisse's art on several occasions,
describing him as: "One of the rare artists who is completely freed from
impressionism, He strives not to imitate nature but to express what he sees
and what he feels through the actual material of the picture, in the same way
that a poet uses the words of the dictionary in order to express the same
nature and same feelings."[4] Apollinaire was commenting on the early
expressionist work of Matisse, particularly his well known paintings, *Dance*
and *Music* (1909-10).

The writer's complimentary words were a constant source of support for
Matisse. There were several occasions when Matisse's work would generate
nearly complete negative response with the exception of Apollinaire. As time
went on the two men grew in different directions. There were no harsh words
between them, yet Apollinaire began to push art in a different direction than
the one toward which Matisse was headed. As the public gradually accepted
Matisse, Apollinaire's interests shifted toward encouraging the highly
criticized movements of Cubism (catalogue 90) and Surrealism (catalogue
86A and B).

This piece is striking in its bold linear conception. It combines several thin
black lines on a white background. It truly shows the ability of the painter to
reduce character and mass to the simplest of forms. This work may not be
one of his most famous, but the simplicity of its drawing reveals the true
talent of this artist. In contrast to the struggle and time an artist would
normally put into an average oil painting, black and white lithographic
sketches may have been a great release for Matisse. The depth and character
achieved through his masterful and spare use of line and contour allowed him
to further refine his drawing skills.

In 1908, Matisse revealed his *Notes d'un peinture*, first published in *La Grande
Revue* on Christmas Day. In it, he presented his most authoritative statement
on his personal philosophy, remaining today, one of the most important
theoretical pronouncements in modern art. He described the essence of his
less is more approach in order to: "condense the meaning…by seeking its
essential lines…What interests me most is…the human figure. It is that which
permits me to express my almost religious awe towards life. I do not insist
upon all the details of the face, on setting them down one-by-one with
anatomical exactitude…I penetrate amid the lines of the face those which
suggest the deep gravity which persists in every human being."[5]

Matisse's portrait of Apollinaire, stands as a monument to the important
relationship between twentieth-century artists and writers, just as artist
Edouard Manet's portrait of poet and critic Charles Baudelaire (catalogue 41)
does for the nineteenth century. The merging of such parallel artistic
statements, defined within their context, was essential toward framing
modern art. Apollinaire's 1907 interview with Matisse included important
quotes by the artist that helped to explain the depth of his passion to his
public. Matisse related that he always returned to *fundamentals*: "…I must
express myself with purity , even though I do it in the briefest manner…by
drawing four or five lines which have a plastic expression…I believe that the
personality of the artist develops and asserts itself through the struggles it
goes through when pitted against other personalities. If the fight is fatal and
the personality succumbs, it means that this was bound to be its fate."[6]
Matisse's fate, on the other hand, was clearly destined to be one of the shining
lights of twentieth-century modernism.

[Gayln Landem, *Class of 2007* and
Catherine Carter Goebel, *Professor of Art History,
Paul A. Anderson Chair in the Arts*]

[1] Robert Couffignal *Apollinaire* (Tuscaloosa: University of Alabama, 1966).

[2] Roger Benjamin, *"Matisse's Notes of a Painter" Criticism, Theory, and Context, 1891-1908*
(Ann Arbor, Michigan: UMI Research Press, 1987), 130.

[3] Images Fine Art Dealers, http://www.images-art.co.uk/stockDetailTA42.htm (07 May
2005).

[4] Benjamin, 130.

[5] Jack D. Flam, *Matisse on Art* (New York: E. P. Dutton, 1978), 36-38.

[6] Ibid., 32.

ep d'artiste   Henri Matisse

88

After Henri Matisse (French 1869–1954), etched by Jacques Villon (French 1875–1963)
Odalisque sur la terrasse [Odalisque on the Balcony], 1922–1923, published by Bernheim-Jeune, Paris
Color aquatint, 64/200
Signed b.l. in image "Henri Matisse" and b.r. below image in ink "Henri Matisse" and b.r. in plate edge "*Gravé par Jacques Villon*"
48.3 x 60.5 cm., 19 x 24" image
54.2 x 64.3 cm., 21-5/16 x 25-3/4" sheet
Paul A. Anderson Chair in the Arts Purchase, Augustana College Art Collection, 2001.16

In 1908 artist Henri Matisse stated: "what interests me most is neither still life nor landscapes but the human figure."[1] This foremost figural concern resulted in a number of stylistic choices, including the absence of facial detail (catalogue 87). As the leader of the *Fauves (Wild Beasts)* of French Expressionism, Matisse preferred *expression* or feeling versus reality in his drawings and paintings, stating: "...one cannot do successful work which has much feeling unless one sees the subject very simply...."[2] He used space and color to create images that would ultimately please the viewer. Matisse's almost sketchy style reflected his attempt to construct an image with a "wider meaning, a more comprehensively human image."[3] His overall goal was to create an experience for the viewer that made a lasting impression at the same time that it expressed a universal understanding of humanity. Toward this goal, he traveled to Tangiers and Morocco, further influencing his style toward experimentation with *odalisques*.

Matisse's interest in the exotic is clearly visible in *Odalisque sur la terrace* (1922–23). He worked largely in both Paris and the French Rivera during this odalisque period. The setting for this work consists of an exotic looking room with a terrace view of the beach. The costuming of the nudes also appears to have eastern influence. Matisse was first introduced to eastern art in Munich, where he attended an Islamic art exhibition in 1910. He was impressed with the permanence and spirituality that he perceived the works communicated to the viewer.[4]

Odalisques, or the painting of nudes read as concubines, became a common subject for Matisse because it provided a means by which he could present nude women to the public in an acceptable manner.[5] In the choice of this subject, Matisse was highly influenced by the work of nineteenth-century Neoclassical-Romantic artist, Jean-Auguste-Dominique Ingres, who shocked his audience by painting nudes, devoid of any *goddess* connotation, as in the *Grande Odalisque* (1814). She was indicative of the contemporary fascination with exotic women and harems, as well as sensuous pleasure in general. Matisse struggled during his experimentation with the odalisque theme stating "I do odalisques in order to do nudes. But how does one do the nude without it being artificial?"[6]

The imagery in this piece typifies Matisse's work. His figures are central to the interior space and dominate the work. He expressed this principle,

stating, "My models, human figures, are never just 'extras' in an interior. They are the principal theme in my work. I depend entirely on my model, whom I observe at liberty, and then I decide on the pose which best suits her nature."[7] The woman in the foreground is most likely the model Henriette Darricarrère, who monopolized his works following their meeting in 1920.[8] She had the features and physical characteristics he sought, to his eye, classical in feel. In *Odalisque sur la terrace*, Matisse's figures appear flattened and although they maintain their central importance, they seem almost to become a part of the overall decorative interior.[9] In fact, Matisse himself held that "A picture should...always be decorative..."[10] Because Matisse believed that "the chief aim of color should be to serve expression as well as possible,"[11] the choices in this piece appear striking, making the piece aesthetically pleasing to the viewer.

Many schools of thought influenced Henri Matisse throughout his life. As a leader of the *Fauves*, he emphasized color associated with feeling. As a Neoclassicist, he attempted to achieve an aesthetic balance between line and color. His formal training introduced him to the works of French Post-Impressionist, Paul Cézanne. In fact, even when he really could not afford it, he purchased the small version of Cézanne's *Bathers* in 1899. Cézanne had a formative influence on Matisse, who later admitted that this particular painting, "sustained me spiritually in the critical moments of my career as an artist."[12] The works of Romantic artist Eugène Delacroix (catalogue 34) further encouraged Matisse's interest in exotic subject matter. Whatever the influences in his life, Matisse's intentions were clear: "What I dream of is an art of balance, of purity and serenity devoid of troubling or depressing subject-matter...."[13] Matisse indeed searched for this ideal through a combination of color, subject and feeling. *Odalisque sur la terrace* is a beautiful example of his attempt to create a lasting and aesthetically pleasing image, balancing past tradition with a modern feel for original and individual *expression*.

[Mikeda Cannon, *Class of 2007*]

[1] Robert Goldwater and Marco Treves, *Artists in Art: from the XIV to the XX Century* (New York: Pantheon Books, 1972), 412.

[2] John Elderfield, *The Drawings of Henri Matisse* (New York: The Museum of Modern Art, 1984), 50-51.

[3] Goldwater and Treves, 411.

[4] Françoise Gilot, *Matisse and Picasso: A Friendship in Art* (New York: Doubleday, 1990), 169.

[5] Ibid., 170.

[6] Margrit Hahnloser, *Matisse: The Graphic Work* (New York: Rizzoli, 1988), 74.

[7] Ibid., 72.

[8] Ibid., 70.

[9] Elderfield, 90.

[10] Ibid., 51.

[11] Goldwater and Treves, 412.

[12] Herbert Read, ed., *The Thames and Hudson Dictionary of Art and Artists* (London: Thames and Hudson, 1984), 217.

[13] Goldwater and Treves, 413.

89

Sven Birger Sandzén (Swedish American 1871–1954)
Golden Aspen [Rocky Mountain National Park Colorado], 1928
Oil on board
Signed b.r. "Birger Sandzén"
30.4 x 35.3 cm., 11-15/16 x 13-7/8"
Gift of Dr. Eugene C. and Mrs. Barbara B. Wittenstrom and Mr. Clarence
F. and Mrs. Barbara B. Wittenstrom, Jr., In Memory of Their Parents,
Rev. Clarence F. and Mrs. Edna A. Wittenstrom, Sr., Class of 1928, and
In Memory of Their Grandparents, Rev. Carl J. and Mrs. Anna A.
Johnson, Treasurer of Augustana College under President Andreen,
Augustana College Art Collection, 86.12.8

Sven Birger Sandzén is classified as a Post-Impressionist and is in fact one of
the few artists of this movement to extensively practice the style in the United
States. He ultimately became one of the most influential artists in the history
of Kansas.[1] For decades, however, he was unfortunately not well recognized
within American art history.

Sandzén was born the son of a Lutheran minister in the village of Blidsberg,
Sweden in 1871. In early 1894, he left Sweden for Paris, the world's center for
modern art at the time, where he enrolled in the studio of Edmond F. Aman-
Jean. Here, he immersed himself in painting and visiting galleries, museums
and art salons as Post-Impressionist styles were just emerging. Because his
mature style developed about 1919, it is not clear if he first viewed the works
of Vincent Van Gogh and Paul Cézanne (who seem to have provided the basis
from which Sandzén's style evolved) in Paris or if he encountered these styles
in America.

In the fall of 1894, Sandzén accepted a teaching position at Bethany College, a
liberal arts institution in Lindsborg, Kansas and made the journey to the
United States. It was here, in the heartland of America, that the Swedish
painter found his muse. Beneath the layer of Kansas landscape stereotyped as
blank prairies and colorless farmland, Sandzén uncovered a vibrant, beating
heart. Barren rock formations were transformed into "high and gay colored
palaces"[2] and meager creeks became reflecting pools in which the wide
prairie sky was mirrored. Through his love of striking colors and plays of
light, Sandzén captured the elusive beauty of the Kansas landscape as no one
had ever done before, laying it out in shades of lavender, magenta and
turquoise.

Golden Aspen is a typical Sandzén work in both subject and technique. His
Post-Impressionist approach is seen in the high-key palette and the thick
daubs of color. This painting portrays a still body of water with a stand of
slim golden trees reflected in the shallows along the stark rocky banks. Taller,

twisted trees are delineated against a pale sky whose tone suggests either early
morning or late afternoon, and in the distance, a steep embankment rimmed
with pines stoops down to the water's edge.

Upon his arrival in America, Sandzén met Olaf Grafström, art instructor at
Bethany College. Grafström later became the art professor at Augustana
College, Rock Island. Through this connection, Sandzén came to be
supported by members of the Augustana Art Association and, in 1935,
received an honorary degree from Augustana.[3]

Birger Sandzén would spend the rest of his life on the Kansas plains, with
summers in the Rocky Mountains, which also became a favorite scene among
his subjects. He was just as prolific a printmaker as painter. Although his
artwork was exhibited widely throughout the United States and Europe in the
1930s,[4] his reputation rested in the Midwest, especially among Swedish-
American circles. Here it remained for decades until the 1990s, when his role
in mainstream American art history was recognized by William H. Gerdts.
In his 1992 foreword to Emory Lindquist's biography on the artist, Gerdts
concluded:

> But Birger Sandzén's significance is greater than his role as an
> important influence on other artists or even upon the artistic and
> cultural development of his adopted Kansas.... The artist should be
> recognized, I believe, as a significant figure in the development of
> modernism in America in the early decades of the twentieth century.
> He was a painter whose perceptions of the power and dynamics of
> color ally him with those other Americans who have rightly been
> recognized as leaders in the introduction of postimpressionism in
> America—artists such as Arthur Dove, John Marin, Alfred Maurer,
> Marsden Hartley, Max Weber, and others.[5]

While Sandzén did not lead the avant-garde of New York City, he extended
the influences of modernity west of the Mississippi, and the potency of his
paintings has finally been acknowledged.

[Tiffany Chezum, *Class of 2008* and
Sherry C. Maurer, *Director of Augustana College
Art Museum*]

[1] William H. Gerdts, *Art Across America: Two Centuries of Regional Painting, 1710-1920,* vol.
III (New York: Abbeville Press, Publishers, 1990), 71.

[2] Emory Lindquist, *Birger Sandzén: An Illustrated Biography* (University Press of Kansas,
1993), 65.

[3] Ann Boaden and Sherry C. Maurer, *Dr. Fritiof Fryxell: Explorer in Search of Beauty* (Rock
Island: Augustana College, Rock Island, Illinois, 1991), 10.

[4] Janet Knowles Seiz, "Birger Sandzén: A Painter in His Paradise" in *Härute—Out Here:
Swedish Immigrant Artists in Midwest America,* eds. Mary Em Kirn and Sherry Case Maurer
(Rock Island: Augustana College, 1984), 60.

[5] Lindquist, xvi.

90

Perle Fine (American 1908–1988)
Sketch for a Cubist Still Life, 1938
Charcoal drawing
Signed b.r. in graphite "Perle Fine 2.11.'38"
15.3 x 35.3 cm., 6 x 13-15/16" image
21.0 x 41.2 cm., 8-1/4 x 16-1/4" sheet
Gift of Dr. Thomas B. Brumbaugh Art History Collection, Augustana
College Art Collection, 2002.18.14

Perle Fine was an artist who loved to experiment; to this end she practiced many different styles of art ranging from Cubism to Abstract Expressionism. Her family emigrated from Russia in 1905 and settled on a dairy farm outside of Boston. Although they did not have the means to fund private art lessons, they encouraged her natural abilities, providing ample crayons and wall space for her early expression. As her sister-in-law, Charlotte Fine recalled: "Her parents were so proud of her, they never took them [her drawings] off. They were all over, everywhere she could reach, even over the bed. And she started drawing them—flowers, everywhere—well before she was old enough to go to school. Art was her life from the day she was born."[1] Unlike the existential angst of many modern artists' beginnings, Fine herself described that she "had a marvelous childhood."[2]

Fine never finished her formal education, dropping out of high school to pursue artistic training. She moved to Boston and eventually around 1927, to New York. Alfred Stieglitz's *291* gallery on Fifth Avenue, which opened in 1905, presented cutting-edge European art to a mostly reluctant American audience. The infamous *Armory Exhibit* (International Exhibition of Modern Art) of 1913, exposed a larger public to *decadent* avant-garde creations with Marcel Duchamp's Cubist-Futurist contribution representing the cause célèbre. In the year 1927, seventy drawings by Cubist Pablo Picasso were on exhibition at the Wildenstein Galleries. Art critic Henry McBride wrote in *The Sun* that Picasso was a powerful new force in modernism and should be thus "recognized even by those who fear that he is a pernicious influence upon the young."[3] As French art critic Guillaume Apollinaire (catalogue 87) predicted: "In my opinion what people have decided to call *Cubism* is the most important artistic phenomenon of our time."[4]

Fine settled in Greenwich Village and attended the grand opening exhibition of the Museum of Modern Art in 1929, soon after the stock market crash. The show exposed her to works by the French Post-Impressionists, Georges Seurat, Paul Gauguin, Vincent Van Gogh and Paul Cézanne. She later declared that from this point, she was now "a life-long Francophile…[and that] those four great painters really set me off. I loved everything French from then on."[5] She transferred from the Grand Central School of Art for illustrative training to the Arts Students League. She married fellow artist Maurice Berezov, a marriage that lasted fifty-seven years, until Fine's death in 1988. At a time when most women artists were not taken seriously, she valued his role, later stating that: "I could never have been an artist without Maurice's encouragement."[6] She determined to keep her maiden name and to not have children in order to focus on her profession, fairly radical decisions for the day.

While at the Arts Students League, Fine chose to study under Kimon Nicolaides, rather than Thomas Hart Benton (catalogue 96). Although other modernists such as Jackson Pollock chose to work with Benton, Fine likely knew that Benton did not encourage women in his classes and despised the "intellectually diseased"[7] modernists of the Stieglitz circle. Nicolaides, on the other hand, encouraged anyone willing to work, promising that: "I do not care who you are, what you can do, or where you have studied, if you have studied at all. I am concerned only with showing you some things which I believe will help you to draw."[8]

The Great Depression and its aftermath made it difficult for young American artists to travel to Europe. Fine did a great deal of independent study, particularly gravitating toward the works of Cézanne, Henri Matisse (catalogue 87 and 88) and Picasso, with such recorded comments as: "Great Picasso show. Went again and again. More students followed."[9] She later reflected that: "When Picasso was doing what appeared to be non-representational work, it was certainly extremely beautiful, and when he was painting Analytical Cubism it too was very moving, very beautiful. Every phase of his work, without any symbolical connotation, has extremely beautiful examples in it."[10]

She and Maurice determined to move to the innovative classes of Hans Hofmann who was a nurturing teacher (and perhaps the first Abstract Expressionist) who brought sophisticated European modernist theory to America. She later estimated that: "The great value of Hofmann's teachings is that he combined the flat two-dimensional with a strong feeling for the three-dimensional in volume, with movement and a great deal of expression."[11] *Sketch for a Cubist Still Life* reflects her period of formative study under Hofman. In particular, it demonstrates her own independent research into *Analytical Cubism*, invented twenty years earlier by Picasso and Georges Braque. Its sources in Cézanne and African art (catalogue 80A and B), broke down subjects into *cubistic* shapes, still retaining aspects of their original source, through studies generally progressing from three dimensions toward abstraction. Color was secondary to form, and the sense of the fourth dimension of time was implied to reflect a shifting eye considering the facets of the subject.

Created on paper with charcoal, this drawing is a beautiful exercise in *Analytical Cubism*. A guitar might be discerned in the lower left corner. The title of *still life* suggests objects arranged within a display. The linear patterns surrounding them, however, seem to set them in motion. The viewer can see elements that might resemble a hand or a rounded object, perhaps fruit, a ball or a swinging pendulum. Fine's drawing is so exquisite that it might be favorably compared to works by Vasily Kandinsky (catalogue 85). Her approach, however, was more in line with the formalist approach of Picasso, rather than the explosive emotional effects of Kandinsky. The chiaroscuro brings the whole to life, against a seemingly vibrating mathematical grid.

Perle Fine would go on to establish herself as one of the most talented Abstract Expressionists of her generation. A close friend and colleague to Willem de Kooning and Jackson Pollock, she regretted the *destructive* qualities of *action painting* and ultimately developed an original style based in meditative beauty, the roots for which might be traced to this contemplative Cubist drawing. Important contemporary critic and theoretician, Harold Rosenberg, aptly perceived in 1958 that Fine developed "within the changing [modern] art movements…an intelligence in [her] work that is beyond concept."[12]

[Jennifer Banaszak, *Class of 2005* and
Catherine Carter Goebel, *Professor of Art History,
Paul A. Anderson Chair in the Arts*]

[1] Kathleen L. Housley, *Tranquil Power: The Art and Life of Perle Fine* (New York: Midmarch Arts Press, 2005), 1.

[2] Ibid.

[3] Ibid., 8.

[4] Pierre Daix, *Picasso* (New York: Frederick A. Praeger, 1965), 90.

[5] Housley, 11.

[6] Ibid., 16.

[7] Ibid., 18.

[8] Ibid.

[9] Ibid., 28.

[10] Ibid., 29.

[11] Ibid., 33.

[12] Ibid., 197.

sketch for Cubist Still-life

233

91

Nampeyo (Hopi-Tewa North American Indian ca. 1860–1942), painting attributed to Fannie Polacca Nampeyo (Hopi-Tewa North American Indian 1900–1987)
Olla, ascribed title, ca. 1920–1925
Ceramic, hand coiled and traditional open pit firing
Unsigned
47.2 x 42.2 x 43.1 cm., 18-1/4 x 16-1/2 x 16-7/8"
The Olson-Brandelle North American Indian Art Collection, Augustana College Art Collection, 2005.1.35

This beautiful *Olla* was made by Nampeyo and painted by her daughter, Fannie Nampeyo. Called *snake girl* by people in her tribe, Nampeyo was born around 1860 to a Tewa mother and Hopi father on the Hopi Reservation in Arizona. Fascinated by pottery as a young girl, she learned her craft from her grandmother and quickly became one of the finest potters at First Mesa; adept by the 1880s, and at full flower during 1890-1915. She demonstrated her Indian craftsmanship twice at The Hopi House, a store for selling Native American crafts, and at the 1893 Chicago Exposition. "She was described as a small woman, less than five feet tall, a gentle woman, gracious to outsiders."[1] When she was only twenty years old, she married her first husband who left her because he feared that her beauty would make her search for other men.

Nampeyo's second and final marriage, to a man named Lesso, lasted fifty-two years and produced five children: Annie, William, Nellie, Wesley and Fannie. By 1920, because Nampeyo became legally blind, her daughters often helped her in painting designs on the vessels.[2] Due to the recognition collectors and promoters of Indian handcrafts accorded her pottery, she ultimately became a symbol for Hopi culture. She was very close to her family and inspired subsequent generations to continue the family tradition of making pottery.

What made Nampeyo stand out from other potters was her new *modern* style, which was rooted in ancient pottery. Even as a young girl, her designs were distinctive, and she was later influenced by the *Sikyatki* style, one of the most famous prehistoric Hopi wares (from the 14th-century C.E. village of Sikyatki at the base of First Mesa). Her fascination with this style is reflected not only in her designs but also in the quality of her pots. She and her mother discovered clay that was similar to the ancient Sikyatki type.

The base of every pot was started within another kind of saucer (*puki*), on which thick coils of clay were attached until the pot reached its desired height. In order to thin and smooth the wall, Nampeyo first scraped the exterior with a gourd rind and then with a sandstone. The unusually smooth surface ranged in color from yellowish to red, and even light brown colors, resembling Sikyatki pottery. Nampeyo learned to duplicate traditional paints as well, and used the same Sikyatki palette (red, brown, and black). Her interpretation, however, was not a copy of a Sikyatki vessel, and clearly was a modernist interpretation of a traditional cultural theme.

Sikyatki pottery generally had many painted geometric and life designs, applied to flat-sided jars without necks, or to the center of the bottom of shallow, wide bowls with incurved rims. Nampeyo's pottery, on the other hand, produced jars with prominent necks, and her designs covered most of the entire surface of the pot. Bowls retained their low, wide shape, but the interior design varied greatly. Sikyatki designs included elements of geometric shapes, lines, heavy crosses, humans, rabbits, snakes, deer, *kachinas* (supernatural spirit beings) and birds, from which Nampeyo drew her own kachina masks, with life forms and feathers being her most frequent motifs.[3]

Furthermore, Nampeyo's pottery included much iconography which related to Sikyatki style. It may be questionable whether or not all of the signs had a particular meaning; however, considering the importance of religious feasts and living in harmony with nature, many of the symbols were related to Hopi culture. Some of the most important include the *kachinas*, the spirits said to "live" among the Hopis from approximately February through July, and then "live" in the San Francisco Peaks, north of Flagstaff, Arizona, for the other half of the year. *Kachinas*, always portrayed as wearing a mask, were an important part of ceremonial life such as the Snake Dance, and usually appeared on pottery.

Rick Dillingham's 1981 appraisal of this *Olla* describes it as: "...a major example of the work of Nampeyo and its condition is fine considering the age."[4] The pot was made between 1920–1925 and was likely painted by Nampeyo's daughter Fannie. According to scholar Susan Peterson, "[Nampeyo's] lack of sight did not seem to diminish her art....She began to add tactile decoration, such as corrugated coils that she textured with a pointed stick, in place of some of her painting."[5] The globular shape of the jar, called *globose* by Barbara Kramer, was a type usually used for storage. "Nampeyo varied this shape from a taller globose storage jar to one with slightly flattened shoulders."[6] However, this shape and large size are uncommon for her productions, which—along with the corrugation around the neck, the appliqué interlocking fillets around the shoulder, and the band of black parrot-like birds—are what make this piece even more exceptional.

As far as iconography is concerned, it is hard to relate all the designs on this jar to particular symbols, because some are unique. There are many U-shaped cloud emblems, feather symbols, an arrow, and the *gnwela* pattern with a unique texture. It may be questionable whether the arrow symbolizes the sky god's arrow, or if it represents a beak slowly changing its shape into a wing located above two legs. Attached to the tail of the bird is a sign of *gnwela* (from above) and clouds (from below), both seen in other examples of Hopi pottery. The *Olla* displays unusual patterns of black, parrot-like birds around the rim, which resemble those on the prehistoric pottery made by the Anasazi, and peoples associated with Sikyatki and Four Mile Polychrome.[7] The painting on this particular piece is clearly more abstract than that on earlier pieces by Nampeyo, a reflection of Fannie's style.

Designs of eagle, owl or wild turkey feathers were also used for decoration, their purpose being to "mimic the wish to carry airborne prayers from the Hopi."[8] Clouds, lightning, rain, seeds and corn depictions symbolized "the transmittal of prayers for these things to the deities."[9] Many times an eagle was portrayed with storm clouds on his wings, which related to one of the Hopi legends.[10] *Gnwela*, drawn as a curved stick, also frequently appeared as a symbol and had multiple inferences.[11] The symbol referred to the wooden structure used by maidens for dressing their hair into round disks on both sides of the head, a statement of their unmarried status. On pottery, the *gnwela* decoration further signified a root, growing from the seed/plant to sustain life, suggestive of the germination point and spreading of life. When the symbol was repeated and linked like scrolling waves, as in the connected pattern of swirling shapes around the rim of this *Olla*, there resulted a suggestion of the vivid proliferation of life.

Hopi pottery designs from prehistoric Sikyatki, as well as the modern interpretations by Nampeyo, serve as primary sources of inspiration for many contemporary Hopi potters and painters. The iconography of Sikyatki and Nampeyo's designs are now a basis for modern art. They stand as a vital creative force that fuses the past and present times of this mysterious and fascinating Native American culture.

[Ewa Wojewoda, *Class of 2006* and
Mr. Kent R. Olson]

[1] S. Lucas, "Nampeyo Hopi Master Potter," Canyon County Originals, LLC, 1998, http://www.canyonart.com/Nampeyo.htm.

[2] T. R. Frisbie, "Nampeyo," Houghton Mifflin Company, Encyclopedia of North American Indians, http://college.hmco.com/history/readerscomp/naind/html/na-024600-nampeyo.htm).

[3] D. K. Washburn, *Hopi Kachina Spirit of Life* (California: California Academy of Sciences, 1980), 76.

[4] Kent Olson, *Notes*, unpublished typescript, Augustana College Thomas Tredway Library Special Collections, file 34-56HOP.

[5] Susan Peterson, *Pottery by American Indian Women: The Legacy of Generations* (Washington, D.C.: Abbeville Press, 1997), 57.

[6] B. Kramer, *Nampeyo and Her Pottery* (Albuquerque, NM: University of New Mexico Press, 1996), 180.

[7] Olson, file 34-56 HOP.

[8] Washburn, 76.

[9] Ibid.

[10] A. Patterson, *Hopi Pottery Symbols* (Boulder: Johnson Printing Company, 1994), 230.

[11] Ibid., 52, 62, 167.

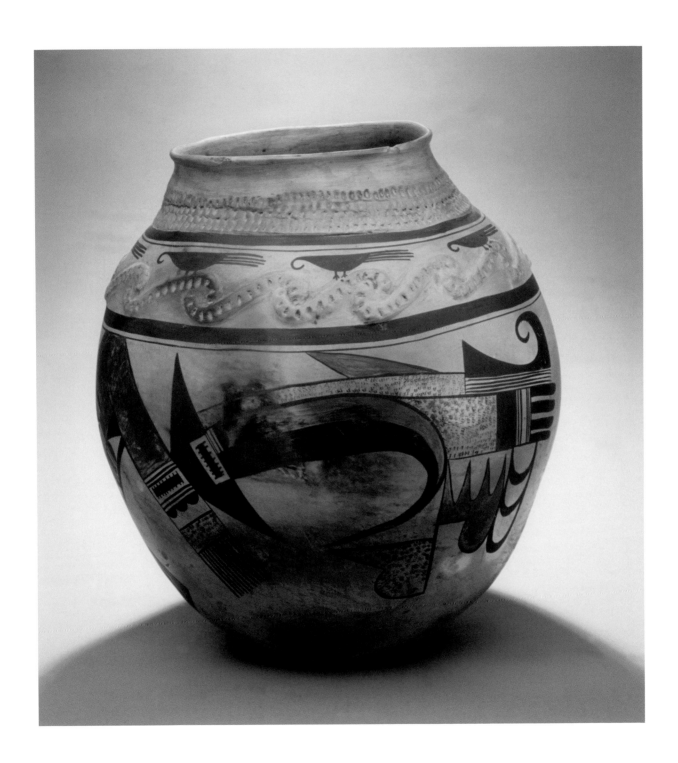

92

Artist unknown
Arts and Crafts Inkwell, ca. 1910
Hammered copper, milk glass insert
Unsigned
5.4 x 9.0 x 9.0 cm., 2-1/8 x 3-1/2 x 3-1/2"
Purchase with Gift of Mr. James Beebe, Augustana College Art
Collection, 2003.15

Since antiquity, inkwells have performed the basic function of dispensing ink until their general disuse by the mid-twentieth century with the invention of reliable pens capable of carrying their own supply of ink.[1] Inkwells are single receptacles for the short-term storage of a small amount of ink to slow its evaporation until its eventual use. A variety of materials was suited to this task and was fashioned in various ways. Hence, inkwells contained not only ink, but were also imbued with the aesthetic trends of a particular time and place. This copper and glass inkwell, although not marked or dated, is characteristic of the type of Arts and Crafts metalwork produced in the United States around 1910.

The Arts and Crafts Movement began in England during the nineteenth century as a reaction against nearly a century of rampant industrialization and what was then seen as the undesirable effect it had on the design and manufacture of goods. It was largely inspired by the ideas of John Ruskin and William Morris, who eschewed the factory system and its use of divided labor, advocating instead for a return to an idealized, pre-industrial past via a romanticized, albeit flawed, notion of the medieval guild system. It was not conceived as a new style, but was a new philosophy for living, working and making objects, which in turn effected a change in domestic design. Though unified by a set of ideals, various groups emphasized some principles more than others, which became aesthetically apparent in different ways. However, the general preference for handcraftsmanship, straightforward construction, organic design suited to purpose (the beginning of the "form follows function" idiom) and simple, (and generally) inexpensive materials established, in varying degrees, a noticeably consistent rustic tone, that could be called a style.[2]

Non-precious metals were favored, but copper, in particular, was the preferred metal of choice by Arts and Crafts metalworkers and revealed the various trends within the movement rather fully. The use of glass and copper for this inkwell typifies the Arts and Crafts' preference for simple, proletarian materials. The glass insert, likely mass-produced, could have been readily and inexpensively purchased at any purveyor of writing supplies. Inserts such as this were not necessarily made for specific inkwells, but were stock items made to a standardized shape and size, or "universal" fit. They were intended to be replaceable, if broken. Since copper was relatively inexpensive, it too, was well aligned with the "democratic" ideals of the Arts and Crafts philosophy. In addition, pure copper was highly malleable and easily hand-worked by amateur craftsmen, thus lessening this inkwell's extrinsic costs. Lowering the amount of time, labor and grade of labor required to produce this inkwell would have aided in reducing its overall cost.

Within the revival of medieval techniques fostered by the Arts and Crafts Movement, a distinctive style of metalwork developed.[3] On assembled pieces, the construction was often left exposed, although soldering was sometimes used. The flange of this inkwell's rudimentary hinge is soldered to the body and then crimped to the lid. Simple forms further emphasized the qualities of the material and clarified an object's function. This inkwell's strong geometric shape upholds the Arts and Crafts' preference for simple forms and straightforward, functional design. Its austerity is softened only

by rounded edges, a slightly flared base, and an overall roughly hammered finish. Typically, the surfaces of hand-wrought items were roughly hammered or planished to a smooth texture of evenly distributed, yet visible hammer marks. These marks, which generally distinguish Arts and Crafts metalwork, conveyed the imprint of the craftsman as well as the method of manufacture. Unlike figural or heavily ornamented inkwells that disguised or complicated their functions (catalogue 73), this inkwell's hammered-copper surface is its only pretense at decoration. The hammer marks have not been planished smooth, but are distinctly visible, being uniform in size, of medium depth and evenly spaced. Patination, or the chemical alteration of metal to change its color, further emphasizes the character and manipulation of the copper on this inkwell. Overall, the inkwell's patina is medium brown in color, though this appears bright in places; either from polishing or normal wear. Unlike the hammer strikes of English copperwork, which were generally restrained, this inkwell's hammer marks are more characteristic of the robust handling of American metalwork. In addition, American Arts and Crafts copperwork was routinely patinated, while English metalsmiths only occasionally patinated their wares. The hammer marks and patination of this inkwell indicate that it is likely of American make.

The Arts and Crafts philosophy was transplanted to the United States around 1897, first taking root in Boston and then dispersed throughout the country. Under the movement's influence, academic institutions and museums, in cooperation with manufacturers, began offering metalwork training. Journal publications and instruction manuals also promoted the metalwork revival. Several Arts and Crafts communities were formed, helping to establish the taste for hand-wrought metal articles. Hundreds of Arts and Crafts societies, workshops and summer schools were formed from coast to coast, providing amateur and professional metalworkers with training on hand techniques. The movement peaked in the United States around 1910, but continued to flourish until 1915.

Within this renaissance of pre-industrial American metalwork, there existed three major Arts and Crafts centers that exhibited certain, distinct regional characteristics: New York State, Chicago and northern California.[4] This inkwell seems to be typical of the type of work made by the New York "school" at the height of the movement, which is characterized by mostly utilitarian wares, roughly planished surfaces composed of detached and evenly-spaced, medium-depth hammer strikes and medium to dark-brown patination.[5] Based on these general characteristics, it seems that this inkwell was made under the influence of the Arts and Crafts Movement's Northeastern interpretation. However, exceptions do exist. A tighter attribution may yet be made when a catalogue raisonné has been compiled for the numerous American Arts and Crafts enterprises and a similar inkwell appears within a known body of work. It is, however, unlikely that a positive conclusion for this inkwell could ever be made, given the number of "guild" communities, societies, and instructional programs that existed nationwide that were producing work for both commercial and private use.

[James Beebe, *Class of 1988*]

[1] Joe Nickell, *Pen, Ink, and Evidence* (New Castle, DE: Oak Knoll Press, 2003) surveys writing implements and mediums from ancient times through the 20th century.

[2] See John Fleming and Hugh Honour, *The Penguin Dictionary of Decorative Arts* (New York: Penguin Books, 1989), 45-6. for general survey of the movement. Entry also provides ample bibliography for further reading.

[3] For an explanation of metal composition and medieval manufacturing techniques, see John Blair and Nigel Ramsay, eds., *English Medieval Industries: Craftsmen, Techniques, Products* (London: Rio Grande, OH, U.S.A.: The Hambledon Press, 1991); and Richard Newman, "Materials and Techniques of the Medieval Metalworker," in Nancy Netzer, *Catalogue of Medieval Objects: Metalwork* (Boston: Museum of Fine Arts, 1991), 19-41.

[4] David Rago, "Regionalism in American Coppersmithing," in *Reflections: Arts & Crafts Metalwork in England and the United States* (New York: Kurland-Zabar, 1990), 11.

[5] Barry Harwood, Introduction to *Reflections: Arts & Crafts Metalwork in England and the United States* (New York: Kurland-Zabar, 1990), 11.

93

Harriet W. Frishmuth (American 1880–1980)
Playdays, original model 1923; 1925 small version
Cast bronze with verdigris patina on marble base
Marked verso at bottom of base "Harriet W. Frishmuth © 1925 Gorham
Co Founders OFHL"
59.6 x 21.2 x 18.6 cm., 23-1/2 x 8-3/8 x 7-3/8"
Paul A. Anderson Chair in the Arts Purchase, Augustana College Art
Collection, 2001.40

Harriet Whitney Frishmuth's *Playdays* gracefully captures the exuberant
spirit of early twentieth-century modernist sculpture. Sculpture historian
and critic Loring Holmes Dodd wrote in the 1930s that Frishmuth's nude
figures "represent the modern ideal of energy, of action, of swift movement...
as representative of our times as the Venus of Melos of its [time]."[1]
Frishmuth's sensual style and impression of captured motion evolved from
the academic training she obtained at the Académie Rodin. She enrolled in
the only open female class at age nineteen and studied briefly with the
premier modernist French sculptor Auguste Rodin (1840–1917).[2]

Ruth Talcott, Frishmuth's secretary-companion, related the story of *Playdays'*
creation:

> Harriet wanted to do a study of a young girl just entering adolescence, and
> Desha [Frishmuth's favorite model-dancer and muse] said she knew just the girl:
> a very young pupil at the school of the dance, a Madeleine Parker...Whitney
> asked the young Madeleine what she would do if she were standing on a flat rock
> in a shallow pool and there were frogs nearby, and the girl said that she would
> probably try to tickle the back of one of the frogs. "Like this." And that is the
> pose of Playdays.[3]

The playful spirit of the slender nude adolescent girl embodies the signature
style of Frishmuth's most notable decorative bronzes and garden sculptures.
The young girl's lyrical pose with extended arms and raised tip-toe position
reflects Frishmuth's interest in the new free-form dance movement, a style
popularized by Isadora Duncan that later became known as *Modern Dance*.
Frishmuth's rendering also typifies her appropriation of the feminine ideal of
slender androgyny popular in the 1920s era of the flapper and suffragette.

Born in Philadelphia and privately educated abroad, Frishmuth pursued
extensive academic training in Paris, Berlin and New York, to become one of
the most highly trained sculptors among her American contemporaries. After
studying with Rodin, she trained in the atelier of Académie Colarossi with
Henri Desiré Gauquié and Jean Antoine Injalbert. After returning to New
York, Frishmuth studied at the Art Students League with Gutzon Borglum (of
Mt. Rushmore fame) and Hermon A. MacNeil. Frishmuth also undertook
dissection for two years at Columbia University's College of Physicians and
Surgeons. She exhibited her works widely, most notably at the National
Academy of Design, and won the prestigious St. Gaudens award in 1910.

Frishmuth's figurative mode carried over sculptural methods from her
background in the lingering *Beaux-Arts* manner, the complex Parisian-
influenced art style from the turn of the nineteenth century. Created in a
transitional period for American sculpture, *Playdays'* naturalistic subject also
represents the move beyond French academicism toward the modern abstract
idiom. The modernist tendencies in *Playdays*—the rhythmic contours of the
figure and the slight sleek stylization—reflect aspects of both the curvilinear
designs of *Art Nouveau* and streamlined aesthetic of the emerging *Art Deco*
movement. As sculpture historian Penelope Curtis notes, "Playfulness is a
large part of the inter-war figurative mode which became known as Art
Deco."[4] While Frishmuth's work bridged the academic figurative tradition
with the modernity of avant-garde sculpture, she frequently expressed dislike
for the new modern abstract and social realist art becoming popular by the
1930s.[5]

In the early twentieth century, decorative bronze sculptures graced the
interiors and exteriors of wealthy country estates and modest suburban
homes. Frishmuth joined the new generation of admired and financially

successful women sculptors like Janet Scudder (1869–1940), who specialized
in small parlor statuettes and garden sculpture.[6] *Playdays'* lighthearted motif
with frogs echoes Scudder's *Frog Fountain* of 1901, inspired by Italian
Renaissance sculpture. Yet, Frishmuth chose a more naturalistic source—the
modern dancer. Frishmuth first used the motif of a female form teasing a
water creature in her small utilitarian bronze *Girl and Frog Ashtray* of 1910,
which sold well for many years. Three years later she created *Girl with Fish,
Fountain*, in which she also began to explore the use of water sprays as a
compositional device.

In 1913, Frishmuth and her mother purchased a house in Sniffen Court, an
artists' enclave between East 35th and East 36th Streets in New York City.
From Sniffen Court, Frishmuth taught younger sculptors and created the bulk
of her sculptural oeuvre over the next twenty years. She began working with
the Yugoslav-born ballet dancer Desha Delteil as a model and in 1916 created
a series of sensuous nudes bending, swaying or on tiptoe. The eroticism of
these nude figures, most evident in her best-known work *The Vine* (1921,
1923), was unprecedented in mainstream art of the time.[7]

While in demand as a garden sculpture designer, Frishmuth stated she
"decided to model small, decorative figures whenever commissions for large
pieces allowed me the time. The small pieces were for purposes of bread and
butter...."[8] *Playdays*, modeled in 1923 without a specific commission, was
intended as a marketable sculpture in the small version. In 1924, she pointed
up the larger fifty-four inch version as a piped fountain, and in 1925, the
Gorham Company, one of the preeminent foundries during the early
twentieth century, fabricated this small version of *Playdays* in Augustana's
collection. That same year it won the Allied Artists of America's Brown and
Bigelow Silver Medal. Frishmuth astutely marketed her statuettes and garden
sculptures through commercial galleries, exhibitions and decorative firms
such as Tiffany and Co. (NY) and Marshall Field (Chicago).[9] In 1928,
Gorham Galleries published *Famous Small Bronzes*, a sales catalogue that
featured nine Frishmuth sculptures including *Playdays*, with the large
fountain version commanding the highest price in the catalog at $3,000.[10]

The emergence of abstract art and the Depression adversely affected
Frishmuth's sales, resulting in her creating very few new works after 1930.
She spent her remaining fifty years overseeing the production and sales of her
existing works. During the past few decades, Frishmuth's charming statuettes
and lively garden sculptures have sparked renewed interest among scholars
and collectors. [11]

[Cynthia Wiedemann Empen, *Class of 1992*]

[1] Loring Holmes Dodd, *The Golden Age of American Sculpture* (1936), 53, as quoted in
Charlotte Streifer Rubenstein, *American Women Sculptors: A History of Women Working in
Three Dimensions* (Boston: G.K. Hall & Co., 1990), 153.

[2] Rodin's *The Age of Bronze* (1875-76) played a significant role in the modernization of
sculpture. See Ilene Susan Fort, "The Cult of Rodin and the Birth of Modernism in
America," in Ilene Susan Fort, et al., *The Figure in American Sculpture: A Question of
Modernity* (Los Angeles: Los Angeles County Museum of Art, 1995), 34.

[3] Ruth Talcott to Frishmuth's patron and biographer, Charles Aronson, as quoted in Charles
N. Aronson, *Sculptured Hyacinths* (New York: Vantage Press, 1973), 140. Frishmuth
attempted to prevent publication of Aronson's subjective biography.

[4] Penelope Curtis, *Sculpture 1900-1945: After Rodin* (Oxford: Oxford University Press, 1999),
231.

[5] See n. 20 in Page Talbott & Patricia Tanis Sydney, *The Philadelphia Ten: A Woman's Artist
Group, 1917-1945* (Philadelphia: Galleries at Moore; Kansas City, MO: American Art Review
Press, 1998), 114.

[6] See Rubenstein, Chapter 5, "Fauns and Fountains—Traditional Women Sculptors: 1905-
1929," pp. 145-208; and Michele Bogart, "American Garden Sculpture: A New Perspective" in
Fauns and Fountains: American Garden Statuary, 1890-1930 (Southampton, NY: The Parrish
Art Museum, 1985), n.p.

[7] *The Vine* (1923), bronze, Metropolitan Museum of Art, American Wing, Engelhard Yard
Court.

[8] Frishmuth quoted in Aronson, 28.

[9] See n. 19 in Janis Conner and Joel Rosenkranz, *Rediscoveries in American Sculpture: Studio
Works, 1893-1939* (Austin: University of Texas, 1989), 42.

[10] *Famous Small Bronzes: A Representative Exhibit Selected from the Works of Noted
Contemporary Sculptors* (New York: Bronze Division of the Gorham Company, 1928), 43.

[11] See the catalogue raisonné: Thayer Tolles, Janis Conner, and Leah Rosenblatt Lehmbeck,
Captured Motion: The Sculptures of Harriet Frishmuth (Hudson Hills Press, forthcoming).

94

After Fernand Léger (French 1881–1955), etched by Jacques Villon (French 1875–1963)
Femme à la cruche [Woman with Pitcher], 1928
Color aquatint, engraving and roulette, proof aside from the edition of 200
Signed b.l. in plate *"Gravé par Jacques Villon 1928"*
47.6 x 31.4 cm., 18-11/16 x 12-5/16" image
57.2 x 41.4 cm., 22-1/2 x 16-1/4" sheet
Paul A. Anderson Chair in the Arts Purchase, Augustana College Art Collection, 2001.18

While serving as a stretcher-bearer in the French army during World War I, Fernand Léger wrote:

> I came out of a milieu of intellectuals made up of Apollinaire, Max Jacob and other friends and found myself with peasants, labourers, miners and bargemen. But I was built as they were, and as strong. I wanted my work as a painter and the imagery which would emerge from that work to be as tough as their slang, to have the same direct precision, to be as healthy…I felt the body of the metal in my hands, and allowed my eye to stroll in and around the geometry of its sections. It was in the trenches that I really seized the reality of objects. I thought back again on my first abstract studies, and a quite different idea concerning the means, the use and the application of abstract art took root in my mind.[1]

Before his involvement in the war, he was in the same artistic milieu as Cubists Pablo Picasso and Georges Braque. His early works had their basis in geometry, while simplifying objects into shapes and dehumanizing people into tubular constructions. After the war, Léger continued with Cubism; he applied more industrial themes to his paintings. His subjects took on a more machine-like design, almost to the point of seeming robotic. Arthur Danto aptly considered that "…the term 'mechanical' seems fitter than 'cubist' to represent his [paintings]."[2]

Léger wrote: "It is my ambition to achieve the maximum pictorial realization by means of plastic contrasts."[3] In *Femme à la Cruche* (1928), it is immediately apparent that each segment of the woman is individual from the next. Each body part is its own shape, except for the continuity of the neck and chest, which is broken up by the yellow necklace. The right forearm is particularly rounded as if a tear was turned horizontally—even the fingers are drawn as being separate from the hand, as though they are an entirely different entity.

The face of the figure is nearly expressionless, appearing impassive or trance-like. When this print was created in 1928, industrialization was nearing full swing and some expressed concern as to what the future held for humans. This dehumanization of the figure into a robotic form might thus represent a frightening premonition toward this new world. Yet, at the same time, Léger echoed classical tradition by making the figure the focal point of the painting.

The vase that she holds represents the strong vertical element that is present in nearly every work by Léger. This is caused by his Cubist influence, which, along with its emphasis on geometry, generally represented the same object from different perspectives. Still, the figure overlaps the vase when at all possible, helping to bring the figure to the front of the painting. A similar vase may be found in Léger's *Le Profil au Vase*.[4]

The color scheme is bold and simple, made up of primary and secondary colors that are outlined in black. The simplicity echoes the paintings of Paul Cézanne, who often simplified his composition into a few colors—consisting primarily of orange and blue. In his early works, Léger used a wide range of colors, but by 1910 he had begun to limit his palette. *The Bay at L'Estaque* (1886-1890) by Cézanne has a similar color scheme, with blue occupying the majority of the piece. The sheer physical upheaval of structure in Cézanne's late works influenced Léger to stress form (or volume) over color.[5] While the color in *Femme à la Cruche* contributes to the plastic contrast, the form takes precedence and lets the color complement it.

Léger's evolution to industrial or *mechanical* art influenced aspiring and upcoming artists who moved into abstraction. The idea that form was more important than color might not continue, but form remained important as artists such as Piet Mondrian composed works in reductive abstractions. Mondrian demonstrated that primary colors were universal, and in his typical works, used rectangles as the basis for form. This simplification of pattern might be interpreted as taking Léger's body forms, still based in nature, to an extreme with total abstraction. Countless artists have been influenced by Léger's work to a certain degree, and thus he should be viewed as an influential force for his time. As he stated in 1954: "My era was one of great contrasts, and I am the one who made the most of it. I am the witness of my time."[6]

[Dan Pearson, *Class of 2007*]

[1] André Verdet, *Fernand Léger et le dynamism pictoral* (Geneva: Editions P. Cailler, 1955), quoted in Peter de Francia, *Fernand Léger* (New Haven: Yale University Press, 1983), 31.

[2] Arthur C. Danto, *The Madonna of the Future* (New York: Farrar, Straus and Giroux, 2000).

[3] Fernand Léger, "Correspondance," *Bulletin de L'Esprit nouveau*, No. 4 (1924), quoted in *Leger and Purist Paris* (London: Tate Gallery, 1970), exhibition catalog, 85.

[4] *Léger and Purist Paris*, 71.

[5] Verdet, 12.

[6] Carolyn Launchner, *Fernand Léger*, Exhibition organized by Carolyn Lanchner (New York: Museum of Modern Art, in association with Harry N. Abrams, 1998), 15.

95

Grant Wood (American 1891–1942)
Seed Time and Harvest, 1937
Lithograph, edition of 250, published by Associated American Artists,
New York
Signed b.r. below image in graphite "Grant Wood 1937"
18.9 x 30.7 cm., 7-7/16 x 12-1/8" image
30.0 x 40.3 cm., 11-7/8 x 15-7/8" sheet
Paul A. Anderson Chair in the Arts Purchase, Augustana College Art
Collection, 2000.30

During the 1930s, a popular artistic genre emerged out of America's
heartland. Grant Wood, along with other notable midwestern artists, such as
Thomas Hart Benton (catalogue 96) and John Steuart Curry, developed the
idea of *Regionalism* for a country that was weak and torn apart by the *Great
Depression*. Wood, as illustrated in *Seed Time and Harvest*, felt the need to
portray an Agrarian myth—the need to work by hand. He refused to
recognize the age of industry that was sweeping the nation. "In his farm
pictures Wood not only forbade the machine, but also eliminated the
industrial allusions of utility poles and wires, railroad tracks, and billboards.
He chose to avoid the permanent signs and scars of industrial-electronic
civilization as it invaded and occupied the countryside."[1]

Born and raised in Iowa, Wood took his turn in the international study of
European forms of modernist art. This piece reflects the influence of French
Post-Impressionist *pointillist* artists like Georges Seurat and Henri-Edmond
Cross (catalogue 67B). The pointillist technique is evident in *Seed Time and
Harvest* in his use of tiny dots to represent highlights and shadows that
ultimately consume the entire work. Also, in the 1930s, "Wood's major
stylistic transformation coincided with Art Deco adaptations of
aerodynamics…"[2] apparent in the streamlined contours of this midwestern
landscape. The precision and alignment of the fields is almost abstract in that
they seem *too* perfect, yet the piece portrays a glimpse of the reality of hard-
working midwestern farmers in the midst of a profound socioeconomic
drought.

Wood's most famous painting, *American Gothic*, presents a sort of zoom-lens
view of stereotypical Iowa farmers. In *Seed Time and Harvest*, however, we
see his more typical genre scene framed within a Regionalist landscape.
Wood created numerous works depicting the fertile rolling hills of the
heartland and the labor needed to tend to those farms. As seen in this piece,
he used simplified figures in order to achieve a sense of realism. On the
whole, the composition seems rather plain, yet upon closer examination, the
minute details in the grass, haystacks and corn become evident.

Wood first pursued lithography in the 1930s. An important nineteenth-
century technique, it was utilized as a black and white vehicle for French
Realist Honoré Daumier (catalogue 44) and colored process for Post-
Impressionists Cross (catalogue 67B) and Henri de Toulouse-Lautrec

(catalogue 69 and 70). Wood made nineteen lithographs between 1937 and
1941 for Associated American Artists, a New York based mail-order business.
These lithographs and their marketing through the company's catalogue,
illustrate important artistic strategies of the Depression era. Such
merchandising offered artists much needed work, and the nature of the
multiple lithographic images made them affordable to a larger audience. The
publishers appealed to the patriotism of their patrons to support American
artists during this tough economic period. The number produced depended
on the quantity of orders received, but never exceeded 250, as in the case of
this lithograph. The dealers only supported artists like Wood who painted
the *American scene*.[3]

There is a deep sense of iconography rooted in this lithograph. Wood wanted
the American people to understand the dignity of hard work that still
survived in the rural communities of this country. At a time when many were
moving to industrialized cities, he reminded Americans that there were still
farmers who remained in the country and made their living through
traditional manual labor. Wedged between the Depression and the Nazi
movement toward World War II, this image provided a comforting reminder
of simpler and better times and helped viewers appreciate ordinary farm
routines. A man carries a bushel of corn into the shed, yet the wagon full of
corn and the vast field behind him suggest that he still has much work to do.

Wood engaged his audience through his use of *chiaroscuro* (shading with
black and white.) The presence of the haystacks is emphasized through the
long shadows, indicating early morning or late afternoon, depending on the
vantage point. The dark interior of the shed leaves the viewer pondering what
might be inside. The shadows also perhaps allude to the idea of a long
summer's day coming to an end, as if he is working from dawn until dusk,
and must complete his tasks before the cold winds of winter blow.

Seed Time and Harvest conveys the intended message that Grant Wood wanted
America to hear. He was proud to create a more *patriotic* form of art that
demonstrated that there was still room for hard-working citizens in this
country who believed in the dignity of manual labor, despite the advance of
industrialization. Our nation should be grateful to artists like Grant Wood.
These talented individuals provided inspiration and solace to people of their
time and important memories for the future, to remind us of the proud
foundation of this country. Wood himself later revealed his inspiration: "the
rhythms of the low hills, the patterns of crops upon them, the mystery of the
seasons, and above all, a feeling for the integrity of the ground itself—these
are my deep-rooted heritage."[4]

[Mary Feeney, *Class of 2007*]

[1] James M. Dennis, *Grant Wood: A Study in American Art and Culture* (New York: W. W.
Norton, 1975), 216.

[2] *Grant Wood Collection: Davenport Municipal Art Gallery* (Davenport: Davenport Municipal
Art Gallery, 1966), 43.

[3] Wanda M. Corn, *Grant Wood: The Regionalist Vision* (New Haven and London: Yale
University Press, 1983), 49-51.

[4] Corn, 90.

96

Thomas Hart Benton (American 1889–1975)
Sunday Morning, 1939
Lithograph, edition of 250, published by Associated American Artists, New York
Signed b.r. below image in graphite "Benton"
24.4 x 32.3 cm., 9-1/8 x 12-3/4" image
28.2 x 35.7 cm., 11-1/16 x 14-1/16" sheet
Purchase with Gift of Jeff Abernathy and Rebecca Wee, Augustana College Art Collection, 2005.9

Thomas Hart Benton's 1939 lithograph, *Sunday Morning,* is a noteworthy example of the work of an important American artist whose production ran counter to the major artistic movements of his time. Benton (1889–1975) was born in Missouri, went to high school in Alton, Illinois, and spent a formative year as an artist at the Art Institute of Chicago. He is best known for his portrayals of rural America, which often glance nostalgically toward a fading past.

The scenes Benton depicted were decidedly American and most often reflective of the Middle West in which he was raised. Though he himself dismissed the "Regionalist" label as too narrow and, indeed, sought to portray America from a modern vantage point—"I was after a picture of America in its entirety"[1]—his work, along with that of Grant Wood (whose iconic *American Gothic* exemplifies the regionalist impulse) has come to define this traditionalist genre. He specifically rejected the abstract work of European artists he had studied early in his career, claiming that art should be "arguable in the language of the streets."[2]

Published by Associated American Artists (AAA), this lithograph was one in a series of prints sold cheaply through department stores, paid advertisements and mail order. The means of distribution suggest the purpose: AAA intended to bridge the gulf between art and the masses. Benton's lithographs in the series primarily portrayed the same rural Americans to whom they were often sold. In *Sunday Morning,* Benton worked against the modernist impulses of so many of his contemporaries in nostalgically recalling a lost America.

White American artists and writers—often despite deep sympathy for African-Americans—have regularly portrayed the black figure in the context of a narrow, essentialist view of African-American identity. Benton often depicted African-American subjects, but even as that work has been influential on African-American artists—Benton's contemporary William Johnson developed his primitivist works partly in response to Benton, for example—it has also been constraining and one-dimensional in its portrayal. For example, his multiple depictions of Huck Finn's companion, Jim, are instructive: in 1936, Benton portrayed the escaping slave as strong, intelligent and independent, plainly the superior to Huck, but in a 1942 edition of the novel, Benton included confining, stereotypical depictions of a comic Jim deeply indebted to the minstrel tradition.

Here, Benton described a rural Arkansas sharecropping community from a sentimental vantage point that flies in the face of the reality of southern communities at the time. The lithograph depicts a sharecropping community that was fading swiftly in 1939. At the end of the nineteenth century, the sharecropping system had replaced slavery throughout the deep South. In debt to white land owners, unable to vote because of poll taxes, their freedom restricted by the Black Laws, the plight of African-Americans in sharecropping communities differed from that of their parents' slavery too little, and sometimes only in name. The appeal of northern jobs and the manufacture of automated farming equipment in the early decades of the twentieth century had caused the transformation of communities such as the one portrayed here, as millions of African-Americans left the South for the 'promised land' in northern cities. Benton nostalgically recalled an earlier time.

Like the Agrarians of the 1930s—literary critics at Vanderbilt University who sentimentalized the passing of the rural values—Benton showed a lost America threatened by modernism (and he declared himself to be an "enemy of modernism"). Andrew Lytle, one of the more reactionary of the Agrarians, argued that modern life augured not merely the loss of human functions but the loss of human life itself, as the movement to new technologies becomes "to follow the matter to its conclusion, a moral and spiritual suicide, foretelling an actual physical destruction."[3] Benton's portrayal here reveals his sympathies for the Agrarian view since his subjects could describe the nineteenth century as easily as the twentieth.

In portraying an African-American community coming to church, Benton manipulated perspective, such that the church itself is hardly bigger than the people preparing to enter it. The landscape sweeping toward the church, faceless figures make their way to worship: the stoop-shouldered couple about to enter the church is followed by two slumping girls. Figures in the distance come to church with their heads down. If the lithograph suggests nostalgia for the nineteenth African-American church as hub of community, there is also tension over the burden of social obligations. Even as the church calls the community together, it also serves to constrain, small as it is.

By contrast, the young couple that has paused below a tree outside the chapel brings much energy to the image: the young man leans in, his right hand reaching toward her—or perhaps pulling back after a proffered advance?—his left hidden but apparently holding her arm. Their delay before going into the church goes unnoticed by the parishioners filing in, but they gain the viewer's interest. The apparent drama of the lithograph lies in the tension between the parishioners, lined up as they prepare for service, and the romance outside.

As observers of Benton's work, we find more drama still in the tensions behind his impulse to recreate the past and reorder the present. In *Sunday Morning,* Benton reveals sympathy for his subjects as well as a conservative response to the changes brought on by modernism.

[Jeff Abernathy, *Dean of the College*]

[1] Quoted in *American Life and Lore: Thomas Hart Benton and the Associated American Artists from the Hugh Taylor Collection* (Tempe: University Art Museum, 1989), 5.

[2] Ibid., 4.

[3] Andrew Nelson Lytle, "The Hind Tit," in *I'll Take My Stand: The South and the Agrarian Tradition* (Baton Rouge: Louisiana State UP, 1977), 202-03.

245

97

Erich Heckel (German 1883–1970)
Sächsische Arbeiter [Saxon Workers], 1946
Woodcut
Unsigned
Stamped verso, along bottom edge "*Erich Heckel, Sächsische Arbeiter, Original-Holzschnitt, 1946*"
17.4 x 12.2 cm., 6-15/16 x 4-13/16" image
21.5 x 15.5 cm., 8-1/2 x 6-1/8" sheet
Gift of Dr. Thomas B. Brumbaugh Art History Collection to Augustana College Art Collection, 2002.18.25

Erich Heckel began his career as an architectural student at the Technical Academy in Dresden, along with his childhood friend, Karl Schmidt-Rottluff. Together, with Ernst Kirchner and Fritz Bleyl, they co-founded the important German Expressionist group *Die Brücke* (The Bridge). All four were self-taught painters and printmakers. Schmidt-Roluff named the association, inspired by a passage from Nietzsche's *Thus Spoke Zarathustra*: "What is great in man is that he is a bridge and not an end: what can be loved in man is that he is a going across and a going under."[1] The group eventually included other notable figures such as Emil Nolde, Max Pechstein, and Otto Mueller. Heckel's participation in *Die Brücke* directly influenced his artistic style, which led to his successful painting career.[2]

The *Brücke* was considered less cosmopolitan and revolutionary in comparison to the *Blaue Reiter* (Blue Rider), another German Expressionist group, founded by Franz Marc (catalogue 84) and Vassily Kandinsky (catalogue 85). The *Brücke* kept their artistic styles closer to earlier Nordic art, with influences from such Old Masters as Matthias Grünewald and Rembrandt van Rijn. The *Fauvist* and *Cubist* movements also inspired the *Die Brücke*, as well as the expressionist works of Vincent Van Gogh and Edvard Munch. The most popular theme of the Brücke included human figures and their relation to either nature or urban life.[3]

The *Brücke* disbanded in 1913, probably due to the rising tensions of World War I. Heckel volunteered for service but was deemed unfit to fight, and instead worked for the Red Cross. His commander, an art historian, scheduled Heckel's hours so he could continue painting while serving as a medic. After his service he went back to Berlin and spent several years traveling throughout Europe.[4]

In 1919 he became a member of both the *Novembergruppe* (November Group) and *Arbeitsrat für Kunst* (Workers' Council for Art) in a further attempt to break away from academic constraints. Heckel's works from the early 1920s reflect his dedication to the belief that "the unconscious and the involuntary are the sources of artistic power [and can thus create]…a spiritualized apocalyptic atmosphere."[5] During this time, he focused on human themes and his figures expressed the depression and loneliness of the human condition. Heckel also became interested in landscapes through his travels with the Red Cross during the war.[6] As he traveled through Europe's countryside, he sketched scenic pictures, especially of the mountains.[7]

His 1945 woodcut titled *Sächsische Arbeiter (Saxon Workers)* is a copy of his earlier 1924 oil painting titled *Junge Arbeiter or Arbeiter aus dem Erzgebirge (Young Workers or Workers Out of the Ore Mountains)*. In these works, Heckel reflected his German heritage by relating a sympathetic view of three working-class German men. Both his woodcut and oil painting depict these men standing next to either a doorway or window that is overlooking several pine trees atop the Ore Mountains. The seated man displays a sense of frustration and disappointment, based on the empty look in his eyes and the manner is which he supports his head with his hand. The man in the center seems to be in a state of disbelief because his eyes, although wide open, are framed within a blank stare. The third man on the left appears to be deep in thought because of his furrowed brow and gaze. These workers represent a realistic look at the emotional stress felt by German working-class individuals at this time, and the confusion, frustration and emptiness that they were consequently experiencing.

Heckel probably got his inspiration for these works while visiting the Ore Mountains near the historical region of northern Germany called Saxony, which forms the western border of the Ore Mountains and was the original land of the Saxon people. These mountains can be seen behind the three Saxon workers in Heckel's oil painting and woodcut. Both works include the theme of human sadness and despair, as well as the artist's new scenic mountain motif. *Junge Arbeiter* was not Heckel's only work that depicted these mountains. In 1925, he again painted this scenic landscape in *Steinklopfer im Erzgebirge (Stone Knockers in the Ore Mountains)*.[8]

The reason why the images of *Sächsische Arbeiter* and *Junge Arbeiter* are mirror images of each other is due to the process of translating a composition from a painting or drawing into a woodcut, a Germanic tradition since Albrecht Dürer defined the medium in the Northern Renaissance (catalogue 6). The artist must first draw the design onto a block of wood, cutting away the background which appears as white space in the print, leaving the higher positive areas in relief, which then print as black. Ink is placed on the raised surfaces of the woodblock and the image is transferred to paper. Through the printing transfer process, the finished impression is reversed from the original design. Woodcuts are easier to mass-produce than paintings, since in order to create copies of a woodcut, the artist only has to add more ink to the raised surfaces of the woodblock print.[9] With time, however, and the pressure of the process, the wood lines become worn and the details in the prints blur.

As with most avant-garde art of his generation, the Nazis labeled Heckel's works as *degenerate* in 1937. Consequently, 729 of his pieces were barred from museums throughout Germany. Furthermore, just before the end of World War II, his studio was bombed in an air raid, destroying much of his collection. After the bombing, he moved to Lake Constance where he began to produce art again.

His later works, however, were clearly overshadowed by his earlier artistic productions. In this woodcut, for example, he translated an earlier oil painting. Heckel simplified his detail and color by using the woodcut medium, which added a more reductive modernist quality to the composition. The inspiration for translating a painting into a woodcut can be traced back to his days with *Die Brücke*. The members of this group would often paint together and were known to translate each other's oil paintings into fine woodcuts.[10]

In 1949, Heckel became a professor of visual arts at the Academy of Art, where he taught for six years. He died in 1970, but before his death he donated many of his works to the *Brücke*-Museum, which he was instrumental in founding.[11] In all, he created hundreds of woodcuts, etchings and lithographs, many of which were unfortunately destroyed during the bombing of his studio. Through these works, Heckel proved to be a major artistic influence for the German Expressionist movement, particularly during World War I.

[Jason Myers, *Class of 2005*]

[1] Gunther Thiem, *Prints by Erich Heckel and Karl Schmidt-Rottluff: A Centenary Exhibition* (Los Angeles: Los Angeles County Museum of Art, 1965), 5.

[2] Stephanie Barron, *Degenerate Art: The Fate of the Avant-Garde in Nazi Germany* (Los Angeles: Los Angeles County Museum of Art, 1991), 13.

[3] Victor H. Miesel, ed., *Voices of Expressionism* (Englewood Cliffs: Prentice-Hall, 1970), 13.

[4] Barron, 250.

[5] Ibid.

[6] Ibid.

[7] Brücke Museum, "Erich Heckel (1883–1970)," 9 Mar. 2005, Brücke-Museum.de, http://bruecke-museum.de/englheckel.htm (20 Apr. 2005).

[8] For more information on Erich Heckel, see Paul Vogt, *Erich Heckel* (Recklinghausen: Aurel Bongers, 1965).

[9] Michael Delahunt, "Woodcut," ArtLex.com, 2005, http://www.artlex.com/ArtLex/wxyz/woodcut.html (20 Apr. 2005).

[10] William S. Bradley, *Emil Nolde and German Expressionism: A Prophet in His Own Land* (Ann Arbor, Michigan: UMI Research Press, 1986), 54.

[11] Barron, 251.

98

Marc Chagall (Russian/French 1887–1985)
Nocturne à Vence, 1963, from **The Lithographs of Marc Chagall,**
Volume 2
Color lithograph
Unsigned
31.8 x 24.1 cm., 12-1/2 x 9-1/2" sheet sight
Lent Courtesy of Private Collection

Marc Chagall (1887–1985) needs little introduction in a discourse on twentieth-century art. He was, among other breakthrough artists such as Pablo Picasso, at the very reigns of the modern art movement. Images derived from his Russian Jewish heritage often filled his imagination as he interacted with the French avant-garde, creating magical and original impressions. As an artist who drew his inspiration from interpreting dreams and dissecting allegories, a certain elegant innocence emerged in his art. Spanning a life of nearly one hundred years, Chagall exercised his art expertise in multiple media and varying methods, including aquatints, etchings, oil painting and stained glass.

His favorite medium was clearly the lithograph, evidenced by the fact that he created over a thousand editions of them in his lifetime. As he stated: "Whenever I bent over the lithography stone…it was as though I was touching a talisman. It seemed as though I could pour all my sadness and joy into it."[1] Lithography is an art form that bases its existence on the principle that oil and water do not mix. A greasy crayon is used to create a drawing on a flat surface such as limestone, metal or plastic. Chemicals are used to *fix* the image to the surface, so that when the artist applies ink, it adheres only to the greasy lines and not to the moistened areas. Although time-consuming and dependent on an artist's dedication and attention to detail and procedure, it is quite easy to rework or correct a design, and multiple images can be produced without loss of quality. Lithography is likely the most unrestricted type of printing. It produces tones ranging from intense black to the most delicate gray, and can be printed in a full range of colors. It also simulates the effects of pencil, pen, crayon or brush drawing, retaining the immediacy of the original sketch. White lines can be produced by scratching through the drawing on the stone.

At first sight, Chagall's lithograph *Nocturne à Vence* is a breathtaking dreamlike vision, powerfully highlighted by its blue background. While most artists worked on a naturally white background, this particular example of Chagall's genius is especially unique because of the depth and intensity of the blue. When comparing this element to his other lithographs such as *Acrobats at Play* (1963), which has a blank background, something is fundamentally lost. The colored environment adds to the fulfillment one experiences upon observing *Nocturne à Vence*. Since it is a night scene, the dark background is both intoxicating, drawing the observer into the scene, but it is also logical. Even among Chagall's other lithographs that feature a fully-colored background, none seem as captivating and solid as the deep blue observed here.

Chagall's depiction of a night at Vence, a French town located near the Côte d'Azur in the chic French Riviera, features a collection of small objects or people that became familiar to him as the embodiment of the Vence lifestyle. A concept that reappears in this work is the idea of flight. The first and most obviously linked object is the airplane in the upper left corner. There also seems to be an angelic creature with the ability to fly, directly below. Flying was freedom, real and imagined, instilled not only in the pilot of the aircraft, but in the hearts and minds of those who witnessed the flight. For many artists, the concept of flight changed the world just as dramatically as Cubist paintings and sculptures. Perspectives changed as to how people looked at their work, at art and at their relationship to nature.

Chagall also took artistic ideas from the Bible. This angel seems to be presenting something, perhaps to a god, or God, among the heavens through which she flies. Her arms are thrust to the sky, which directs the observer's eye to the next object in the painting: a couple, appearing to be lovers, who seem content, although solemn, at the top of the work. One might suggest that they could be Chagall's representation of Mary and Joseph, anxiously awaiting the birth of the baby Savior. Chagall, in his own life, was greatly influenced by his religious heritage, with multiple themes reoccurring in his works.

Also pointed toward the couple is a third object, which appears to be an animal. This could perhaps be a sacrificial offering made in celebration of the arrival of baby Jesus. In any case, Chagall put great emphasis on the importance of the couple in the upper middle section of the work by directing three other objects toward them. The bottom half of the work also seems to illustrate Biblical elements. On the left side, a round table is featured with emphasis on a central large chair, perhaps focusing on Jesus. At the right, a woman appears to be riding a donkey with her baby, possibly Mary and Jesus returning home to Jerusalem from Bethlehem; the direct answers are few, but the suggestions are intriguing.

Marc Chagall had a long life as an artist, working constantly until his death in 1985. It is not surprising that he would be strongly influenced by the Bible for his given name was actually Moses, not Marc. Living until the age of 98, Chagall is still considered one of the frontrunners of progressive modern art. His paintings and prints are treasured by collectors around the world. In an interview from 1960, the period in which he created this lithograph, he described his own perception of his legacy: "Today or yesterday—what is good will remain. That's the way art is: what you give you receive. You have to work. No theories! God in heaven is the greatest *théoricien*, if you understand what I mean…You have to believe in your work—that's all."[2]

[Beth Biercz, *Class of 2007*]

[1] Ulrike Gauss, *Marc Chagall: The Lithographs: La Collection Sorlier* (New York: Distributed Art Publishers, 1998), frontispiece.

[2] Ibid., 9.

99

Alexander Calder (American 1898–1976)
Spiral Composition, n.d.
Color lithograph, artist's proof (*épruve artiste*)
Signed b.r. in image in graphite "Calder"
66.3 x 97.4 cm., 26-1/8 x 38-5/16" image and sheet
Gift of Mr. and Mrs. Michael Moss, Augustana College Art Collection,
95.15.14

Alexander Calder (1898–1976) was born in Lawton, Pennsylvania to a highly artistic family. His father and grandfather were both sculptors and his mother was a painter. They nurtured his own natural creativity and often used him as a model for their various artistic pursuits.[1] Even as a young boy, Calder was fascinated with three-dimensional sculpture and the possibilities of motion. Because of this natural inclination toward building things out of metal and wood, he enrolled in engineering school.

This formal education proved instrumental toward Calder's later artistic career, where his training led him to devise a whole new sculptural medium—the *mobile*.[2] After graduating from engineering school, he went through a series of unsuccessful jobs that did not satisfy his expectations. A moment of resolution presented itself during an interview for an engineering job. Encouraged by the sympathetic would-be employer, Calder made a fateful decision. "He advised me to do what I really wanted to do—," Calder recalls, "he himself often wished he had been an architect. So, I decided to become a painter."[3]

To this end, Calder enrolled in the Arts Students League where he took classes from the innovative American *Ashcan* painters, John Sloan and George Luks, friends of his parents.[4] Yet his inspiration seemed to be less based in their largely realist works than on the new European abstract movements that invaded the American consciousness through the infamous *Armory Exhibit* in 1913, as well as various exhibitions at Alfred Stieglitz's modernist gallery *291*, located at *291* Fifth Avenue in New York.

Fascinated with the simplicity yet expressive capacity of *line*, Calder began experimenting with linear designs on paper aimed at depicting the traditional life-drawing exercise of drawing the nude. At this time, he also worked for two years as a tabloid illustrator.[5] Eventually this interest evolved from the paper surface to wire, where Calder was able to create simple sculptures as the three-dimensional counterpart of line, his *stabiles*. *Calder's Circus*, an assembly of handcrafted toys which he himself brought to life, was a complex array of such figures which immediately brought him to the attention of various critics.[6]

As his early *toys* and wire figures illustrated, although Calder abstracted his art through simplification, his forms were still based on nature. Like most Americans at the time, he was not initially sympathetic to the complete abstraction seen in his later *Spiral Composition* as well as in his innovative invention of the *mobile*. This ultimate and complete reliance on line, shape and color to create meaning rather than relying on replicating nature can be, in part, attributed to the influence of Dutch *De Stijl* painter, Piet Mondrian. In confronting the artist's completely abstracted walls of shape and color, which Mondrian termed *pure* abstraction or *Neo-plasticism*, Calder fully embraced abstraction.[7] He adopted Mondrian's philosophy that "The emotion of beauty is always obstructed by the appearance of the object; therefore the *object* must be eliminated from the picture."[8] His floating *mobiles* as well as *stabiles* convey a sense of harmony, balance and movement through their organic shapes, bold colors and simplicity of line. Calder said that rather than depicting individual, recognizable pieces of observed reality, "the underlying sense of form in my work has been the system of the Universe, or part thereof."[9]

Although much of Calder's focus was directed toward his *mobiles*, he created modern two-dimensional works as well. As in many other modern artists' pieces, such as abstract works by Mondrian and Calder's close friend, Joan Miró, *Spiral Composition* employs bold primary colors which help to simplify the work to the basics of art—pure color and line. When comparing *Spiral Composition* to Calder's mobiles, many of the same elements are apparent. By creating a simple form through line and color, the observer is encouraged to look at the creation as a whole, rather than merely focusing in on one particular section. Also, by intermeshing colors in a swirl-like pattern, the entire creation is effectively tied together.

The dominant shape of the red and yellow swirl, punctuated with blue, white and orange triangular forms, is repeated in the black line curl on the right, which plays with the thickness of line and draws the eye to the center of its pinwheel. Organic shapes float along the left edge and the top right corner. This purely abstracted image creates its own meaning, one of rhythm and balance. The overall effect, although defined in two dimensions, parallels the fragile *kinetic* quality of his *mobiles*.

Through his intuitive combination of art and engineering, Calder brought movement and motion into art, creating original and lyrical abstract art. Never humble in his zeal for the pursuit of artistic excellence, he once stated, while recalling a lecture from the president of his former school, that: "there was one phrase that stayed with me, the idea that 'good enough was best.' But while this might hold for engineering, it is not [true] for artists."[10] It was this continual search, never content to *settle*, which led Calder to achieve greatness in his art. Just a few weeks after attending the opening of yet another retrospective of his work, *Calder's Universe*, at the Whitney Museum of American Art in New York (1976), Calder died at the age of seventy-eight, ending perhaps the most innovative artistic career of the twentieth century.[11]

[Errin Copple, *Class of 2005* and
Jennifer Lams, *Class of 2007*]

[1] Alexander Calder, *Calder: An Autobiography with Pictures*, Introduction by Jean Davidson (New York: Pantheon Books, 1977), 11.

[2] Joan M. Marter, *Alexander Calder* (New York: Cambridge University Press, 1991), 13.

[3] Calder, 59.

[4] Marter, 15.

[5] In 1924 and 1925, Calder was employed by the *National Police Gazette*. Marter, 20.

[6] An example of Calder's playful and often humorous nature, between 1926 and 1930, he progressively developed *Calder's Circus*, which was comprised of handmade characters including jugglers, sword swallowers, clowns, and animals. These figures, crafted from a collection of cork, wire and various other materials, were each assigned a series of movements and manipulated by the artist to perform specific circus acts. This novel performance caught on quickly, and Calder and his *Circus* were in high demand. Ibid., 64.

[7] Elizabeth Hutton Turner, "Calder and Miró: A New Space for the Imagination," *Calder/Miró*, ed. Elizabeth Hutton Turner and Oliver Wick (Washington, D.C.: Philip Wilson Publishers, 2004), 34.

[8] Herbert Reid, *The Thames and Hudson Dictionary of Art and Artists* (London: Thames and Hudson, 1985), 228.

[9] Quoted in Turner, 35.

[10] Calder, 41.

[11] Marter, 250.

100

Pablo Ruiz y Picasso (Spanish 1881–1973)
Yan Face, 1963
Painted red earthenware pitcher, numbered 99/300
Inscribed on underside of base "Edition Picasso" with Madoura and
Edition Picasso stamps
25.8 x 11.3 x 15.6 cm., 10-1/8 x 4-3/4 x 6-5/8"
Paul A. Anderson Chair in the Arts Purchase, Augustana College Art
Collection 2001.10

Pablo Ruiz y Picasso was surrounded by art throughout his life. His father
was an art teacher who was his foremost mentor during his formative years.
At the age of eleven, he entered the fine arts school in La Coruna, Spain.
Despite such formal training, it was primarily his father who taught him.[1]
While studying, he quickly mastered techniques and demonstrated
exceptional talent. He continued to progress, exploring the Classical
tradition and the Old Masters, art sources which would continue to influence
him throughout his life. Picasso's desire to express himself and his ideas led
him to constantly experiment and alter his approach. His primary evolution
of style can be traced through his *Blue Period, Rose Period* and *Cubism*. Later
in life he also returned to Classicism and dabbled in Surrealism. Picasso did
not become interested in clay as an art medium until later in his career, and
then only began to seriously pursue it after 1946.

The *Yan Face* pitcher, along with a majority of Picasso's clay works, was
created in Vallauris in the *Madoura* studio. Vallauris is a small town on the
French Riviera that since ancient times has been an important pottery center
because of the fine clay found in the area. Invited by Georges and Suzanne
Ramié to visit their pottery studio called *Madoura*, Picasso first went to
Vallauris in 1946.[2] He returned a year later with several ideas he hoped to
flesh out in clay. Picasso himself never actually threw the pieces on which he
worked. He attempted a few times, but when these failed, he decided to let a
potter create the body which he would then alter. While the *Yan Face* pitcher
was modified by adding black slip and closing the pot at the top, he altered
others by carving into them, adding pieces, brightly painting them or
bending them into diverse shapes.[3]

Picasso's earthy red pitcher with its straightforward black design recalls the

much earlier ancient Greek form of black-figure painting (catalogue 1).
When observing the front of the pitcher, two faces greet the viewer. The
zoomorphic image of a bird is formed at the top by thickly painted black lines
in the shape of eyes and a beak. The pinched rim of the pot further
emphasizes this beak. Along the belly of the pitcher, a face is painted with
eyebrows, eyes and a mouth. A nose is produced by the addition of two
vertical lines, starting above the eyebrows and ending before the mouth,
punctuated by two small dots for nostrils. Ears are found at the sides of the
pitcher, and short black lines representing hair, sweep behind them to the
back of the pot. These strokes of hair also cover the handle. Deceptively
simple in style, the faces resemble many of Picasso's previous paintings, as
well as other ceramic pieces, in which he reduced the details of the human
form to resemble primitive art and masks, an effect he first realized in his
famous painting, *Les Demoiselles d'Avignon* (1907).

In return for letting him use their studio, Picasso allowed the Ramiés to
produce copies of his work, called *Edition Picasso*, and to sell them for profit.[4]
Yan Face is one of these copies, numbered 99 out of 300 and marked with
Edition Picasso and *Madoura* stamps at the base. These pots may have been
replicated from originals by Picasso or simply taken from one of his designs.
It is also not entirely clear whether the black slip faces on *Yan Face* were
painted by Picasso himself, or whether, as is more likely with three hundred
pots, they were painted by others in the studio who followed his model.
Picasso did not allow many of his works to be copied for fear that confusion
would arise as to which were the *true* originals. He eventually bought an old
warehouse and transformed it into his own studio where he continued to
experiment with the pliable medium of clay.[5] Through such
experimentation, the creative genius of Picasso successfully transformed an
ancient medium into a new approach to modernity.

[Errin Copple, *Class of 2005*]

[1] Hans L. C. Jaffé, *Pablo Picasso* (New York: Harry N. Abrams, Inc., Publishers, 1964), 13.

[2] Marilyn McCully, ed., *Picasso: Painter and Sculptor in Clay* (New York: Harry N. Abrams, Inc., Publishers, 1998), 26.

[3] Ibid., 34–35.

[4] Ibid., 38–39.

[5] *Picasso in Clay: Three Decades of Ceramics from the Marina Picasso Collection* (Santa Fe: Gerald Peters Gallery, Inc., 2000), 5.